TABL

Element	Sym-bol	Atomic Number		Element	Sym-bol	Atomic Number	Atomic Weight
Actinium	Ac	89		Mercury	Hg	80	200.59
Aluminum	Al	13	26.9815	Molybdenum	Mo	42	95.94
Americium	Am	95		Neodymium	Nd	60	144.24
Antimony	Sb	51	121.75	Neon	Ne	10	20.183
Argon	Ar	18	39.948	Neptunium	Np	93	
Arsenic	As	33	74.9216	Nickel	Ni	28	58.71
Astatine	At	85		Niobium	Nb	41	92.906
Barium	Ba	56	137.34	Nitrogen	N	7	14.0067
Berkelium	Bk	97		Nobelium	No	102	
Beryllium	Be	4	9.0122	Osmium	Os	76	190.2
Bismuth	Bi	83	208.980	Oxygen	O	8	15.9994[a]
Boron	B	5	10.811[a]	Palladium	Pd	46	106.4
Bromine	Br	35	79.909[b]	Phosphorus	P	15	30.9738
Cadmium	Cd	48	112.40	Platinum	Pt	78	195.09
Calcium	Ca	20	40.08	Plutonium	Pu	94	
Californium	Cf	98		Polonium	Po	84	
Carbon	C	6	12.01115[a]	Potassium	K	19	39.102
Cerium	Ce	58	140.12	Praseodymium	Pr	59	140.907
Cesium	Cs	55	132.905	Promethium	Pm	61	
Chlorine	Cl	17	35.453[b]	Protactinium	Pa	91	
Chromium	Cr	24	51.996[b]	Radium	Ra	88	
Cobalt	Co	27	58.9332	Radon	Rn	86	
Copper	Cu	29	63.54	Rhenium	Re	75	186.2
Curium	Cm	96		Rhodium	Rh	45	102.905
Dysprosium	Dy	66	162.50	Rubidium	Rb	37	85.47
Einsteinium	Es	99		Ruthenium	Ru	44	101.07
Erbium	Er	68	167.26	Samarium	Sm	62	150.35
Europium	Eu	63	151.96	Scandium	Sc	21	44.956
Fermium	Fm	100		Selenium	Se	34	78.96
Fluorine	F	9	18.9984	Silicon	Si	14	28.086[a]
Francium	Fr	87		Silver	Ag	47	107.870[b]
Gadolinium	Gd	64	157.25	Sodium	Na	11	22.9898
Gallium	Ga	31	69.72	Strontium	Sr	38	87.62
Germanium	Ge	32	72.59	Sulfur	S	16	32.064[a]
Gold	Au	79	196.967	Tantalum	Ta	73	180.948
Hafnium	Hf	72	178.49	Technetium	Tc	43	
Helium	He	2	4.0026	Tellurium	Te	52	127.60
Holmium	Ho	67	164.930	Terbium	Tb	65	158.924
Hydrogen	H	1	1.00797[a]	Thallium	Tl	81	204.37
Indium	In	49	114.82	Thorium	Th	90	232.038
Iodine	I	53	126.9044	Thulium	Tm	69	168.934
Iridium	Ir	77	192.2	Tin	Sn	50	118.69
Iron	Fe	26	55.847[b]	Titanium	Ti	22	47.90
Krypton	Kr	36	83.80	Tungsten	W	74	183.85
Lanthanum	La	57	138.91	Uranium	U	92	238.03
Lead	Pb	82	207.19	Vanadium	V	23	50.942
Lithium	Li	3	6.939	Xenon	Xe	54	131.30
Lutetium	Lu	71	174.97	Ytterbium	Yb	70	173.04
Magnesium	Mg	12	24.312	Yttrium	Y	39	88.905
Manganese	Mn	25	54.9381	Zinc	Zn	30	65.37
Mendelevium	Md	101		Zirconium	Zr	40	91.22

[a] The atomic weight varies because of natural variations in the isotopic composition of the element. The observed ranges are boron, ±0.003; carbon, ±0.00005; hydrogen, ±0.00001; oxygen, ±0.0001; silicon, ±0.001; sulfur, ±0.003.

[b] The atomic weight is believed to have an experimental uncertainty of the following magnitude: bromine, ±0.002; chlorine, ±0.001; chromium, ±0.001; iron, ±0.003; silver, ±0.003. For other elements the last digit given is believed to be reliable to ±0.5.

Printed by permission of the International Union of Pure and Applied Chemistry and Butterworths Scientific Publications.

CHEMISTRY

A TutorText

PUBLISHED BY

DOUBLEDAY & COMPANY, INC., GARDEN CITY, N.Y.

1966

CHEMISTRY

by Royal B. Leach
and Galen W. Ewing

PREPARED UNDER THE DIRECTION OF

EDUCATIONAL SCIENCE DIVISION

U. S. Industries, Inc.

Library of Congress Catalog Card Number 65–19870

Printed in the United States of America
First Edition

Contents

NOTE TO THE READER

This is not an ordinary book. Its pages are not numbered in the usual way, and are not to be read in the usual order. The material is divided into convenient sections, and at the end of each section, you will find instructions indicating which section is to be read next. Please follow the instructions carefully.

You will find that reading this book is very much like having an individual tutor. The book will continually ask you questions and correct your errors, to test how well you have grasped the information presented.

Your progress through this course will depend wholly on your ability to choose right answers instead of wrong ones. It is recommended that you do not try to go through this course in one sitting, or even two or three. As a rule, several short learning sessions are more productive than a few long ones.

Follow instructions accurately and you will find it difficult to reach the final section without a good knowledge of the fundamentals of chemistry.

Chapter 1

THE ATOM

The chemical events that are constantly going on about us in our world—the burning of coal, the rusting of iron, the tarnishing of silver, the corrosion of copper, the souring of milk, the decay of meat, the "browning" of a peach, the yellowing of white paint—all of these are large-scale chemical events which we can see with our eyes. Such events have been noted by man since antiquity, but the understanding of these events, and the ability to predict and to control them, has come about only in recent years. Indeed, chemistry became a science only after the invention of the modern atomic theory in 1808 by John Dalton, a Quaker schoolteacher who wanted to understand more about the things he saw in the world about him.

The atomic theory is not something that was discovered; rather, it was an invention of Dalton's vivid imagination. Just as a map pictures the geography of a land, so the atomic theory pictures a vision of atoms. This was John Dalton's great contribution to the world's knowledge.

Which of the two statements below is the better summary of the material you have just read?

John Dalton *discovered* the atomic theory and announced it to the world. **section 5**

John Dalton *invented* the atomic theory to explain observed facts, and announced it to the world. **section 9**

2

You have failed to note the instructions for reading this book. You do not turn directly from one page to the next, and so on.

At the bottom of section 1, you will find a multiple-choice question. Select the answer that you feel is correct, then turn to the section indicated alongside the answer you chose. If you have chosen the correct one, you will be proceeding smoothly. If, on the other hand, you have chosen your answer neither wisely nor well, you will be referred back for a second reading of the section where you missed the question.

Now, return to section 1.

3

[*from section 9*]

YOUR ANSWER: The importance of Dalton's atomic theory rests in the fact that it provided an atomic model that was capable of growth and development so as to be adaptable to new facts as they were discovered.

You are correct. Dalton's theory has indeed been greatly modified and vastly improved in the 250 years since Dalton announced it. Since our prime concern is with present-day chemical science and not with the history of chemistry, let us consider a simplified version of present-day atomic theory. Such a simplified version will be:

(1) Capable of explaining and predicting much of elementary chemical data.

(2) Easier for the student to master than a more complete and detailed version.

Later, the student will find that more complex facts may require a more complex theory; whenever our simplified version requires more details we will expand it. (This is exactly the way a scientist uses his "theories"; he often has several versions of a single theory, and uses the simplest version that is adequate for his purpose.)

The material world is made up of many different pure substances and mixtures, but all substances can be analyzed into one or more chemical elements. There are now 103 known elements; a list is given on the inside front cover of this book.

Turn to the front cover; glance down the alphabetical list of the elements, and note that each element is followed by a chemical *symbol.* Study this list for a few moments and decide whether the following statement is true or false.

"Every symbol is taken from the first one or two letters of the name (in English) of the corresponding element."

This statement is false. **section 8**

This statement is true. **section 15**

4

[*from section 8*]

YOUR ANSWER: The symbol column appears to be the most orderly and simple of the three columns.

Sorry, you are not correct. This symbol column is *not* arranged in the most orderly way of the three columns.

Turn back to section 8 and look these three columns over more carefully.

5

[*from section 1*]

YOUR ANSWER: John Dalton *discovered* the atomic theory and announced it to the world.

Sorry, you did not choose the *best* answer. John Dalton is the man responsible for the beginnings of our modern atomic theory, and he did announce it to the world, but it was an *invention,* a construction of John Dalton's mind, rather than a *discovery.*

Turn back to section 1 and reread the text; then compare the two answers to the question and note the difference between them.

6

[*from section 13*]

YOUR ANSWER: The following group of elements contains an erroneous atomic number:

Group A:	Hydrogen	1
	Lithium	3
	Cadmium	48
	Lead	82

You are wrong. Recheck the list of elements, and you will see that each of these elements has exactly the atomic number quoted. Be sure you don't read the atomic weight column by mistake.

Return to section 13 and try again.

7

[*from section 23*]

YOUR ANSWER: I am confused; I need a bit of a review about electricity.

Very well, let's nail down a few essential facts about electricity. If you rub a plastic rod or comb on a piece of fur, it will acquire the ability to pick up bits of paper and dust. We say it has become *electrified.* If we touch this comb to a pair of light metallic objects hanging on threads, we will find that the two objects *repel* each other, and swing apart.

If we repeat the same experiment using a glass rod and a piece of silk or Nylon, the results will appear identical; the two metallic objects again will *repel* each other and swing apart.

But now if we combine the two experiments, by touching one object with the plastic comb (rubbed on fur) and the other with the glass rod (rubbed on silk or Nylon), we will find that the two objects now *attract* each other, and will cling together.

From this set of observations it is evident that there are *two kinds of electricity*. These have been named (by Benjamin Franklin) positive and negative.

Any body is electrically neutral if it contains equal numbers of positive and negative charges. The positive charges are carried by fundamental particles called protons; the negative charges are carried by fundamental particles called electrons.

A positively charged body must contain more protons than electrons; the reverse is true for a negatively charged body, i.e., it must contain an excess of electrons over protons.

Now please return to section 23, reread the text, and then choose a different answer to the question.

8

[*from section 3*]

YOUR ANSWER: The statement, "Every symbol is taken from the first one or two letters of the name (in English) of the corresponding element," is false.

You are correct. These symbols are used by all chemists throughout the world, and it is just a lucky break for English-speaking chemistry students that so many of the official internationally accepted symbols are related to the names *we* commonly use for the elements.

However, these names were chosen for the chemical elements for rather insignificant reasons:

(1) Ag was chosen as the symbol for silver because the Roman name for silver comes from the name of the largest Roman silver mine, located near the town of Argentum.

(2) Helium was so-named, and given the symbol He, because it was first discovered by the study of spectrograms of the light from the sun (the word for sun in Greek is *helios*).

(3) Bromine was given this name because the element is a foul-smelling liquid, and the Greek word for stink (or stench) is *bromos*. (Bromine by any other name would smell as bad.)

Obviously, the names and symbols have been assigned to the elements for rather trivial reasons. Can we find any fundamental relationship among various elements? Turn to the inside front cover of this book and use the list to fill in the table below (as we have done for hydrogen):

Name of Element	*Symbol*	*Atomic Number*	*Atomic Weight*
Hydrogen	H	1	1.00797
Helium	______	______	______
Lithium	______	______	______
Beryllium	______	______	______
Boron	______	______	______
Carbon	______	______	______
Nitrogen	______	______	______
Oxygen	______	______	______
Fluorine	______	______	______

Now, study the filled-in table and answer the following question. Which of the three columns, the *symbol column,* the *atomic number column,* or the *atomic weight column,* appears to you to be the most orderly and most simply arranged?

The symbol column. **section 4**

The atomic number column. **section 13**

The atomic weight column. **section 19**

9

[*from section 1*]

YOUR ANSWER: John Dalton *invented* the atomic theory to explain observed facts, and announced it to the world.

You are correct. Dalton conceived the atomic theory as a means of explaining chemical reactions. However, he made many palpable errors, mostly as a result of the scarcity of reliable quantitative data. Lacking any indication to the contrary, for example, he assumed that one atom of hydrogen and one atom of oxygen combined to form one "atom" of water. In his pictographic symbols:

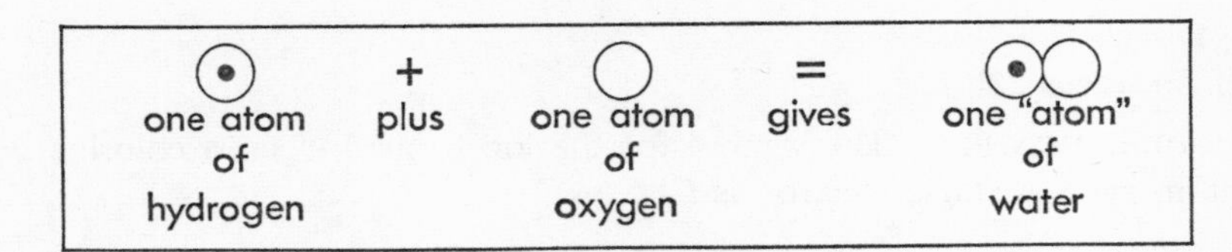

Today we say that a molecule of water consists of two atoms of hydrogen and one atom of oxygen, and we also know that this molecule has a definite angle between the bonds, as in Figure 1.

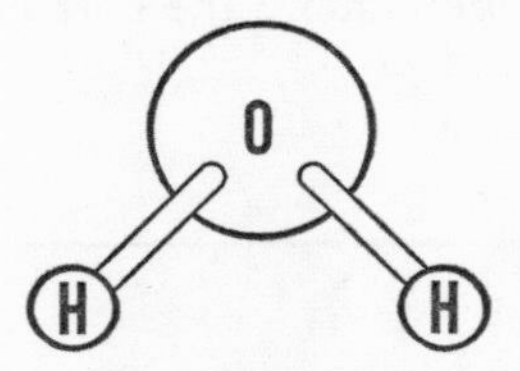

Figure 1. The water molecule. Formula H_2O or HOH.

Which of the two statements below is the better summary of the foregoing material?

The importance of Dalton's atomic theory rests in the fact that his work was for the most part free from errors, and can be used today in essentially its original form. **section 14**

The importance of Dalton's atomic theory rests in the fact that it provided an atomic model that was capable of growth and development and was thus adaptable to new facts as they were discovered. **section 3**

10

[*from section 22*]

YOUR ANSWER: The charge will be −2.

Sorry, your answer is wrong. If a neutral body (a calcium atom) consisting of positive protons and negative electrons *loses* electrons, it is *not* reasonable to judge that this loss would confer a *negative* charge on the atom.

Restudy section 22 and then make a better choice.

11
[*from section 32*]

YOUR ANSWER: The symbol for the ion formed when a chlorine atom gains a single electron is Cl^+.

You are wrong. A chlorine atom, being electrically neutral, has 17 protons and 17 electrons. If this atom gains an electron the ion formed will have 17 protons and 18 electrons, and this excess of electrons could not cause the net charge to be positive.

Return to section 32 and choose the correct answer.

12
[*from section 23*]

YOUR ANSWER: I feel sure from the above information that the charge on an electron must be negative.

You are correct. Electrons carry unit negative charges and protons carry unit positive charges; a body is neutral when it has an equal number of each kind of these fundamental particles.

Let us see if you can apply this knowledge.

How many electrons does a calcium atom have?

A calcium atom has 40.08 electrons. **section 17**

A calcium atom has 20 electrons. **section 22**

I am not sure how to figure this out. **section 29**

13
[*from section 8*]

YOUR ANSWER: The atomic number column is the most orderly and simple of the three columns.

You are correct. The list of integers in increasing order, one through nine, is certainly more orderly than either the list of symbols or of atomic weights.

These integers, the atomic numbers, were assigned to the various elements only fairly recently in the development of chemistry, after it was discovered that the most fundamental difference between any two atoms, from the chemists' viewpoint, was the number of *protons* that the atom contains. The significance of this fundamental fact, the proton number of an element, is the reason for the use of atomic numbers. There are 103 known elements, each element differing from every other element in the number of protons that it contains, thus:

Chlorine (atomic number 17) contains 17 protons;
potassium (atomic number 37) contains 37 protons;
an element with 51 protons is antimony (atomic number 51).

Thus every element has its own atomic number which specifies the number of protons the atom contains.

Let's be sure that you are clear about this and that you can use the list of elements satisfactorily.

Which of the following groups contains an element with an atomic number which is incorrect?

Group A:	Hydrogen	1	**section 6**
	Lithium	3	
	Cadmium	48	
	Lead	82	
Group B:	Tin	50	**section 18**
	Strontium	38	
	Zinc	30	
	Nitrogen	7	
Group C:	Fluorine	19	**section 23**
	Boron	5	
	Silver	47	
	Iodine	53	

14
[*from section 9*]

YOUR ANSWER: The importance of Dalton's atomic theory rests in the fact that his work was for the most part free from errors, and is used today in essentially its original form.

Sorry, you seem to have misunderstood the text.

Dalton was one of the earliest of "modern" chemists, and many of his "known facts" are, by today's standards, false statements. In fact, every one of the four major hypotheses in his original theory has been largely revised in the modern theory of the atom.

Turn back to section 9, restudy the text, and then choose a better answer to the question.

15
[*from section 3*]

YOUR ANSWER: The statement, "Every symbol is taken from the first one or two letters of the name (in English) of the corresponding element," is true.

Sorry, you are incorrect. You must not have checked the list very carefully, or you would have seen several elements whose symbols are *not* the initial one or two letters of the English name. For example,

The symbol for chlorine is Cl, not Ch.
The symbol for magnesium is Mg, not Ma.

Besides these and other comparable ones, there are some elements with symbols taken from their old Latin names, such as

Silver (Latin, *argentum*), symbol Ag;
Iron (Latin, *ferrum*), symbol Fe;
Copper (Latin, *cuprum*), symbol Cu;
Sodium (Latin, *natrium*), symbol Na;
Potassium (Latin, *kalium*), symbol K;
Mercury (Latin, *hydrargyrum*), symbol Hg.

Turn back to the front cover, review the list of the element names more carefully, and then turn back to the question in section 3 and choose a better answer to this question.

16
[*from section 22*]

YOUR ANSWER: The charge will be +18.

Sorry, your answer is not correct. You are right in thinking that the calcium atom, consisting of 20 protons (positively charged) and 20 electrons (negatively charged), would acquire a net *positive* charge when it loses electrons, but your arithmetic is very bad. Surely a neutral atom cannot acquire a net excess of protons over electrons equal to 18 by the loss of only 2 electrons.

Return to section 22, rethink your arithmetic and choose a better answer.

17
[*from section 12*]

YOUR ANSWER: A calcium atom has 40.08 electrons.

Sorry, you made a mistake and used the atomic weight column. Turn back to section 12 and choose another answer.

18
[*from section 13*]

YOUR ANSWER: The following group of elements contains an erroneous atomic number:

Group B:		
	Tin	50
	Strontium	38
	Zinc	30
	Nitrogen	7

You are mistaken. Recheck the table of elements, and you will find that these elements have exactly the atomic numbers given in the question. Be sure you don't read the atomic weight column by mistake.

Return to section 13 and try again.

19
[*from section 8*]

YOUR ANSWER: The atomic weight column appears to be the most orderly and simple of the three columns.

Sorry, your answer is wrong; you are not being logical.

The atomic *weight* column is orderly in that the numbers in it increase from top to bottom, but the increase is *not regular*.

Look again at the three columns in section 8. The atomic *number* column increases from top to bottom also, and the increase is *regular,* each atomic number being greater by one than the atomic number that precedes it.

Turn to section 8 and choose another answer.

YOUR ANSWER: Since the particles that make up atoms are so much smaller than the size of the atom, every atom must consist largely of empty space.

You are correct. The atom, as conceived by modern science, consists of a very small central body (made up of protons and neutrons, and called the nucleus), surrounded by a kind of cloud of electrons. Remember that since all atoms are neutral, in every atom the number of electrons is equal to the number of protons, which is the atomic number.

The electrons in the "cloud" external to the nucleus are arranged in a very definite way, in a series of *shells* or *energy levels*. The successive shells, starting with that closest to the nucleus, are designated by the capital letters *K, L, M,* etc. Each of these has a maximum number of electrons which it can hold:

Shell	Maximum complement of electrons in known elements
K	2
L	8
M	18
N	32
O	32
P	9
Q	2

The *O, P,* and *Q* shells can presumably hold more than shown here, and if more elements are discovered, the additional electrons will undoubtedly be in these levels.

Electrons have a strong tendency to occupy energy levels as close to the nucleus as possible. This is quite reasonable when you consider that the negative electrons are strongly attracted by the positive nucleus. Why the electrons remain in these levels rather than falling all the way into the nucleus is a complex problem which we will not tackle in this TutorText* book.

* Trademark registered in U. S. Patent Office by U. S. Industries, Inc.

Let us now draw a rough picture of an atom of argon (atomic number 18). (See Figure 3)

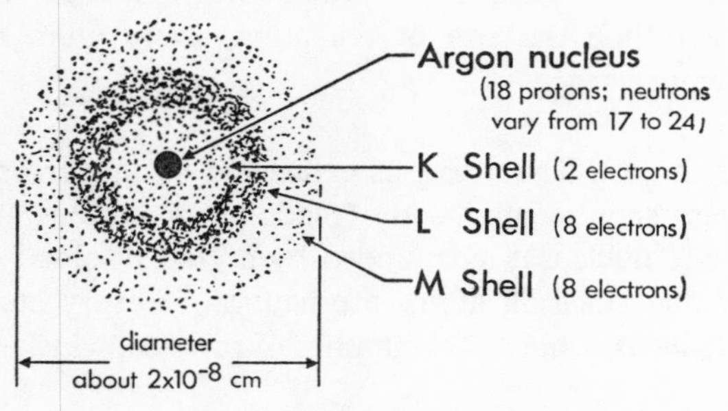

Figure 3. Argon atom.

From this knowledge of energy levels it is possible to determine the electronic arrangement in simple elements. For example, the nitrogen atom has seven protons, hence it must have a *total* of seven electrons. Of these, two are in the *K* level (the limit which it can hold) and the other five are in the *L* level.

Now you try one:

How are the electrons of an oxygen atom arranged in levels? (The atomic number of oxygen is 8.)

The oxygen atom has 8 electrons in the *K* shell. **section 25**

The oxygen atom has 8 electrons in the *L* shell. **section 30**

The oxygen atom has 2 electrons in the *K* shell and 6 in the *L* shell. **section 35**

The oxygen atom has 6 electrons in the *K* shell and 2 in the *L* shell. **section 39**

21
[*from section 31*]

YOUR ANSWER: (*a*) and (*b*) are isotopes of the same element.

Well, let's see. Two isotopes of the same element must be alike in number of protons (atomic number). (*a*) contains 32 protons and (*b*) contains 33 protons; therefore, they are *not* the same element and your answer was wrong.

Return to section 31 and make another choice.

22

[*from section 12*]

YOUR ANSWER: A calcium atom has 20 electrons.

Quite correct. A calcium atom has 20 protons (20 positive charges) and hence to be neutral must have 20 negative charges (20 electrons).

The number of protons in a calcium atom is the most fundamental thing about the calcium atom. If a calcium atom should gain or lose a proton it would no longer be calcium. (Such a change would not be a chemical change but would be a nuclear transformation. This subject will be discussed in Chapter 8.)

But it is possible for a calcium atom to gain or lose *electrons* in a number of ways. The most important of these ways is for the atom to take part in a chemical reaction. When a calcium atom takes part in a chemical change it characteristically loses 2 electrons. Whenever an atom has gained or lost electrons, it is no longer neutral, and should be referred to as an *ion* rather than as an atom. *An atom that has gained or lost one or more electrons is called an ion.*

When the calcium atom loses 2 electrons it becomes a calcium ion; when a barium atom loses electrons it becomes a barium ion.

When a calcium atom loses 2 electrons, what will the charge on the calcium ion be?

The charge will be -2. **section 10**

The charge will be $+18$. **section 16**

The charge will be $+2$. **section 32**

The charge will be -18. **section 37**

23
[*from section 13*]

YOUR ANSWER: The following group of elements contains an erroneous atomic number:

Group C:	Fluorine	19
	Boron	5
	Silver	47
	Iodine	53

You are correct. Very good; 19 is not the atomic number of fluorine. Its atomic number is, of course, 9.

Protons are one of the fundamental building blocks of matter, and they are found in the nuclei of all atoms. These protons are particles which have mass and carry a unit charge of positive electricity.

All atoms are electrically neutral bodies. The positive charge of the protons in the nucleus of an element is exactly neutralized by the charge of electricity that is carried by a cloud of electrons that surrounds the nucleus.

From the above statement, a person who is familiar with electricity can immediately deduce what the nature of the charge on the electrons must be. Test yourself!

What is the sign of the charge on an electron?

I am confused; I need a bit of a review about electricity. **section 7**

The charge on an electron must be negative. **section 12**

The charge on an electron must be neutral. **section 28**

The charge on an electron must be positive. **section 33**

YOUR ANSWER: The symbol for the ion formed when a chlorine atom gains a single electron is Cl^-.

You are correct. A neutral chlorine atom has 17 protons and 17 electrons. The gain of one electron will result in an ion with 17 protons and 18 electrons, with a net excess of one electron, which we represent by the symbol Cl^-. This ion is called a *chloride* ion.

Notice that it is the *difference* between the number of electrons and protons that determines the net charge on the ion; an excess of protons over electrons gives a positively charged ion, and an excess of electrons over protons gives a negatively charged ion.

Study the table below:

Symbol of Ion	*Name of Ion*	*Number of Protons*	*Number of Electrons*
Cl^-	Chloride	17	18
Br^-	Bromide	35	36
I^-	Iodide	53	54
O^{--}	Oxide	8	10
S^{--}	Sulfide	16	18

(Notice that negative ions, which are formed by removing electrons from atoms, are named after the atom, and always end in "ide.")

Li^+	Lithium	3	2
Na^+	Sodium	11	10
K^+	Potassium	19	18
Ca^{++}	Calcium	20	18
Sr^{++}	Strontium	38	36
Ba^{++}	Barium	56	54

Remember that *atoms* are always electrically neutral. Atoms can gain or lose electrons and through this process become charged bodies, but we should not call them charged atoms; when an atom *gains* one or more electrons it becomes *a negative ion;* when an atom *loses* one or more electrons it becomes *a positive ion.*

Electrons with a unit charge of -1, and *protons* with a unit charge of +1, are two of the three kinds of fundamental particles that are required for an understanding of modern atomic theory.

The third particle, called the *neutron,* appears to be very much like an intimate combination of a proton and an electron. The neutron carries no electrical charge. Neutrons are found, together with protons, in the nuclei of atoms. For example, the nucleus of the helium atom contains 2 protons and 2 neutrons.

What is the charge on a helium *nucleus,* consisting of 2 protons and 2 neutrons?

The charge on the helium nucleus is +2. **section 31**

The charge on the helium nucleus is neutral. **section 36**

The charge on the helium nucleus is positive. **section 40**

25
[*from section 20*]

YOUR ANSWER: The oxygen atom has 8 electrons in the *K* shell.

You are wrong. The *K* level can never hold more than 2 electrons. Return to section 20 and make a better choice.

26
[*from section 31*]

YOUR ANSWER: (*b*) and (*c*) are isotopes of the same element.

You are correct. (*b*) has 33 protons and (*c*) has 33 protons; 33 is the proton number (usually called *atomic number*) of arsenic, and both these atoms are arsenic atoms. The neutron number of these two isotopes has *no* bearing on the question of the identity of the atom.

The number of neutrons is important when we are considering the weight of the atom. All arsenic atoms have 33 protons, but the number of neutrons is not the same in all arsenic atoms. An arsenic atom with 42 neutrons has a mass number of 75; one with 43 neutrons has a mass number of 76. *For every atom* its mass number is the sum of the number of protons and neutrons in its nucleus.

All hydrogen atoms have a single proton in the nucleus; almost all of these hydrogen atoms are without neutrons and so have a mass number of 1; a very few hydrogen atoms have a single neutron in their nucleus, and hence have a mass number of 2.

ATOMIC WEIGHT

The atomic weight of a chemical element may be defined as the average of the weights of the atoms of this element in the proportion or mixture in which they exist in nature. Since most hydrogen atoms have a mass number of 1, and only a few have a mass number of 2 (and an exceedingly small proportion of hydrogen atoms have a mass number of 3), the average weight of hydrogen atoms turns out to be 1.00797, which is just slightly greater than one.

The atomic weight, the average weight of all the isotopes of each element as they are found in nature, is given on the inside front cover. We will need to refer to this list from time to time. This concept of atomic weight will be discussed further in later sections.

Let us now see if we can visualize what an atom would "look like" if we had superman vision. Superman vision is needed because atoms are such very small objects indeed. It would take about 1,000,000,000 atoms lined up in a single file across this page to extend from:

·here   to   here·
↑   ↑

The nucleus of an atom is *much smaller* than is the atom itself. Let us *suppose* that the circle below represents the size of an atom (remember, 1,000,000,000 atoms would only extend 4 inches):

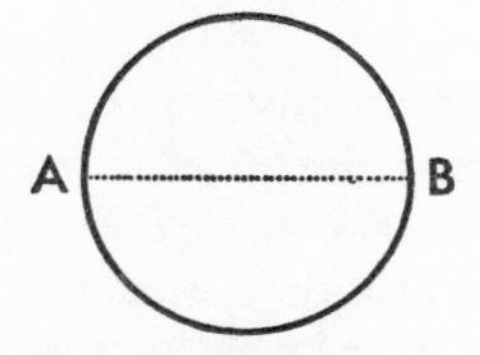

Figure 2. Size comparison: nucleus and atom.

It would take 10,000 nuclei lined up to extend from *A* to *B*. (The circle represents the size of an atom.)

Since the nucleus is made up of protons and neutrons, these particles must themselves be even smaller than the nucleus that contains them. While the size of the electrons is not known to any great degree of accuracy, we do know that electrons are only about as big as the atomic nucleus, and this is small indeed.

As you must now realize, atoms are so small that we will certainly never be able to see one; when we see a chemical reaction we are actually seeing billions and billions of atoms doing the same things. We can "see" atoms mentally, with our mind's eye, but can never actually see them even with the most powerful microscope.

Thus, an atom is made up of protons, neutrons, and electrons, particles which are (in volume) one thousand million million times smaller than the atom itself.

Considering what you have learned about atoms so far, which one of the statements below is correct?

Since the particles that make up atoms are so much smaller than the size of the atom, every atom must consist largely of empty space. **section 20**

Since the particles that make up atoms are so much smaller than the size of the atom, every atom must contain many billions of such particles.
section 34

27

[*from section 35*]

YOUR ANSWER: No, the electron arrangement of iodine *in the highest electron level* is not similar to the arrangement in chlorine and bromine.

Sorry, you either made a mistake in your electron count, or you do not understand the question.

Let's do the count together in Figure 7. Remember that we fill up the orbitals one electron at a time, starting from the bottom, and taking them in the order of their height on the chart, NOT in the sequence connected by lines.

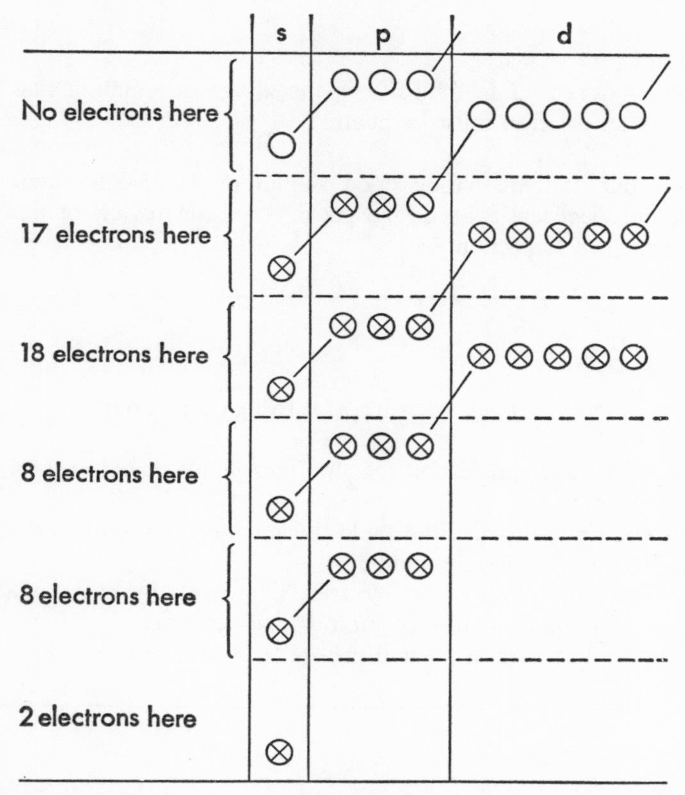

Figure 7. Diagram of electron energy levels (orbitals). (It is important to remember that in this diagram the energy levels are schematic and not drawn to scale. The diagram indicates electron displacement only.)

Now go to section 41 and study the discussion of the meaning of these similar electron arrangements.

28

[*from section 23*]

YOUR ANSWER: I feel sure from the above information that the charge on an electron must be neutral.

Sorry, but you are wrong. You should review the fundamental facts about electrical charges. To get a very brief review of this information, turn to section 7.

29

[*from section 12*]

YOUR ANSWER: I am not sure how to figure this out.

It is really quite simple. Put together two simple pieces of information you know:

(1) You can tell from the table the number of protons an atom of calcium has (its atomic number).

(2) You know that to be electrically neutral the calcium atom must have an equal number of protons and electrons.

Now return to section 12 and choose the correct answer.

30

[*from section 20*]

YOUR ANSWER: The oxygen atom has 8 electrons in the *L* shell.

Your answer is not correct. It is true that the *L* shell can hold 8 electrons, but if the *L* level in oxygen has 8 electrons the *K* shell can have none, since the oxygen *atom* only has 8 electrons. The lower *K* shell must be full before we assign electrons to the higher *L* level.

Return to section 20 and make a better choice.

YOUR ANSWER: The charge on the helium nucleus is +2.

You are correct. Every nucleus (with the single exception of the nucleus of the common hydrogen atom, which contains only *one* proton and *no* neutrons) consists of one or more protons combined with one or more neutrons.

The number of neutrons that are found in the nucleus of an element may vary. For example, while all chlorine atoms contain 17 protons, about one-quarter of all chlorine atoms have 20 neutrons in the nucleus and about three-quarters have 18 neutrons. Atomic nuclei of a given element, that have the same number of protons and a different number of neutrons, are called *isotopes* of each other. They are both atoms of the same element and their chemical properties are virtually the same.

The masses (weights) of these two isotopes of chlorine are different. The mass number of any isotope is determined by the sum of the number of protons and neutrons.

$$\text{mass number} = \text{number of protons} + \text{number of neutrons}$$

Which two of the following are isotopes of the same element?

(*a*) an atom with 32 protons and 43 neutrons.
(*b*) an atom with 33 protons and 42 neutrons.
(*c*) an atom with 33 protons and 43 neutrons.

(*a*) and (*b*) are isotopes of the same element. **section 21**

(*b*) and (*c*) are isotopes of the same element. **section 26**

(*a*) and (*c*) are isotopes of the same element. **section 38**

32
[*from section 22*]

YOUR ANSWER: The charge will be +2.

You are correct! A neutral calcium atom has 20 protons and 20 electrons. The loss of 2 electrons results in a positively charged body, the calcium ion. The symbol for a calcium ion is Ca^{++}, sometimes written Ca^{+2}.

By applying the same type of reasoning, decide what would be the symbol for the ion formed if a chlorine atom *gains* a single electron.

The symbol for the ion formed is Cl^{+}. **section 11**

The symbol for the ion formed is Cl^{-}. **section 24**

33
[*from section 23*]

YOUR ANSWER: I feel sure from the above information that the charge on an electron must be positive.

Sorry, but you are wrong. You should review the fundamental facts about electrical charges. To get a very brief review of this information, turn to section 7.

34
[*from section 26*]

YOUR ANSWER: Since the particles that make up atoms are so much smaller than the size of the atom, every atom must contain many billions of such particles.

Your answer is wrong, and is not consistent with the facts at your disposal. A hydrogen atom contains *only* 1 proton, and *only* 1 electron; it may contain 1 or possibly 2 neutrons: hence a hydrogen atom contains at most 4 particles. Four particles is *not* "many billions."

Perhaps a crude analogy will help you to "see" the atomic picture. Our solar system consists of relatively few bodies: a single sun, nine planets, about twenty-five satellites, and a few hundred known asteroids. These relatively few bodies move about and "occupy" our solar system, most of which consists of empty space.

Return to section 26 and choose the correct statement.

35

[*from section 20*]

YOUR ANSWER: The oxygen atom has 2 electrons in the *K* shell and 6 in the *L* shell.

You are correct. The oxygen atom, having a total of 8 electrons, has its lowest level (*K* level) filled with 2 electrons, leaving 6 electrons over to partially fill the *L* level.

The entire scheme of electron energy levels, as now known to science, is displayed in the diagram below.

In this chart are plotted a number of small circles, each representing a location which *may* be empty, *may* contain a single electron, or *may* contain 2 electrons (never more than 2). The individual circles are called *orbitals*. The vertical height from the bottom of the chart represents the relative energy content of the various levels. The numbers 1, 2, 3, etc., correspond to the letters *K, L, M,* etc., which we have used previously. Within each numbered "shell" (except No. 1) sub-shells exist. These are designated by lower-case letters *s, p, d,* and *f*. As seen from the chart (Figure 4), an *s*-sublevel can only contain a single orbital (perhaps 2 electrons), a *p*-sublevel can contain three orbitals (up to 6 electrons), a *d*-sublevel five orbitals (up to 10 electrons), and an *f*-sublevel seven orbitals (a maximum of 14 electrons).

The chart shows that the five 3*d* orbitals are at a higher energy level than the 4*s*, and similarly for other *d* and *f* orbitals. This means that the "shells" actually interpenetrate each other to some extent.

The chief utility of this chart is in the determination of the location of electrons in any specified atom. For this purpose, one additional rule is required, namely that a *second* electron never enters an orbital until every orbital in the same group has at least one in it. We then proceed to assign electrons to orbitals, starting with the lowest (1*s*) and proceeding upward, until all electrons have been assigned. When doing this, it is convenient to use a copy of the orbital chart, and make a diagonal mark within each circle for each electron. Thus

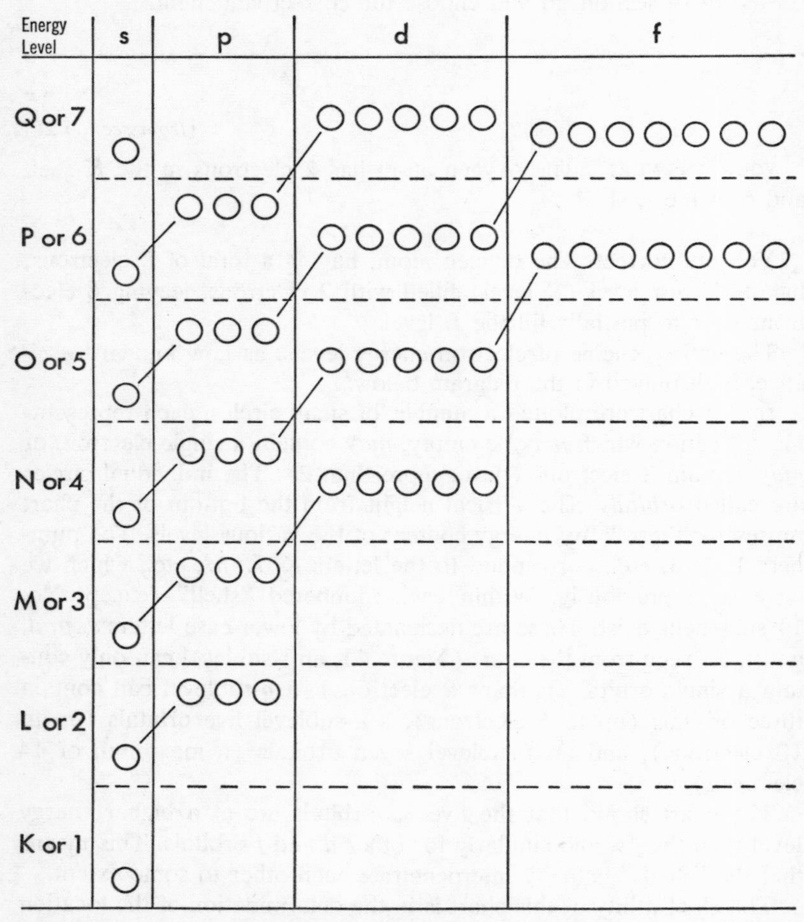

Figure 4. Diagram of electron energy levels (orbitals). (It is important to remember that in this diagram the energy levels are schematic and not drawn to scale. The diagram indicates electron displacement only.)

○ represents an empty orbital, ⦸ an orbital with one electron, and ⊗ an orbital with two electrons (i.e., full).

For example, consider the element chlorine, atomic number 17. A portion of the chart (Figure 5) is shown filled in for 17 electrons.

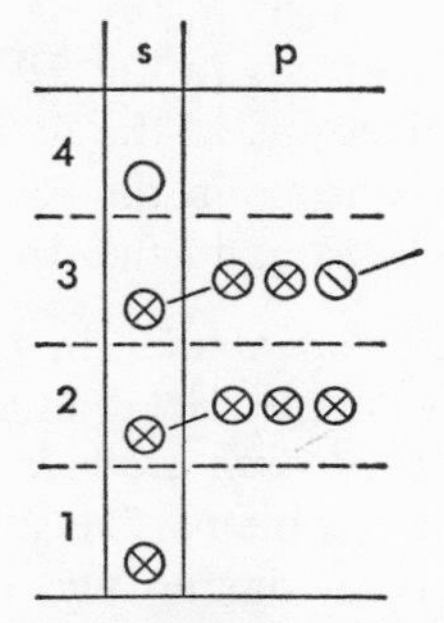

Figure 5. Same as Figure 4.

It has the following assignments:

2 electrons in the 1*s* level
2 electrons in the 2*s* level
6 electrons in the 2*p* level
2 electrons in the 3*s* level
and 5 electrons in the 3*p* level

for a total of 17.

Consider also bromine, atomic number 35. Again a portion of the chart (Figure 6) is given.

	s	p	d
5	○		
4	⊗	⊗⊗⦸	
3	⊗	⊗⊗⊗	⊗⊗⊗⊗⊗
2	⊗	⊗⊗⊗	
1	⊗		

Figure 6. Same as Figure 4.

Bromine thus has:

2 electrons in the 1*s* orbital
2 electrons in the 2*s* orbital
6 electrons in the 2*p* orbitals
2 electrons in the 3*s* orbital
6 electrons in the 3*p* orbitals
2 electrons in the 4*s* orbital
10 electrons in the 3*d* orbitals
and 5 electrons in the 4*p* orbitals

These two elements are very similar in chemical properties, and we attribute this similarity to the fact that *the number of electrons in the highest electron level of each atom is the same.*

Now you try a similar problem. Consider the element iodine, atomic number 53. Start by assigning two electrons to each of the circles, starting with the lowest circle. Keep a record of the number of electrons by marking a diameter to indicate each electron, and a crossed diameter to indicate a pair of electrons.

Now use your diagram to decide the following question:

Is the electron arrangement for iodine *in the highest electron level* similar to the highest-level electron arrangement for chlorine and bromine?

No, the electron arrangement of iodine *in the highest electron level* is not similar to the arrangement in chlorine and bromine. **section 27**

Yes, the electron arrangement of iodine *in the highest electron level* is similar to the arrangement in chlorine and bromine. **section 41**

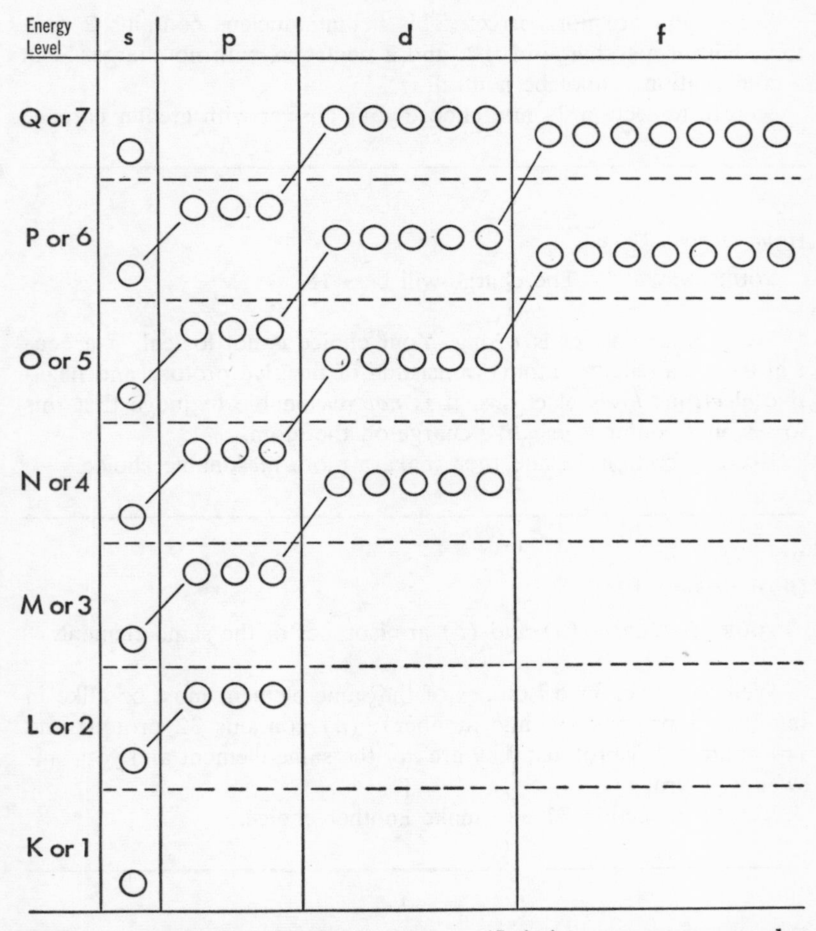

Figure 8. Available orbitals in an atom. (It is important to remember that in this diagram the energy levels are schematic and not drawn to scale. The diagram indicates electron displacement only.)

36
[*from section 24*]

YOUR ANSWER: The charge on the helium nucleus is neutral.

Sorry, you are not correct. This helium nucleus contains 2 protons, with a net charge of +2, and 2 neutrons, with no charge. Such a combination cannot be neutral!

Return to section 24 and choose your answer with greater care.

37
[*from section 22*]

YOUR ANSWER: The charge will be −18.

Sorry, your answer is wrong. Your choice is not logical. If a neutral body (a calcium atom) consisting of positive protons and negative electrons *loses* electrons, it is *not* reasonable to judge that this loss would confer a *negative* charge on the atom.

Restudy section 22 and then make a more reasonable choice.

38
[*from section 31*]

YOUR ANSWER: (*a*) and (*c*) are isotopes of the same element.

Well, let's see. Two isotopes of the same element must be alike in number of protons (atomic number). (*a*) contains 32 protons and (*c*) contains 33 protons; they are *not* the same element and your answer was wrong.

Return to section 31 and make another choice.

39
[*from section 20*]

YOUR ANSWER: The oxygen atom has 6 electrons in the *K* shell and 2 in the *L* shell.

Sorry, this answer is not correct. You should realize that the *K* shell can *never* have more than two electrons.

Return to section 20, reread the text carefully, and then choose the correct answer.

40
[*from section 24*]

YOUR ANSWER: The charge on the helium nucleus is positive.

You are correct. The charge will certainly be positive.

But, although correct, your choice was not the *best* answer available to you. A quantitative answer, being more explicit, would have been better.

Return to section 24 and choose a better answer.

41
[*from section 35*]

YOUR ANSWER: Yes, the electron arrangement of iodine *in the highest electron level* is similar to the arrangement in chlorine and bromine.

You are correct. Iodine is similar to bromine and chlorine in that chlorine has 5 electrons in the $3p$ level, bromine has 5 electrons in the $4p$ level, and iodine has 5 electrons in the $5p$ level.

The arrangements of electrons in the highest level in each atom is identical–and hence we predict that chlorine, bromine, and iodine have similar chemical properties. Experiment verifies our prediction; they are similar elements.

Remember that the number of protons determines the number of electrons; this number of electrons together with the energy level diagram allows us to predict the number of electrons in the highest electron level. This level for any atom is called the "valence" level.

In the next chapter we will use the arrangement of electrons in the various levels to organize a complete chart of all the known elements. Such an arrangement, called the *Periodic Table of the Elements,* is dependent on atomic structure and electron levels, and is the most valuable tool ever devised to enable the chemist to obtain an overview of the properties of the elements in relation to each other.

Now go on to the next section for a summary of what you have just learned.

CHAPTER 1—THE ATOM—SUMMARY

All substances are made up of *elements,* of which 103 are known. Each element has been given a distinctive *name* and a *symbol* consisting of one or two letters of its name (English or Latin) to represent the element.

Each element contains a characteristic number of positively charged particles called *protons,* and this number is designated as the *atomic number.*

To maintain electrical neutrality in the atom, it must contain an amount of negative charge just sufficient to counterbalance the positive protons. The negative charge is carried by particles called *electrons,* each of which has a charge exactly equal to that on a single proton, but of opposite sign.

An atom which has gained one or more excess electrons is a *negative ion;* one which has lost one or more electrons has a residual positive charge and is a *positive ion.* The names of negative ions consisting of a single atom correspond to the name of the element, but end in "*-ide.*"

Most atoms also contain neutral particles called *neutrons. Isotopes* are atoms with the same number of protons (and electrons) but with different numbers of neutrons.

Essentially all the mass of an atom is carried by the protons and neutrons, which are combined closely together to form the tiny *nucleus* at the center of the atom. The *mass number* of an isotope is given by the sum of the number of protons and neutrons.

The *atomic weight* of an element is the average mass number of the isotopes of the element as found in nature, taking into account the relative abundances of the various isotopes.

The electrons within atoms are arranged in discrete *energy levels* or *shells,* designated by the capital letters *K, L, M, N,* etc. The maximum numbers of electrons which are ever found in each shell are, respectively, 2, 8, 18, 32, 32, 9, and 2.

Sub-shells exist within the main levels, and are designated by the lower-case letters *s, p, d,* and *f*. The disposition of electrons in the sub-shells is conveniently treated by the concept of *orbitals*.

There is only 1 orbital in each *s* sub-shell, 3 orbitals in each *p,* 5 in each *d,* and 7 in each *f* sub-shell. Each orbital may hold 1 or 2 electrons, or it may be empty, but never can it hold more than 2. The sequence in which the orbitals are filled, as the elements are considered in order, can be determined by means of the chart in section 35. This is of importance because elements with similar arrangements of electrons in the outer orbitals show similar chemical properties.

Go on to the next section for a short quiz on this material.

CHAPTER 1—REVIEW QUESTIONS AND PROBLEMS

1. Use the table of elements (inside front cover) to find the symbol, atomic number, and atomic weight of: chlorine, cadmium, chromium, and carbon.

2. Use the same table to find the atomic number, atomic weight, and name of: Mn, Mg, Mo, Hg, H.

3. How many electrons, protons, and neutrons are there in an atom of the most common isotope of: carbon, oxygen, calcium?

4. An atom has 47 protons, 47 electrons, and 64 neutrons. Of what element is it an isotope?

5. How do we know that every *atom* must have the same number of electrons as protons? How do we know that this is *not* true of ions?

6. How are the 15 electrons of phosphorus arranged in orbitals?

Turn to section 544 for the answers, then go on to section 44.

44
[*from section 43*]

Chapter 2

THE PERIODIC TABLE

In Chapter 1 we studied the internal structure of atoms. Now we will consider in more detail the relationships between elements. First a review question:

What feature of an atom determines its chemical identity?

How many isotopes it has. **section 50**

How many neutrons it contains. **section 55**

How many protons it contains. **section 60**

45
[*from section 60*]

YOUR ANSWER: The elements in the Periodic Table are arranged horizontally in increasing order of atomic weights.

This is nearly correct but not quite. There are discrepancies; look at the two elements iodine (I) and tellurium (Te), and the pair of elements cobalt (Co) and nickel (Ni).

Return to section 60 and choose a better answer.

46
[*from section 51*]

YOUR ANSWER: The noble gases are unreactive because they have just enough electrons to completely fill their outer energy levels.

You are correct. Each of these gases has 8 electrons in its outer layer (except helium, which has a *total* of only 2). Furthermore, none of these has any orbitals which are partly but not completely filled. Since the outer shells are complete, these elements do not have the ability to accept an electron to form negative ions nor any tendency to lose an electron to become positive ions.

Refer back to section 41 in Chapter 1 where the properties of chlorine, bromine, and iodine are compared, and answer this question: Which of the following statements best describes the placing of chlorine, bromine, and iodine in the Periodic Table?

They are in a column adjacent to the noble gas column because they so nearly resemble noble gases in properties. **section 52**

They are in a column immediately preceding the noble gases because each is lacking only one electron of being electronically identical with the adjacent noble gas. **section 58**

47

[*from section 58*]

YOUR ANSWER: The alkali metal elements are placed in an adjacent column to the noble gases because they are so similar to the halogens.

No. The halogens are a family of nonmetals; it is not reasonable to suppose that the alkali metal family of elements would closely resemble a nonmetallic family.

Go back to section 58 and reread the text, then choose the correct answer.

48
[*from section 53*]

YOUR ANSWER: The alkaline-earth elements occupy their position in the table because they lack 2 electrons of noble gas structure.

No! You are confused.

Look at the elements with atomic numbers 10, 11, and 12 at the left side of the chart. It is illogical to say that element 11 (with 11 protons and 11 electrons) has 1 more electron than an inert gas, and then to say that èlement number 12 (with 12 protons and 12 electrons) has 2 less electrons than an inert gas.

Return to section 53 and choose the correct answer.

49
[*from section 62*]

YOUR ANSWER: I would expect neodymium to resemble praseodymium more than uranium.

You are correct. There is even more reason to expect these elements to have horizontal similarities than for the rest of the transition metals.

The elements 57 to 71 are called the "lanthanide" elements, after the first member, lanthanum. Numbers 89 to 103, similarly, are named "actinides," after actinium.

Now that we have given detailed consideration to various family relations with respect to the Periodic Table, let us take an over-all view of the chart. Certain general features are easily visible. The active nonmetals occupy a triangular region in the upper right corner, while the bulk of the remainder is taken up by metals, including the transitionals. Between these two major regions lies a small group of elements intermediate in chemical properties between metals and nonmetals. This small group, called *amphoteric* elements or *metalloids,* lies along a diagonal line from boron to astatine and is shown outlined in darker ruling on the chart. These are borderline elements and can be thought of as separating the metallic region from the nonmetallic, or as an area where the metallic and nonmetallic regions tend to overlap.

The Periodic Table is reprinted for ready reference as the endpaper of this book. The symbols for the elements of the various regions are set in different kinds of type for emphasis. Symbols in black letters are for metals, those in open (white) letters are nonmetals, while crosshatched letters, being intermediate between black and white, refer to the intermediate class of metalloids. Noble gas symbols are white against a crosshatched background.

If a metalloid reacts with an active nonmetal, such as fluorine, what type of ion would you expect the metalloid to form?

A negative ion. **section 54**

A positive ion. **section 59**

A neutral ion. **section 64**

50

[from section 44]

YOUR ANSWER: The number of isotopes an atom has determines its chemical identity.

No. There is no relation here. Your selection of this answer suggests that you would do well to study Chapter 1 again.

However, if you wish to continue, then return to section 44 and select another answer.

51

[from section 60]

YOUR ANSWER: The elements in the Periodic Table are arranged horizontally in increasing order of atomic numbers.

You are correct. Starting with hydrogen (H), and proceeding left-to-right across Row 1, then Row 2, Row 3, etc., the atomic numbers increase regularly from 1 to 103. This is not always true of the atomic weights. They also increase, but not regularly, and there are instances where the order is actually reversed; Argon (Ar) and potassium (K) is one of three cases where this happens. In this connection, recall that in Chapter 1 we saw that the atomic number is a more fundamental property of atoms than the atomic weight.

All right. So they are in the order of atomic numbers. But why the odd division into rows of varying lengths? The answer lies in the consideration of other properties of the elements than atomic number. The arrangement in the table is based on the location of electrons in the various energy levels which we have previously designated as *K, L, M,* etc., and in the sublevels designated *s, p, d,* and *f*.

Elements with similar outer electronic arrangements are lined up vertically, since the arrangement of the outer layers of electrons is responsible for the chemical behavior of the elements; this means that elements in the same vertical column are likely to be very similar to each other.

The most striking set of related elements are the six elements of the column numbered "0," which is entered in the chart twice, at extreme right and left. These elements are all gases under normal conditions, and have very little tendency to enter into chemical combinations. Because of this low degree of reactivity, they are known as "inert" or "noble" gases.

What unique characteristic of these noble gases causes them to be so very unreactive?

They are unreactive because they have just enough electrons to completely fill their outer energy levels. **section 46**

They are unreactive because they are gases. **section 56**

They appear unreactive because they exist only in very tiny amounts.
section 61

52
[from section 46]

YOUR ANSWER: The elements chlorine, bromine, and iodine are placed in a column adjacent to the noble gas column because they so nearly resemble noble gases in properties.

No! The properties of these three elements are similar, but they are not similar in properties to the noble gases. Chlorine is found in the compound table salt; bromine is used in gasoline, and as we learned in Chapter 1, smells bad. Iodine is used in medicine as a disinfectant and germicide because it reacts strongly with infectious agents. These elements are decidedly *not* inert; they are in fact a family of active nonmetals.

Go back to section 46 and choose another answer.

53
[from section 58]

YOUR ANSWER: The alkali metals are placed in a column adjacent to the noble gases because each of these metals has just one electron more than the number present in the adjacent noble gas.

You are correct. Since the elements are arranged horizontally in the order of increasing atomic number, and since the atomic number is also the number of electrons in the atom, it follows that an element immediately preceding a noble gas will have one less electron than the noble gas, and an element immediately following a noble gas will have one more electron than the noble gas. Since every halogen has one electron less than a noble gas, and every alkali metal has one electron more than a noble gas, it follows that the noble gas column must be sandwiched between the columns for the halogens and the alkali metals. It is convenient to show the noble gases twice in the Periodic Table, both at extreme right and extreme left, since each gas ends one period of the table and begins the next period.

Now let us extend these ideas to other families. Notice that in the Periodic Table, the column next to the alkali metals contains the elements beryllium (Be), magnesium (Mg), calcium (Ca), strontium (Sr), barium (Ba), and radium (Ra). This is called the "alkaline-earth" family of metals.

What must be the electron structures of these elements to justify their placement in the table at this location?

They must lack 2 electrons of noble gas structure. **section 48**

They must each possess 2 electrons more than the preceding noble gas. **section 62**

54

[*from section 49*]

YOUR ANSWER: I would expect that a metalloid, reacting with fluorine, would form a negative metalloid ion.

No. This is not reasonable. If fluorine acquires an electron to form a negative ion, it would not be possible for the metalloid to gain an electron from fluorine in the same reaction.

Return to section 49 and choose another answer.

55

[*from section 44*]

YOUR ANSWER: The number of neutrons an atom has determines its chemical identity.

No! Isotopes of the same element differ in the number of neutrons they contain. Certainly, then, the number of neutrons cannot determine the identity of the element.

Return to section 44 and select another answer.

56

[*from section 51*]

YOUR ANSWER: The noble gases are unreactive because they are gases.

No. Being gases is not unique with these elements. Hydrogen, oxygen, and chlorine are also gases, and are very reactive.

Return to section 51 and try again.

57

[*from section 62*]

YOUR ANSWER: I would expect neodymium to resemble uranium more strongly than praseodymium.

No. In these groups, sometimes called the inner transitionals, it is reasonable to expect horizontal relationships to be more important than vertical relationships.

Return to section 62 and choose the correct answer.

58

[*from section 46*]

YOUR ANSWER: The elements chlorine, bromine, and iodine are located in a column immediately preceding the noble gases because each lacks exactly one electron of being electronically identical with the adjacent noble gas.

You are correct. As we saw in Chapter 1, each of these elements lacks one electron of having a complete outer shell, whereas the outer shell of each noble gas is complete.

This group of elements—chlorine, bromine, and iodine, with the addition of fluorine and astatine—is called the "halogen family" of elements. Now let us turn our attention to another "family," the alkali metals: lithium, sodium, potassium, rubidium, cesium, and francium. Find this family in the table.

Why do you think the alkali metal elements are also placed adjacent to the noble gas family?

Because they are so similar to halogens. **section 47**

Because they each have just one electron in addition to the number present in the adjacent noble gas. **section 53**

Because they readily form positive ions. **section 65**

59

[*from section 49*]

YOUR ANSWER: I would expect a metalloid, reacting with fluorine, to form a positive metalloid ion.

You are correct. Fluorine has such a great tendency to acquire an additional electron and form a negative fluoride ion, that it causes the metalloid to give up an electron and hence to become a positive ion.

We have now considered all of the known elements, except hydrogen, and assigned them an individual location on our Periodic Table of the elements. Look at the location of hydrogen on the chart and note that hydrogen is all by itself.

Which of the statements below seems more reasonable to you?

Hydrogen is given the position at the top because it is the lightest known element. **section 63**

Hydrogen is placed by itself because its chemical behavior is not closely similar to that of any other element. **section 67**

[*from section 44*]

YOUR ANSWER: The number of protons in an atom determines its chemical identity.

You are correct. All atoms of any one element are alike in the number of protons in their nuclei, hence in the number of positive charges on their nuclei, and the number of electrons which they can hold.

The 103 known elements differ greatly in their properties, both physical and chemical. Fortunately, it is possible to classify and systematize these elements; otherwise chemistry would be a meaningless collection of unrelated facts.

A very useful arrangement of the elements in chart form is the Periodic Table, which was devised by the Russian chemist, Dmitri Mendeleef, about 1870. This table is here printed in a fully extended form, and on the inside back cover in a somewhat more compact version.

Let us examine this chart. You will note that the symbol for each element is given and also its atomic number and atomic weight.

Study this chart and decide which of the three statements below best describes it.

The elements are arranged horizontally in increasing order of atomic weights. **section 45**

The elements are arranged horizontally in increasing order of atomic numbers. **section 51**

The elements are arranged horizontally in increasing sequence of both atomic weights and atomic numbers. **section 66**

---

																								1 H 1.0									
	O	IA	IIA	IIIB															IVB	VB	VIB	VIIB	VIII			IB	IIB	IIIA	IVA	VA	VIA	VIIA	O
1		1 H 1.0																														1 H 1.0	2 He 4.0
2	2 He 4.0	3 Li 6.9	4 Be 9.0																									5 B 10.8	6 C 12.0	7 N 14.0	8 O 16.0	9 F 19.0	10 Ne 20.2
3	10 Ne 20.2	11 Na 23.0	12 Mg 24.3																									13 Al 27.0	14 Si 28.1	15 P 31.0	16 S 32.1	17 Cl 35.5	18 Ar 39.9
4	18 Ar 39.9	19 K 39.1	20 Ca 40.1	21 Sc 45.0															22 Ti 47.9	23 V 50.9	24 Cr 52.0	25 Mn 54.9	26 Fe 55.8	27 Co 58.9	28 Ni 58.7	29 Cu 63.5	30 Zn 65.4	31 Ga 69.7	32 Ge 72.6	33 As 74.9	34 Se 79.0	35 Br 79.9	36 Kr 83.8
5	36 Kr 83.8	37 Rb 85.5	38 Sr 87.6	39 Y 88.9															40 Zr 91.2	41 Nb 92.6	42 Mo 95.9	43 Tc	44 Ru 101	45 Rh 103	46 Pd 106	47 Ag 108	48 Cd 112	49 In 115	50 Sn 119	51 Sb 122	52 Te 128	53 I 127	54 Xe 131
6	54 Xe 131	55 Cs 133	56 Ba 137	57 La 139	58 Ce 140	59 Pr 141	60 Nd 144	61 Pm	62 Sm 150	63 Eu 152	64 Gd 157	65 Tb 159	66 Dy 163	67 Ho 165	68 Er 167	69 Tm 169	70 Yb 173	71 Lu 175	72 Hf 178	73 Ta 181	74 W 184	75 Re 186	76 Os 190	77 Ir 192	78 Pt 195	79 Au 197	80 Hg 201	81 Tl 204	82 Pb 207	83 Bi 209	84 Po	85 At	86 Rn
7	86 Rn	87 Fr	88 Ra	89 Ac	90 Th 232	91 Pa	92 U 238	93 Np	94 Pu	95 Am	96 Cm	97 Bk	98 Cf	99 Es	100 Fm	101 Md	102 No	103 Lw															

PERIODIC CHART OF THE ELEMENTS (LONG FORM)

61

[*from section 51*]

YOUR ANSWER: The noble gases appear unreactive because they exist only in very tiny amounts.

Not so—on two counts!

First, one of the noble gases, argon (Ar), makes up 1 per cent of the air (nearly one hundred times the proportion of carbon dioxide), and hence can hardly be described as existing in a "very tiny amount." Xenon (Xe), krypton (Kr), and radon (Rn), it is true, are quite rare, with helium (He) and neon (Ne) intermediate in abundance.

Second, there are many elements which are less abundant than noble gases, and which are at the same time highly active. A prime example of this is the element francium (Fr) which is one of the two most reactive elements, but one which is extremely rare.

Return to section 51 and try again.

62

[*from section 53*]

YOUR ANSWER: The alkaline-earth elements occupy their position in the table because each possesses 2 electrons more than the preceding noble gas.

You are correct. Each element of this family has 2 electrons in its outer shell, and thus should be located two columns away from the noble gas column.

We can now distinguish between the two great classes of elements, the metals and the nonmetals. The metals are those elements which have a small number of electrons (1, 2, or 3) in their outer shells, and appear in the columns just to the right of the noble gas column. They characteristically form positive ions by loss of external electrons.

Nonmetals, on the other hand, lack a few electrons (1, 2, or 3) of complete outer shells, appear to the left of noble gases in the table, and tend to form negative ions.

So far we have emphasized the similarity of elements in the vertical columns, or families. However, in the central region of the chart, this relation no longer is so important, and is displaced by a similarity between horizontal neighbors. This is because of the fact discussed in Chapter 1 that in the fourth- and higher-periods, electrons successively fill up the *d* levels and, in the sixth and seventh periods, both *f* and *d* levels, before any change appears in the *p* and *s* levels. Hence, there are many elements in each period which have the *same* number of *p* and *s* electrons (2 or 3) in their outer shells, but differ in number of *d* (or *f*) electrons only. All these elements are metals. So it is reasonable to expect these elements to show horizontal similarities. The vertical similarities are more important in the *A* columns, whereas horizontal relationships predominate for elements of the *B* columns.

These elements in the *B* columns are known as "transition metals," though it should be noted that some authorities prefer that zinc, cadmium, and mercury (column II-*B*) not be included with the transition metals.

Consider now the elements with atomic numbers 57 to 71 and 89 to 103. In both of these series a layer of *f*-level electrons is filling up, while the outer *s, p,* and *d* levels remain the same.

Would you expect the element neodymium (Nd) to resemble more closely uranium (U) or praseodymium (Pr)?

Praseodymium. **section 49**

Uranium. **section 57**

63

[*from section 59*]

YOUR ANSWER: Hydrogen is given the position at the top because it is the lightest element known.

Not so. Hydrogen *is* the lightest element known, but that is *not* the reason for its location. Density (or lightness) is a physical property, and chemical properties, not physical properties, are the basis of the periodic chart of the elements.

Return to section 59 and consider the question again.

64

[*from section 49*]

YOUR ANSWER: I would expect that a metalloid reacting with fluorine would form a neutral ion.

A neutral ion? That is a contradiction in terms; there is no such thing as a neutral ion. All ions are charged!

Return to section 49 and choose another answer.

65

[*from section 58*]

YOUR ANSWER: The alkali metals are placed in a column adjacent to the noble gases because they so readily form positive ions.

No. This is not the *best* answer to the question. It is true they do form positive ions, but several families of elements that form positive ions are *not* placed next to the noble gases.

Return to section 58 and choose a better answer.

66

[*from section 60*]

YOUR ANSWER: The elements in the Periodic Table are arranged horizontally in increasing sequence of both atomic weights and atomic numbers.

Not quite. Notice the numerical relations of iodine (I) and tellurium (Te), also cobalt (Co) and nickel (Ni). This should show you that one of these two relationships is not correct.

Return to section 60 and choose the correct answer.

67

[*from section 59*]

YOUR ANSWER: Hydrogen is placed by itself because its chemical behavior is not closely similar to that of any other element.

You are correct. The classification of elements in the table is organized to show chemical similarities. Hydrogen is in many respects a unique element.

Notice that the hydrogen block at the top is tied in by lines to both the alkali metal family and the halogen family. This is because hydrogen reacts with the alkali metal sodium much as would the halogen, chlorine; and reacts with the halogen, chlorine, much as does the alkali metal sodium, thus

Na*Cl* and Na*H*	*Na*Cl and *H*Cl
– similar position –	– similar position –
H acts somewhat like a halogen	H acts somewhat like an alkali

But although hydrogen reacts with both the alkali metals and with the halogen nonmetals, it does not act exactly like either group.

When hydrogen combines with the alkali metal sodium, it forms a salt, sodium hydride, formula NaH, in which the hydrogen forms a negative ion (H^-) much like chlorine which forms Cl^-. When elements combine to form ions, *ionic* compounds are formed; such compounds are sometimes referred to as *electrovalent* compounds.

On the other hand, when hydrogen combines with the nonmetal chlorine it does *not* form a positive ion,* nor does it form a negative ion. This compound, HCl, is *nonionic;* such compounds are often referred to as *molecular* or *covalent* compounds.

The similarities of and differences between these two major classes of compounds, *ionic* and *covalent,* together with the bonding forces within these compounds, will be the subject of Chapter 3.

Now continue with section 68 and a review of this chapter.

* The so-called "hydrogen ion" of acids, whose formula is often written as "H+," will be discussed in detail in Chapter 10, Acid-Base Equilibria.

CHAPTER 2—THE PERIODIC TABLE—SUMMARY

The *Periodic Table* is a two-dimensional array designed to emphasize relationships between the elements. In it the elements are arranged horizontally in the order of their atomic numbers, and vertically according to the configuration of electrons in the outer orbitals. The horizontal rows are called *periods,* and the vertical columns are called *groups* or *families.*

The family similarities are especially marked in the case of the *noble gases,* in which there are no orbitals which are only partly filled; the *halogens,* which lack a single electron of a noble gas structure; the *alkali metals,* which have one electron in addition to those of a noble gas; and the *alkaline-earth metals,* which have two electrons more than a noble gas.

The noble gases have very little tendency to react chemically, the halogens can readily gain one electron to become an ion with a charge of -1, while the alkali and alkaline-earth elements can easily lose electrons to form ions of charge $+1$ and $+2$, respectively.

The elements can be classified as *nonmetals, metals,* or *metalloids,* with the noble gases as a separate category. The nonmetals occupy the upper right corner of the chart as usually presented, and the metals all the rest. The metalloids are elements that lie along a diagonal band separating metals from nonmetals; they show mixed metallic and nonmetallic properties.

The metals through the central portion of the chart are characterized by similarities with their neighbors in the same period, which are sometimes more marked than vertical similarities. This is caused by the fact that they have *d* orbitals which are partly filled, while their outer orbitals are nearly identical. These are the *transition metals.*

Two groups of elements within the transition category show even greater horizontal resemblances. These are the *lanthanide* and *actinide* series, in which *f* orbitals are partly filled.

Hydrogen occupies a special position in the chart, since it has only a single electron (and its reactions are unique).

You will find a brief quiz in the next section.

69
[*from section 68*]

CHAPTER 2—REVIEW QUESTIONS AND PROBLEMS

Use the information contained in the Periodic Table and the list of elements, to answer the following questions.

1. Classify each of the following elements (symbol and atomic numbers given) as an actinide metal, a lanthanide metal, a transition metal, a metal other than the above, a nonmetal, a metalloid, or a noble gas: Al (13), As (33), Ba (56), C (6), Ca (20), Ce (58), Cl (17), Fe (26), Fm (100), Ge (32), Ho (67), I (53), K (19), Kr (36), Mo (42), N (7), He (2), Na (11), O (8), P (15), Pt (78), Rb (37), S (16), U (92), Zr (40).

2. Name the element which lacks one electron of the structure of krypton. Name the element with one electron more than krypton. Name the element with two electrons more than krypton. Name the families to which these three elements belong.

3. Select the *more metallic* element from each of the following pairs:

Na, Rb	Ca, Ra
Na, Mg	Al, B
O, F	Bi, I
Se, Br	Bi, N
As, Sb	As, Ge

4. There are three pairs of elements in which the one with the larger atomic number has the smaller atomic weight. Find these, and explain how it is possible for this to happen.

Turn to section 545 for the answers, then go on to section 70.

[*from section 69*]

Chapter 3

CHEMICAL BONDS

As we have seen in Chapter 2, the Periodic Table is divided into four segments occupied by, respectively, the noble gases, the nonmetals, the metals, and the metalloids. We will now look into the types of combinations that can be formed between elements of the various classes.

Although some of the noble gases can form compounds with active nonmetals such as fluorine, these are so rare that we will not consider them in detail here. We will also neglect compounds formed between metals, as these are of only secondary importance.

At the close of Chapter 2 it was pointed out that hydrogen is unique among elements in that it can act similarly to a halogen in combining with alkali metals, and can also act similarly to an alkali metal in combining with a halogen. Hydrogen plays a distinctly different role in these two types of compounds, representative of the two major kinds of chemical bonding: ionic and covalent. We will consider first ionic, later covalent bonding.

IONIC BONDS

Ionic bonds form readily between metals and nonmetals; metals lose electrons and nonmetals acquire them. This is often thought of as a process of lending electrons by the metal and borrowing them by the nonmetal. The metal is a *donor* of electrons, the nonmetal an *acceptor*. The *process* of electron transfer, its energy relations, etc., will be dealt with in Chapter 12 on oxidation-reduction reactions; our interest here is with the nature of the bond formed.

We can think of this electron transfer as a tendency for both donor and acceptor atoms to attain the electronic structure of a noble gas. For example, consider the reaction of fluorine with lithium. We can write the symbol for each element surrounded by a number of dots representing the external, or valence, electrons. (The inner shells of electrons, since they are not involved in the compound formation, are not indicated by dots.) Thus, for atoms of fluorine and lithium:

$$:\overset{..}{\underset{..}{F}}\cdot \qquad \cdot Li$$

Then when an electron is transferred from lithium to fluorine, we can write an equation (the arrow means "gives," "yields," or "produces"):

$$:\overset{..}{\underset{..}{F}}\cdot + \cdot Li \longrightarrow Li^{+} + :\overset{..}{\underset{..}{F}}:^{-}$$

(Remember that removal of an electron from an atom leaves an unbalanced nuclear positive charge, so that the resulting lithium ion has a positive charge.)

Write the electron-dot formula for a magnesium atom.

$:\overset{..}{\underset{..}{Mg}}:$ **section 75**

$:\overset{..}{\underset{..}{Mg}}::$ **section 81**

$Mg:$ **section 87**

71
[from section 87]

YOUR ANSWER: The electron-dot formula for oxygen is $:\overset{..}{\underset{..}{O}}$

You are correct. The two *K*-level electrons are not shown as they play no part in bonding; the six *L* electrons are shown.

We have determined the dot formulas of magnesium and oxygen to be

$$Mg: \qquad \text{and} \qquad :\overset{..}{\underset{..}{O}}$$

Which equation correctly represents the combination of magnesium and oxygen atoms to give magnesium oxide?

$Mg: + :\overset{..}{\underset{..}{O}} \longrightarrow Mg:\overset{..}{\underset{..}{O}}:$ **section 77**

$$Mg\!: + :\overset{\cdot\cdot}{\underset{\cdot\cdot}{O}} \longrightarrow Mg^{++} + :\overset{\cdot\cdot}{\underset{\cdot\cdot}{O}}:^{--}$$ **section 83**

$$Mg\!: + :\overset{\cdot\cdot}{\underset{\cdot\cdot}{O}} \longrightarrow Mg^{+} + :\overset{\cdot\cdot}{\underset{\cdot\cdot}{O}}:^{-}$$ **section 89**

72
[*from section 83*]

YOUR ANSWER: The equation for the combination of atoms of magnesium and fluorine is

$$Mg\!: + :\overset{\cdot\cdot}{\underset{\cdot\cdot}{F}}\cdot \longrightarrow Mg\cdot^{+} + :\overset{\cdot\cdot}{\underset{\cdot\cdot}{F}}:^{-}$$

No. A metal such as magnesium cannot lose only *one* of its 2 outer electrons. Thus there is no ion such as $Mg\cdot^{+}$

Return to section 83 and choose again.

73
[*from section 88*]

YOUR ANSWER: The equation for the combination of sodium and hydrogen atoms is

$$Na\cdot + H\cdot \longrightarrow H^{+} + Na\!:^{-}$$

No. *Neither* ion in this equation has achieved a noble gas structure. Remember, also, that a metal tends to form *positive* ions.

Return to section 88 and choose another answer.

74
[*from section 98*]

YOUR ANSWER: One electron will be shared in a Cl_2 molecule.

No. It is true that each atom will provide one electron to the sharing arrangement, but if *each atom provides one electron* to be shared, then more than one electron will be shared.

Return to section 98 and choose another answer.

75
[*from section 70*]

YOUR ANSWER: The electron-dot formula for magnesium is

$$:\ddot{\underset{\cdot\cdot}{Mg}}:$$

No. You have shown the magnesium atom as having a complete outer shell, like a noble gas. This cannot be true.

Return to section 70 and try again.

76
[*from section 87*]

YOUR ANSWER: The electron-dot formula for oxygen is O :

No. This would give an oxygen atom 2 outer electrons, like magnesium, whereas it actually *lacks* 2 electrons of a completed shell.

Return to section 87 and choose the correct answer.

77

[*from section 71*]

YOUR ANSWER: The equation for the combination of magnesium and oxygen atoms is

$$\mathrm{Mg}\!:+:\underset{\cdot\cdot}{\ddot{\mathrm{O}}}\longrightarrow \mathrm{Mg}:\underset{\cdot\cdot}{\ddot{\mathrm{O}}}:$$

No. Both atoms are converted to *ions* in this process, and you have not shown ions.

Return to section 71 and try again.

78

[*from section 88*]

YOUR ANSWER: The equation for the combination of sodium and hydrogen atoms is

$$\mathrm{Na}\cdot+\mathrm{H}\cdot\longrightarrow \mathrm{Na}:\mathrm{H}$$

No. The tendency is for *both* atoms to become ions, which this answer does not show.

Return to section 88 and try again.

79

[*from section 91*]

YOUR ANSWER: Four pairs of electrons will be shared in a molecule of CH_4.

You are correct. It is better to regard these as 4 pairs of electrons, rather than just 8 electrons, since the covalent bond is a *shared pair* of electrons. We visualize the CH_4 molecule as in Figure 14.

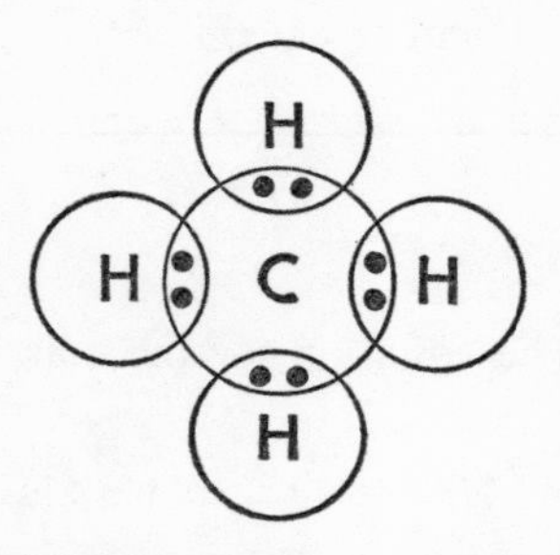

Figure 14. Electron structure of CH_4 molecule.

Note that each hydrogen atom now has 2 electrons (the electronic structure of helium) and that carbon has 8 valence electrons (the electronic structure of neon).

Let us use our ability to interpret the Periodic Table to predict a chemical formula.

If a chlorine atom and a hydrogen atom are combined to form a molecule of hydrogen chloride, how many pairs of shared electrons will be involved?

A hydrogen chloride molecule involves 2 pairs of shared electrons.

section 92

A hydrogen chloride molecule involves 7 pairs of shared electrons.

section 100

A hydrogen chloride molecule involves 1 pair of shared electrons.

section 105

80

[*from section 98*]

YOUR ANSWER: Two electrons will be shared in a Cl_2 molecule.

You are correct. Each atom will contribute one electron to a sharing arrangement, thus forming a covalent bond consisting of a *shared pair* of electrons.

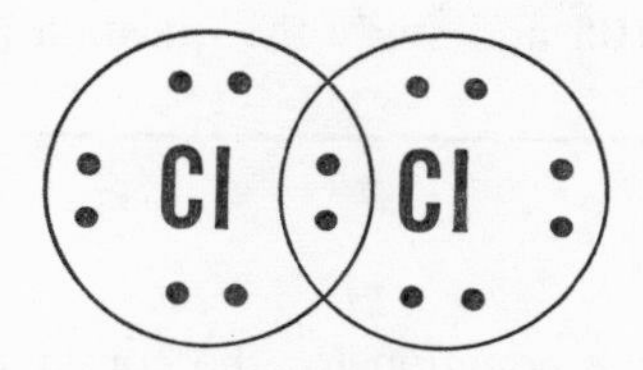

Figure 11. Valence electron arrangement in a Cl_2 molecule.

Hydrogen molecules, H_2, are also formed by the sharing of electrons.

How many electrons will be shared in a molecule of H_2?

One electron. **section 85**

Two electrons. **section 91**

Four electrons. **section 97**

81

[*from section 70*]

YOUR ANSWER: The electron-dot formula for magnesium is $:\overset{\cdot\cdot}{\underset{\cdot\cdot}{Mg}}::$

No. You have indicated dots for the electrons in the two outer shells. The correct notation shows dots for the outermost shell only.

Return to section 70 and try again.

82

[*from section 105*]

YOUR ANSWER: $:\underset{\cdot\cdot}{\overset{\cdot\cdot}{\text{O}}}:\underset{\cdot\cdot}{\overset{\cdot\cdot}{\text{Cl}}}:$ shows the correct structure of the hypochlorite ion.

Sorry, you are wrong. This is *not* an ion because it has no charge. All ions are charged.

Return to section 105 and study the question again.

83

[*from section 71*]

YOUR ANSWER: The equation for the combination of magnesium and oxygen atoms is

$$\text{Mg}: + :\underset{\cdot\cdot}{\overset{\cdot\cdot}{\text{O}}} \longrightarrow \text{Mg}^{++} + :\underset{\cdot\cdot}{\overset{\cdot\cdot}{\text{O}}}:^{--}$$

(MgO is the chemical formula for magnesium oxide.)

You are correct. The magnesium atom donates its two outer electrons to the oxygen atom, which is the acceptor. So the magnesium becomes a doubly positive ion and the oxygen a doubly negative ion in the compound magnesium oxide.

What will happen if a donor atom has two outer electrons, but the acceptor has space for only one?

The equation for the combination of atoms of magnesium and fluorine is written

$\text{Mg}: + :\underset{\cdot\cdot}{\overset{\cdot\cdot}{\text{F}}}\cdot \longrightarrow \text{Mg}\cdot^{+} + :\underset{\cdot\cdot}{\overset{\cdot\cdot}{\text{F}}}:^{-}$ **section 72**

$\text{Mg}: + 2:\underset{\cdot\cdot}{\overset{\cdot\cdot}{\text{F}}}\cdot \longrightarrow \text{Mg}^{++} + 2:\underset{\cdot\cdot}{\overset{\cdot\cdot}{\text{F}}}:^{-}$ **section 88**

$\text{Mg}: + :\underset{\cdot\cdot}{\overset{\cdot\cdot}{\text{F}}}\cdot \longrightarrow \text{Mg}^{++} + :\underset{\cdot\cdot\cdot}{\overset{\cdot\cdot}{\text{F}}}:^{--}$ **section 96**

84

[*from section 93*]

YOUR ANSWER: Water is an ionic compound.

Sorry, you are wrong. Oxygen is a nonmetal and hydrogen is an amphoteric element. It is not reasonable to predict they will lend and borrow electrons from each other to form an ionic compound.

Perhaps you were confused by the fact that hydrogen appears at the top of the alkali metal family. It is to avoid this very confusion that we placed hydrogen in a unique location, entirely by itself, and showed connections to both the alkali metal and halogen families.

Study the location of hydrogen on the chart again. Then turn back to section 93 and choose the correct answer.

85

[*from section 80*]

YOUR ANSWER: One electron will be shared in a molecule of H_2.

Sorry, you are wrong. The bond that holds these two hydrogen atoms together to form the hydrogen molecule is a shared *pair* of electrons.

Return to section 80 and choose another answer.

86
[*from section 98*]

YOUR ANSWER: Seventeen electrons will be shared in a Cl_2 molecule.

No, you are not right. Seventeen is the total number of electrons in *each* chlorine atom. They are not *all* going to be shared!

Return to section 98 and restudy the text material, then choose another answer.

87
[*from section 70*]

YOUR ANSWER: The electron-dot formula for magnesium is $\mathrm{Mg}\!:$

You are correct. We neglect the *K* and *L* levels of magnesium because they are complete and play no part in bond formation. The 2 outer electrons are indicated by a pair of dots.

What is the electron-dot formula for oxygen?

$:\!\ddot{\underset{\cdot\cdot}{\mathrm{O}}}$ **section 71**

$\mathrm{O}\!:$ **section 76**

$:\!\ddot{\underset{\cdot\cdot}{\mathrm{O}}}\!:$ **section 94**

88
[*from section 83*]

YOUR ANSWER: The equation for the combination of atoms of magnesium and fluorine is

$$\mathrm{Mg}\!: + 2\,:\!\ddot{\underset{\cdot\cdot}{\mathrm{F}}}\cdot \longrightarrow \mathrm{Mg}^{++} + 2\,:\!\ddot{\underset{\cdot\cdot}{\mathrm{F}}}\!:^{-}$$

(MgF_2 is the chemical formula for magnesium fluoride.)

You are correct. Since each fluorine atom can accept only one electron, and each magnesium atom can donate two, two fluorines are required to combine with one magnesium (it is impossible for one electron alone to be taken from a magnesium atom to give an ion such as $Mg\cdot^{+}$).

Now think again about the compound of hydrogen with an alkali metal such as sodium, with which we opened this chapter.

Which equation correctly represents the combination of sodium and hydrogen atoms?

$Na\cdot + H\cdot \rightarrow H^{+} + Na:^{-}$ **section 73**

$Na\cdot + H\cdot \rightarrow Na:H$ **section 78**

$Na\cdot + H\cdot \rightarrow Na^{+} + H:^{-}$ **section 98**

89

[*from section 71*]

YOUR ANSWER: The equation for the combination of magnesium and oxygen atoms is

$$Mg: + :\ddot{\underset{..}{O}} \longrightarrow Mg^{+} + :\ddot{\underset{..}{O}}:^{-}$$

This is not right. You have correctly shown ions with noble gas structures as the products, but the ionic charges are not right. There must be one + and one − sign shown for *each* electron transferred.

Return to section 71 and try another answer.

90

[*from section 104*]

YOUR ANSWER: Water has one covalent bond, and the formula HO.

This is what, as we have seen, John Dalton thought water to be. But we know better. Hydrogen needs *one* more electron, oxygen needs *two,* to attain noble gas structures. A molecule made up of *one* atom of each element cannot do this.

Return to section 104 and think this through again.

91

[*from section 80*]

YOUR ANSWER: Two electrons will be shared in a molecule of H_2.

You are correct. Let's visualize your answer:

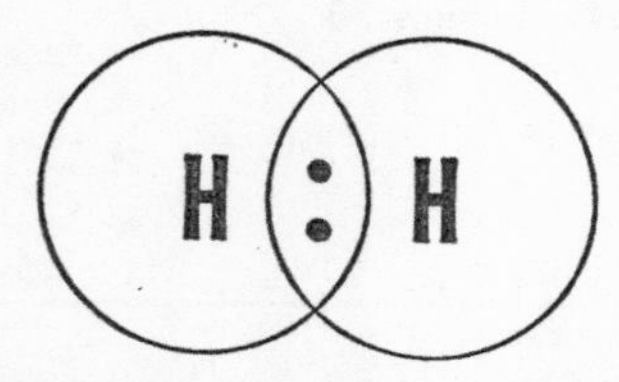

Figure 12. Shared pair of electrons in an H_2 molecule.

Up to this point we have limited our discussion to molecules in which there are only two atoms. Many molecules contain large numbers of atoms. Let us look at a somewhat more complex molecule, a methane molecule, CH_4. The carbon atom, atomic number 6, will of course have 6 electrons; but 2 of these will be in the *K* shell and only 4 of them, the *L* electrons, will be available for bonding. We note from the chart that carbon is an amphoteric element (a metalloid), and that hydrogen is also amphoteric. When these elements combine they will share electrons in such a fashion that both elements will acquire the electron structure of a noble gas.

Let us visualize the valence electron arrangement of a carbon atom as in Figure 13.

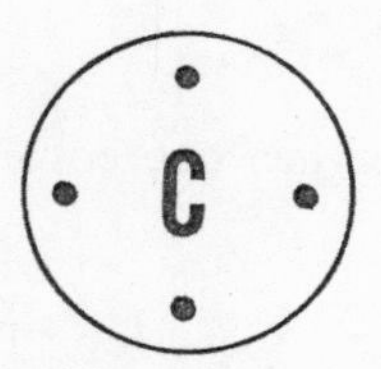

Figure 13. Valence electron arrangement of a carbon atom.

How many electrons are shared in a molecule of CH_4?

Four pairs of electrons. **section 79**

Four electrons. **section 103**

92

[from section 79]

YOUR ANSWER: A hydrogen chloride molecule involves 2 pairs of shared electrons.

You are wrong. Both the hydrogen and the chlorine atoms share electrons with each other in such a way that they *both* attain noble gas structures. Now a chlorine atom only needs *one* more electron; a hydrogen atom likewise needs only *one* more.

Return to section 79 and study it again. Then choose another answer.

93

[from section 105]

YOUR ANSWER: $\left(:\ddot{\underset{\cdot\cdot}{O}}:\ddot{\underset{\cdot\cdot}{Cl}}:\right)^-$ is the correct diagram for a hypochlorite ion.

You are correct. Oxygen has 6 valence electrons and chlorine has 7 valence electrons, and the single negative charge on the ion indicates that 1 electron has been contributed to the group from the outside. The electron count is correct at 14. The shared pair of electrons provides the covalent bond holding the complex ion together.

Other complex negative ions are formed in a similar fashion by covalent bonds linking the atoms, with one or more electrons furnished from an outside source, which provide the excess of electrons over protons required to have a negative ion. Note that two atoms can never form an ion unless electrons are gained or lost by the group. Study the two common complex ions shown below. (The electrons indicated by big black dots indicate the number of electrons furnished by an outside source and this number is identical with the charge on the ion as shown.)

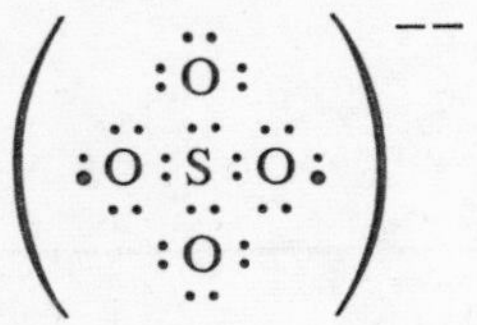

```
  (     ..     )--        (   ..  ..  ..   )-
  (    :O:     )          (  :O : Cl : O:  )
  (  .. .. ..  )          (   ..  ..  ..   )
  ( :O : S : O:)          (      :O:       )
  (  .. .. ..  )          (       ..       )
  (    :O:     )
  (     ..     )
```

sulfate ion
Formula: SO_4^{--}

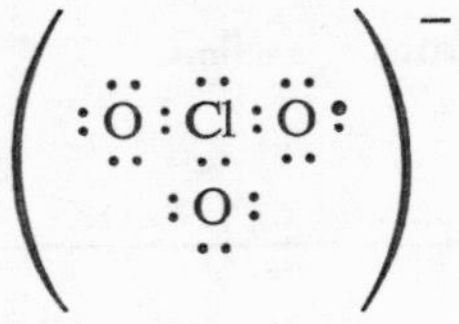

chlorate ion
Formula: ClO_3^-

Almost all of the important complex ions are negative except for the ammonium ion NH_4^+, in which the four hydrogen atoms are each bonded by a shared pair of electrons, with one electron being transferred to an outside group, thus forming the positive ammonium ion.

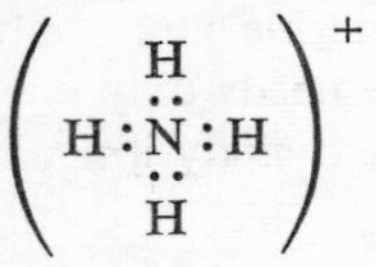

```
  (     H      )+
  (     ..     )
  (  H : N : H )
  (     ..     )
  (     H      )
```

Formula NH_4^+

Let us now take a look at one of the most important substances in the world, and from the chemist's standpoint, one of the most interesting and unique, namely water.

A glance at the Periodic Table will enable us to predict the kind of a compound that will be formed by oxygen and hydrogen when they combine to form water.

Would you predict that water is a molecular compound or an ionic compound?

Water is an ionic compound. **section 84**

Water is a molecular compound. **section 104**

94
[*from section 87*]

YOUR ANSWER: The electron-dot formula for oxygen is $:\ddot{\underset{\cdot\cdot}{O}}:$

No. You have made the oxygen atom resemble a noble gas, with a completed electronic shell. Oxygen lacks 2 electrons of completeness.

Return to section 87 and choose the correct answer.

95
[*from section 104*]

YOUR ANSWER: Water will have two covalent bonds and hence the formula H_2O.

You are correct. Two valence electrons from two hydrogen atoms and six valence electrons from an oxygen atom are just enough—with two shared pairs—to give us the required noble gas structure (shown in Figure 17).

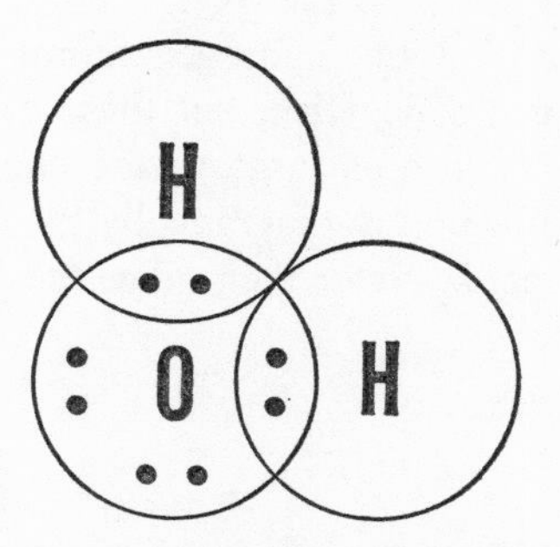

Figure 17. H_2O molecule.

Perhaps you are wondering why we diagram this molecule in this way. The reason is to explain some of the unusual properties of water which depend on a bond angle in the molecule. This bonding angle and its significance are explained in the next section.

INTERMEDIATE BONDS

In the preceding sections we have made the simplifying assumption that there is a clear-cut distinction between ionic and covalent bonds. But this is not always the case. There are many compounds which possess bonds which are intermediate between the two major classes. These are called *polar compounds,* and water is an excellent example. As pointed out already, water is classed as a covalent compound, and has the structure

$$\begin{array}{c} \text{H} \\ \cdot\cdot \\ :\text{O}:\text{H} \\ \cdot\cdot \end{array}$$

where the angle between the bonds is about 104°. We may inquire whether the bonding electrons are evenly spaced between the hydrogen and oxygen atoms. Studies on the relative attraction of various elements for electrons indicate that oxygen has nearly twice the attraction for electrons as hydrogen. Hence, the shared pairs of electrons will be located closer to the oxygen atom than to the hydrogen atoms. The result is that the hydrogen atoms each bear a positive charge and the oxygen a negative, but these can only be considered as *partial* charges, i.e., not as large as the charges of electrons and protons. They are indicated in diagrams by the Greek letter δ (delta) with the + or − symbol. Water then takes the form shown in Figure 18.

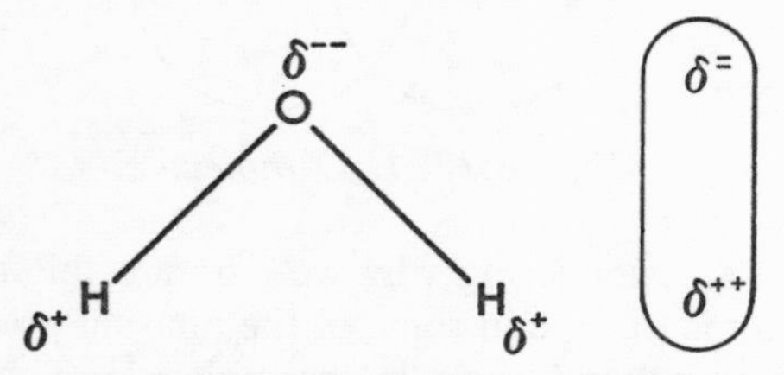

Figure 18. Dipole structure of H_2O.

The negative charge is clearly centered on the oxygen atom, but the center of the positive charge lies out in space, halfway between the hydrogen atoms. Therefore, the water molecule acts as if it were an electrical dipole, the electric analog of a permanent magnet. Water molecules tend to be attracted to and hang onto each other, just as a quantity of tiny magnets would. This may be pictured as in Figure 19.

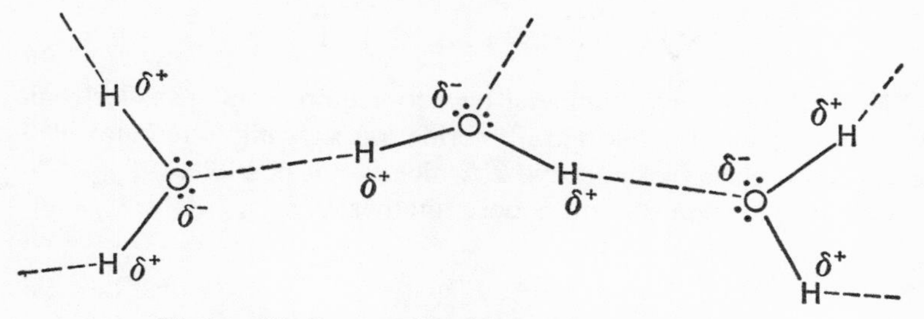

Figure 19. Intermolecular attraction in water.

Note that in Figure 19 there are many hydrogen atoms that serve as a kind of bridge between two oxygen atoms, even though they cannot be covalently bonded to both. This type of bridge plays an important role in chemistry, and is called a *hydrogen bond.* It is not, of course, a true bond in the sense that we have been using that word.

The hydrogen bonding between water molecules accounts for some of the unique properties of water, particularly its high melting and boiling temperatures compared with other similar compounds, and its high solvent power toward ionic compounds.

Which statement below best accounts for the high boiling point of water?

Hydrogen bonds hold the water molecules closer together, resulting in greater density, which raises the boiling point. **section 102**

Hydrogen bonds between water molecules have to be broken before the water can boil, hence the higher boiling point. **section 106**

96

[*from section 83*]

YOUR ANSWER: The equation for the combination of atoms of magnesium and fluorine is

$$\text{Mg}: + :\underset{\cdot\cdot}{\ddot{\text{F}}}\cdot \longrightarrow \text{Mg}^{++} + :\underset{\cdot\cdot\cdot}{\ddot{\text{F}}}:^{--}$$

No. Both metal and nonmetal tend to acquire noble gas electronic structures. You have selected a fluoride ion showing nine outer electrons, and a charge of negative 2, which is not possible.

Return to section 83 and choose another answer.

97

[*from section 80*]

YOUR ANSWER: Four electrons will be shared in a molecule of H_2.

You are wrong! Your answer is nonsense.

Each hydrogen atom has only 1 electron. Two such atoms could not have 4 electrons.

This answer shows that you are confused about covalent bonds. Return to section 80 and enter the sequence there.

98

[*from section 88*]

YOUR ANSWER: The equation for the combination of sodium and hydrogen atoms is

$$\text{Na}\cdot + \text{H}\cdot \longrightarrow \text{Na}^{+} + \text{H}:^{-}$$

You are correct. Sodium is the donor, hydrogen the acceptor, which means that hydrogen resembles a nonmetal in this reaction.

Substances in the solid state are composed of *crystals,* which are regular, three-dimensional, geometric arrays of atoms, ions, or molecules. The crystals of an ionic compound consist of such an array wherein alternate positions in the lattice are occupied by positive and negative ions. An example is shown in Figure 9.

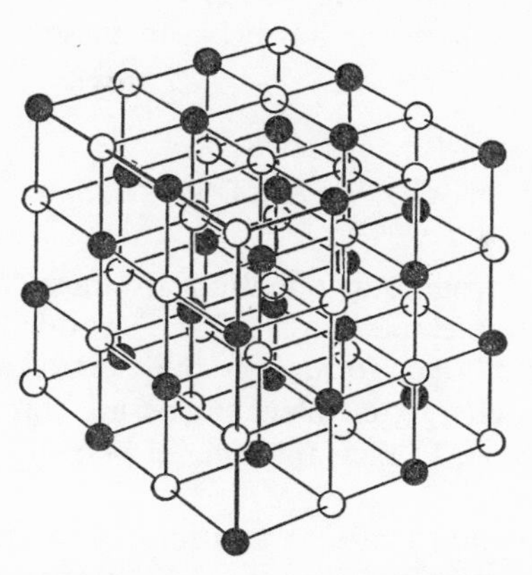

Figure 9. Sodium chloride crystal. Formula NaCl.

Note that each positive ion in this lattice is equally close to 6 negative ions, and similarly that each negative ion is equally close to 6 positive ions. The ions are held together by electrostatic forces of attraction; unlike charges attract. These ionic crystals tend to be hard and to have high melting temperatures, because for the crystal to break apart or melt, strong electrical forces must be broken.

It is interesting to see what happens when an ionic crystal such as solid sodium chloride melts and eventually changes to a gas. In melting, the ions of the crystal remain ions, but break away from each other to move about freely in the liquid state. There is still attraction between oppositely charged ions, so that on the average, each positive ion is surrounded by more negative ions than positive ones, and vice versa.

At the high temperature where NaCl becomes a gas, the picture changes markedly, because of the relatively large distances between the particles of a gas. In this state, the positive and negative ions pair off and form the discrete molecules, which will be discussed in the following section.

Let us summarize. As we have just seen, sodium chloride exists in the solid state as an ordered crystal lattice composed of positive ions and negative ions, and in the liquid state as a disordered collection of these same ions. Sodium chloride also exists at very high temperatures as gaseous molecules of NaCl, in which each sodium ion is effectively paired with a single chloride ion to form a molecule of NaCl, which is gaseous because the temperature is high enough to overcome the forces of attraction between these molecules.

COVALENT BONDS

We will now devote our attention to those compounds whose bonds, at the usual temperatures of our world, are essentially covalent. Unlike ionic bonds formed by the electrostatic forces between particles of unlike charge, covalent bonds are formed by the sharing of a pair of electrons. In fact, this *shared pair of electrons* is the covalent bond.

It is an experimental fact that two fluorine atoms will combine to form a diatomic molecule, F_2.

Note that each fluorine atom, $:\ddot{\underset{\cdot\cdot}{F}}\cdot$, lacks one electron of the favored "noble gas structure," and that a borrowing-lending arrangement is not possible because neither fluorine atom is *able* to lend. The problem is solved by sharing electrons, i.e., sharing a pair of electrons between the two atoms, resulting in the arrangement shown in Figure 10.

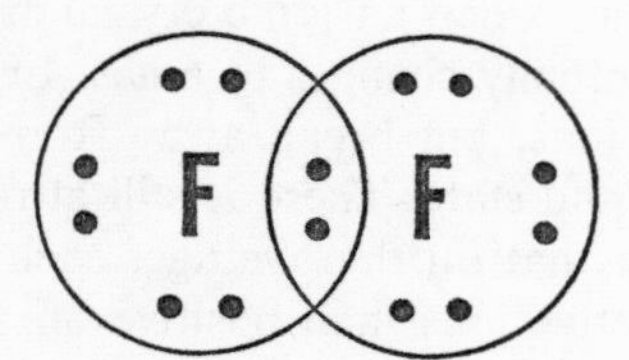

Figure 10. Covalent bonding in F_2 molecule (*compared with noble gas electron structure*).

(The circles are used to assign electrons to atoms; a pair of electrons within *two* circles is a shared pair of electrons, which forms a covalent bond.)

In a similar way, two chlorine atoms, atomic number 17, will form a covalent molecule, Cl_2.

How many electrons will be shared in a molecule of Cl_2?

One electron will be shared in a Cl_2 molecule. **section 74**

Two electrons will be shared in a Cl_2 molecule. **section 80**

Seventeen electrons will be shared in a Cl_2 molecule. **section 86**

99

[*from section 104*]

YOUR ANSWER: Water has three covalent bonds and hence must have the formula H_3O.

No. Three covalent bonds means three *pairs* of shared electrons. But oxygen only needs *two* to give it a noble gas structure.

Return to section 104, study it again, and select a better answer.

100

[*from section 79*]

YOUR ANSWER: A hydrogen chloride molecule involves 7 pairs of shared electrons.

No. It is true that a chlorine atom has 7 electrons, but that doesn't mean that hydrogen chloride has 7 shared pairs!

Go back to section 79, study it again, and choose another answer.

101
[*from section 105*]

YOUR ANSWER: $:\underset{\cdot\cdot}{\ddot{O}}\cdot\underset{\cdot\cdot}{\ddot{Cl}}:$ is the correct diagram for the hypochlorite ion.

Sorry. These two atoms are shown sharing only a *single* electron, which does not constitute a covalent bond. Hence it cannot be correct.

Return to section 105 and consider the question again.

102
[*from section 95*]

YOUR ANSWER: Hydrogen bonds hold the molecules of water closer together, resulting in greater density, which raises the boiling point.

No. Carbon tetrachloride is a liquid much more dense than water; yet, lacking hydrogen bonds, its boiling point is lower than that of water.

Return to section 95 and select the correct answer.

103
[*from section 91*]

YOUR ANSWER: Four electrons are shared in a molecule of CH_4.

Sorry, you are wrong. It is true that the carbon atom shares its 4 outer electrons, but the four hydrogen atoms each shares its 1 electron, so there are a total of 8 electrons shared. It is better, however, to consider them to be 4 *pairs* of electrons rather than 8 separate ones.

Return to section 91 and choose a better answer.

104

[*from section 93*]

YOUR ANSWER: Water is a molecular compound.

You are correct. Oxygen, a nonmetal, and hydrogen, an amphoteric element, are to be expected to form a molecular compound.

Use your knowledge of bond formation in covalent compounds to predict the number of covalent bonds and hence the formula of water.

Water has one covalent bond and the formula HO. **section 90**

Water has two covalent bonds and hence the formula H_2O. **section 95**

Water has three covalent bonds and hence the formula H_3O. **section 99**

105

[*from section 79*]

YOUR ANSWER: A hydrogen chloride molecule involves 1 pair of shared electrons.

You are correct. Hydrogen has one electron less than helium, and chlorine lacks one electron of the structure of argon; if each shares a pair of electrons with the other, each will acquire a noble gas electron structure. Let us diagram this:

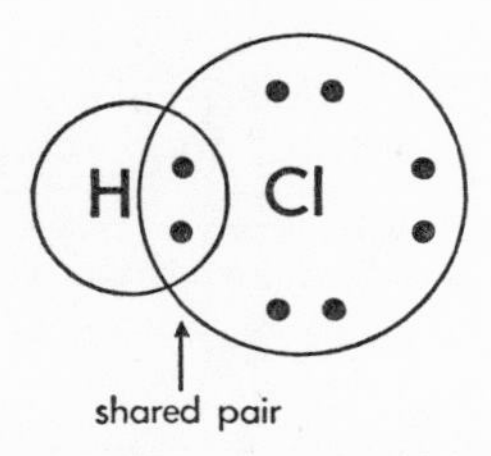

Figure 15. Electron structure of hydrogen chloride (HCl).

This ability of atoms to combine by the sharing of electrons accounts not only for the formation of molecules, but for the formation of covalently bonded units that are able to carry net charges, so that the covalently bonded unit is able to enter into ionic compounds with other ions. Such covalently bonded units that carry charges are called complex ions to distinguish them from simple monatomic ions.

Notice that all ions are charged, as previously discussed, and that all atoms and molecules are neutral.

Let us now consider these complex ions and their bonding. Let us suppose that an oxygen and a hydrogen atom are united by a single shared pair:

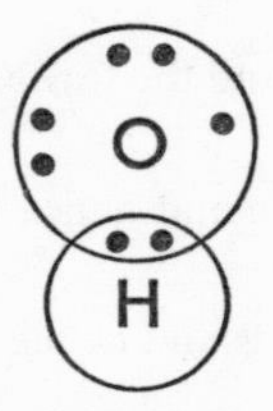

Figure 16. Six valence electrons from oxygen and one valence electron from hydrogen. This is one electron less than the number necessary to produce a molecule.

This group is *not* stable and has a very strong tendency to react with any available electron to form a charged group. Let us see what would occur if this group should react with a metal such as sodium:

$$\text{Na}\cdot + \cdot\ddot{\underset{\cdot\cdot}{\text{O}}}:\text{H} \longrightarrow \text{Na}^{+} + \left(:\ddot{\underset{\cdot\cdot}{\text{O}}}:\text{H}\right)^{-}$$

This forms a positive sodium ion (as has been discussed in the early part of this chapter), and a complex negative ion known as the hydroxide ion.

In a very similar fashion an oxygen atom and a chlorine atom can unite, and, with an electron secured from some metallic atom, form a stable hypochlorite ion.

Which of the diagrams below shows the correct structure of a hypochlorite ion?

$:\ddot{\underset{\cdot\cdot}{\text{O}}}:\ddot{\underset{\cdot\cdot}{\text{Cl}}}:$ **section 82**

$\left(:\ddot{\underset{\cdot\cdot}{\text{O}}}:\ddot{\underset{\cdot\cdot}{\text{Cl}}}:\right)^{-}$ **section 93**

$:\ddot{\underset{\cdot\cdot}{\text{O}}}\cdot\ddot{\underset{\cdot\cdot}{\text{Cl}}}:$ **section 101**

YOUR ANSWER: Hydrogen bonds between water molecules have to be broken before the water can boil, hence the higher boiling point.

You are correct. Breaking the hydrogen bonds requires a considerable amount of energy, so more energy has to be supplied to bring about boiling.

Hydrogen bonds can form between molecules of many kinds if they have a hydrogen atom attached to oxygen. The bond can form from this oxygen-hydrogen grouping to another oxygen atom or sometimes to a nitrogen or fluorine atom. In some instances, the oxygen-hydrogen group can be replaced by a nitrogen-hydrogen or fluorine-hydrogen. Thus, hydrogen bonding is important not only in water but in such comparable compounds as ammonia (NH_3) and hydrogen fluoride (HF). Some carbon compounds, such as sugar which contains several $-OH$ groups, show strong hydrogen bonding.

Another kind of bond that is intermediate between ionic and covalent is found in such compounds as hydrogen chloride (HCl). The pair of electrons which constitute the bond between the two atoms are attracted more strongly to the chlorine atom than the hydrogen, but not enough to cause ionization. The pure substance is a typical covalent compound, but when dissolved in water, ions form according to the reaction

$$HCl + H_2O \longrightarrow H_3O^+ + Cl^-$$

because the H_2O has a greater attraction for the proton (H^+) than the Cl^- has. This kind of reaction will be discussed in Chapter 10.

Now continue with the next section for a chapter summary.

107
[from section 106]

CHAPTER 3—CHEMICAL BONDS—SUMMARY

Three types of bonds have been discussed: the *ionic,* where one or more electrons are *transferred* from one atom (the *donor*) to another (the *acceptor*), resulting in the formation of a pair of ions; the *covalent,* wherein one or more *pairs* of electrons are *shared* between two atoms; and the *hydrogen bond,* which requires a third atom (hydrogen) to form a "bridge" between two atoms, which can only be oxygen, nitrogen, or fluorine.

Examples of ionic bonds are those in:

lithium fluoride	$Li^+ F^-$
magnesium oxide	$Mg^{++} O^{--}$
magnesium fluoride	$Mg^{++} (F^-)_2$
sodium hydride	$Na^+ H^-$

Ionic compounds in the solid state form *ionic crystals,* three-dimensional arrays with positive and negative ions at alternate positions in the lattice. The concept of "molecule" does not apply here.

Examples of covalent bonds are those in:

fluorine gas	F_2
chlorine gas	Cl_2
hydrogen gas	H_2
methane	CH_4

The structures of covalent compounds are often written with dots surrounding the atomic symbols to indicate the location of valence electrons, both those involved in bonding and those which remain unshared. Examples are:

H : H (H_2, hydrogen gas)

$$:\ddot{\underset{\cdot\cdot}{Cl}}:\ddot{\underset{\cdot\cdot}{Cl}}:$$ (Cl_2, chlorine gas)

$$\begin{matrix} & H & \\ & \cdot\cdot & \\ H: & C & :H \\ & \cdot\cdot & \\ & H & \end{matrix}$$ (CH_4, methane gas)

Complex ions, i.e., those which contain more than one atom, have covalent bonds between the atoms within the ion, but the ion is ionically bound to another ion of opposite charge. Examples are:

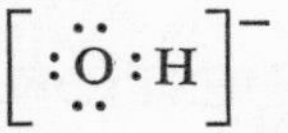

```
 ..    -
[:O:H ]                (OH-, hydroxide ion)
 ..

 .. ..  -
[:O:Cl:]               (OCl-, hypochlorite ion)
 .. ..

[    ..     ]--
[   :O:     ]
[ .. .. ..  ]
[:O:S:O:    ]          (SO4--, sulfate ion)
[ .. .. ..  ]
[   :O:     ]
[    ..     ]

[   H    ]+
[   ..   ]
[ H:N:H  ]             (NH4+, ammonium ion)
[   ..   ]
[   H    ]
```

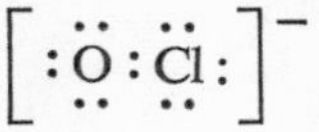

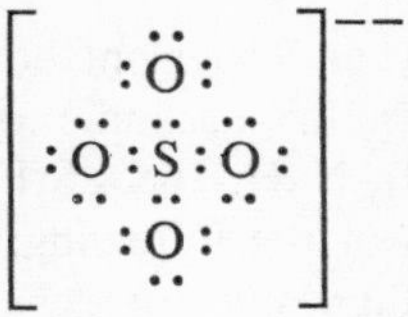

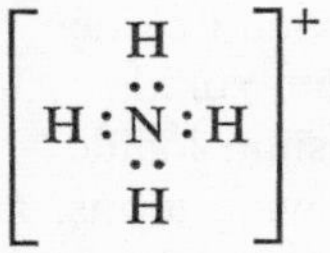

Water, H_2O, is an example of a *polar* compound. The hydrogen atoms have less power to attract electrons than the oxygen, so that the shared pairs are closer to the oxygen than to the hydrogens. This, together with the fact that the water molecule is angular rather than linear, means that the molecule is electrically unsymmetrical. The result is that there is an attraction between the positive part of one molecule and the negative parts of others, so that the water molecules tend to hang on to each other in bunches. This is called *molecular association.*

Go on with section 108 for a short quiz on this material.

[*from section 107*]

CHAPTER 3—REVIEW QUESTIONS AND PROBLEMS

1. Explain the distinction between ionic and covalent bonds.

2. Classify each of the following formulas as ionic or covalent: C_2H_4, NaCl, FeI_3, MgO, NH_3, CCl_4, NaH, H_2O, SrF_2, $C_6H_{12}O_6$.

3. Write a reasonable formula for each of the following:

Barium fluoride	Magnesium oxide
Aluminum bromide	Aluminum oxide
Silicon chloride	Radium sulfide
Actinium chloride	Potassium iodide

4. Tell what is meant by each of the following terms, and give examples:

Ionic crystal
Hydrogen bond
Molecular association
Complex ion

Turn to section 546 for the answers, then go on to section 109.

Chapter 4

UNITS AND DIMENSIONS

When a person asks a question that calls for a numerical answer, it is usually not satisfactory to give *just* a number for an answer. Suppose I ask John how long it took him to read a book and he answers, "Five." Does he mean "five days," "five minutes," or "five hours"?

My question required an answer with the *dimension* of time. Days, hours, minutes, and seconds are some of the various *units* used to indicate this dimension. The answer "Five" to the question has no real meaning unless some unit of time is stated or at least understood by implication or context.

UNITS IN CHEMISTRY

In chemistry, we want to be exact and explicit in our work, and the answer to a problem, in almost every case, *must* have a unit stated. If it is universally agreed and understood what the unit is, it may sometimes be omitted; but if the *slightest* doubt might arise, the unit should be stated.

If you have been reading this thoughtfully, you will realize that you already know a great deal about such matters. Here are a few simple questions that should not cause you any trouble.

Which of these answers is a reasonable response to the question, "How much does it weigh?"

Five. **section 114**

Sixty pounds per cubic foot. **section 119**

Sixty ounces. **section 125**

110

[*from section 125*]

YOUR ANSWER: The response to the question, "What weight of zinc . . . ?" should be expressed in terms of atomic weights.

No. It would be wise for you to take a moment to go back and review the concept of atomic weight as presented in Chapter 1 (section 26). You will then see why this does not represent a correct answer to the question.

Return to section 125, restudy it, and select another answer.

111

[*from section 116*]

YOUR ANSWER: $30 \frac{\text{lbs}}{\text{ft}^2} \times 10 \text{ ft} = 300 \text{ lbs/ft}.$

You are correct.

$$30 \frac{\text{lbs}}{\text{ft}^2} \times 10 \text{ ft} = 300 \frac{\text{lbs} \times \text{ft}}{\text{ft} \times \text{ft}} = 300 \frac{\text{lbs}}{\text{ft}}$$

Let's be sure you understand this. Test each of the following equations to determine whether it is wrong. Then choose the correct statement (or statements) below. Test the equations in alphabetical order —there may be more than one wrong one.

(a) (32 liters) (2.4 grams/liter) = 76.8 grams

(b) (32 grams) $\left(\frac{1}{64} \frac{\text{mole}}{\text{gram}}\right) = 0.50$ mole

(c) (22.4 liters/mole) (3 moles) = 67.2 liters

(d) (38 calories/gram) (14 grams) = 504 calories

(e) (12 liter-atmospheres) (4 grams/liter) = 48 gram-atmospheres

Choose the correct statement below.

(a) contains an error. **section 117**

(b) contains an error. **section 122**

(c) contains an error. **section 127**

(d) contains an error. **section 134**

(e) contains an error. **section 140**

I don't understand the question. **section 148**

112
[*from section 134*]

YOUR ANSWER: To convert 3 hours to minutes, we should multiply by 60.

No, this is not adequate.

$$(3 \text{ hours})(60) = 180 \text{ hours}.$$

This is obviously wrong, on two counts: (1) We *know* that 3 hours cannot equal 180 hours, and (2) we wanted the answer to be in minutes, and it is actually in hours.

Return to section 134 and try again.

113
[*from section 149*]

YOUR ANSWER: Both (a) and (b) are correct conversion factors.

Not quite. Let's check factor (a):

$$\frac{1 \text{ mole of NaOH}}{36.0 \text{ grams of NaOH}}.$$

From the table of atomic weights we find:

atomic weight of Na = 23.0
atomic weight of H = 1.0
atomic weight of O = 16.0

Total = 40.0, which is the formula weight of NaOH.

Therefore,

$$\frac{1 \text{ mole of NaOH}}{36.0 \text{ grams of NaOH}} = \frac{40.0 \text{ grams}}{36.0 \text{ grams}} = 1.11.$$

Hence this fraction has a value that is *not* unity, and therefore it cannot be a correct conversion factor.

Restudy section 149 and choose another answer.

114

[*from section 109*]

YOUR ANSWER: "Five" is a reasonable response to the question, "How much does it weigh?"

No, this is not adequate. Five what? Pounds? Tons? Grams? What unit of weight? Such a response, without any unit specified, is not a satisfactory answer.

Reread section 109 and select another answer.

115

[*from section 129*]

YOUR ANSWER: "1 min = 60 sec" represents a conversion factor relating seconds and minutes.

No. This is a true relation, of course, but it is *not* a conversion factor. Remember that a conversion factor is *always* a fraction equal to unity.

Restudy section 129 and choose another answer.

[*from section 125*]

YOUR ANSWER: The response to the question, "What weight of zinc . . . ?" should be expressed in terms of grams.

You are correct. Always check an answer to see whether it has the correct dimension, and you will have cleared a big obstacle out of your path to success with chemical problems.

MATHEMATICAL OPERATIONS WITH UNITS

Many people multiply and divide numbers without difficulty but do not realize that they can do the same thing with units. For example, how do you find the area of a rectangle 3 feet long and 4 feet wide?

Do you do this . . .	or this?
$3 \times 4 = 12$	$3 \text{ ft} \times 4 \text{ ft} = 12 \text{ ft}^2$*
Answer: 12 sq ft	Answer: 12 sq ft

Or again, how far can a car travel if it goes for 10 hours at an average rate of 50 miles/hour?

Do you do this . . .	or this?
$10 \times 50 = 500$	$10 \text{ }\cancel{\text{hours}} \times 50 \dfrac{\text{miles}}{\cancel{\text{hour}}} = 500 \text{ miles}$
Answer: 500 miles	(cancelling the "hours")
	Answer: 500 miles

It is possible to get the correct answer by either path, but *the best way to avoid mistakes* is to use the method on the right. Put your units with their respective numbers, and multiply and divide these units just as though they were numbers also.

Try this problem:

Multiply $30 \dfrac{\text{lbs}}{\text{ft}^2} \times 10 \text{ ft}$. What is your answer?

* The notation ft^2 means the same as *sq ft*, cm^3 means *cu cm*, and so on. Two units connected by a hyphen are to be considered as multiplied together. Thus 10 ft-lbs is the same as 10 (ft)(lbs); 10 ft^2 is the same as 10 (ft)(ft).

300 lbs/ft. **section 111**

300 lb-ft/ft^2. **section 126**

300 ft/lb. **section 142**

117

[*from section 111*]

YOUR ANSWER: There is a mistake in equation (a):

(32 liters)(2.4 grams/liter) = 76.8 grams.

No, there is no error in this statement. Recheck the problem until you see that it is correct. If you still are doubtful, turn back to section 116 and start in again. If you do see your trouble, return to section 111 and try the next answer.

118

[*from section 134*]

YOUR ANSWER: To convert 3 hours to minutes, we should multiply by 60 minutes.

No, this is not right. Let's try it and see what happens:

(3 hours)(60 minutes) = 180 hour-minutes.

We see at once that our units are wrong, and *if the units are wrong, the answer is wrong.*

Return to section 134 and try again.

119

[*from section 109*]

YOUR ANSWER: "Sixty pounds per cubic foot" is a reasonable response to the question, "How much does it weigh?"

No, this is not right. The unit "lbs/cu ft" has the dimensions of density, not of weight. This would be a step toward answering the question "How much does it weigh?" but for a complete answer you would also need to know the volume of the object.

Return to section 109 and try again.

120

[*from section 141*]

YOUR ANSWER: To find the number of ampere-hours equivalent to 3 faradays, you should multiply 3 faradays by 26.8.

No, you are forgetting about units. Multiplying by a simple number such as 26.8 (no units) cannot change the units of what we start with. In this case we would get

$$(3 \text{ faradays})(26.8) = 80.4 \text{ faradays}$$

whereas our question asked how to find the number of ampere-hours.

Return to section 134 and restudy the material there.

121

[*from section 137*]

YOUR ANSWER: (a) $\frac{1 \text{ atmosphere}}{15 \text{ lbs/in}^2}$ is not a correct conversion factor.

No, you are mistaken. This *is* correct. Since 1 atmosphere = 15 lbs/in^2, the ratio written above is equal to unity. A conversion factor must be a fraction with units stated, and it must be equal to unity.

Return to section 137 and choose more carefully.

122

[*from section 111*]

YOUR ANSWER: There is a mistake in equation (b):

$$(32 \text{ grams})\left(\frac{1}{64}\frac{\text{mole}}{\text{gram}}\right) = 0.50 \text{ mole.}$$

No, there is no error here. Recheck the problem until you see that it is correct. If you are still unconvinced, you had better turn back to section 116 and restudy the material. If you see the source of your trouble, return to section 111 and continue with the next entry.

123

[*from section 129*]

YOUR ANSWER: "60 sec = 1 min" represents a conversion factor relating seconds and minutes.

No. This is a true relation, of course, but it is *not* a conversion factor. Remember that a conversion factor is *always* a fraction equal to unity.

Restudy section 129 and choose another answer.

YOUR ANSWER: (a) is a correct conversion factor, but (b) is in error.

No, not correct. Let us check factor (a):

$$\frac{1 \text{ mole of NaOH}}{36.0 \text{ grams of NaOH}}.$$

From the table of atomic weights we find:

atomic weight of Na = 23.0
atomic weight of H = 1.0
atomic weight of O = 16.0
Total = 40.0, which is the formula weight of NaOH.

Therefore,

$$\frac{1 \text{ mole of NaOH}}{36.0 \text{ grams}} = \frac{40.0 \text{ grams}}{36.0 \text{ grams}} = 1.11.$$

Hence this fraction has a value which is *not* unity, and therefore it cannot be a correct conversion factor.

Restudy section 149 and choose another answer.

125
[*from section 109*]

YOUR ANSWER: "Sixty ounces" is a reasonable response to the question, "How much does it weigh?"

You are correct. Sixty ounces is the only answer given that has the dimension of weight, and hence the only correct answer to the question, "How much does it weigh?"

In chemistry, we commonly use the units of the metric system. When we want to answer the question "How heavy?" for example, our answer *must* have the dimension of weight; by the metric system, our answer will be in grams or some multiple or submultiple of a gram.

To answer the question:	We need the dimension:	And we choose as our unit in the metric system:
How heavy?	weight	gram (g)
How far?	length	meter (m)
How large (in volume)?	volume	liter (l)
How long (a duration)?	time	second (sec)

Now try this question:

To answer the question, "What weight of zinc will react with one liter of one-molar hydrochloric acid?" we should express our answer in terms of—

atomic weights. **section 110**

grams. **section 116**

liters. **section 132**

126
[from section 116]

YOUR ANSWER: $30 \frac{\text{lbs}}{\text{ft}^2} \times 10 \text{ ft} = 300 \text{ lb-ft/ft}^2$.

In a sense this is right, but you have not expressed it in the proper form. You have the unit "ft" in the numerator and "ft²" in the denominator. This should be simplified. Go ahead and do this, then return to section 116 and choose the correct answer.

127
[from section 111]

YOUR ANSWER: There is a mistake in equation (c):

$$(22.4 \text{ liters/mole})(3 \text{ moles}) = 67.2 \text{ liters}.$$

No, this statement contains no error. Recheck it until you see that it is correct. If you don't understand it, return to section 116 and restudy the material there. If you see why it is correct, then return to section 111 and check the next equation.

128
[from section 133]

YOUR ANSWER: Five moles of H_2 (at STP) will occupy 112 liters.

You are correct.

$$(5 \text{ moles})\left(\frac{22.4 \text{ liters}}{\text{mole}}\right) = 112 \frac{\text{liter-}\cancel{\text{moles}}}{\cancel{\text{mole}}} = 112 \text{ liters}.$$

You have learned to convert moles to gas volume (STP), and vice versa; you have also learned to convert moles to grams, and vice versa; therefore, you are in a position to convert grams directly to gas volumes at STP (and, of course, vice versa). For example, 2.0

grams of $H_2 = 1$ mole of $H_2 = 22.4$ liters of H_2 at STP. Using this equality, we can write conversion factors:

$$\frac{2 \text{ grams of } H_2}{22.4 \text{ liters of } H_2} = 1 = \frac{22.4 \text{ liters of } H_2}{2 \text{ grams of } H_2}$$

$$\frac{44.0 \text{ grams of } CO_2}{22.4 \text{ liters of } CO_2} = 1 = \frac{22.4 \text{ liters of } CO_2}{44.0 \text{ grams of } CO_2}$$

To find how many grams of CO_2 gas there are in 67.2 liters (at STP), you would calculate as follows:

$$(67.2 \text{ liters})\left(\frac{44.0 \text{ grams}}{22.4 \text{ liters}}\right) = 132 \frac{\cancel{\text{liter}}\text{-grams}}{\cancel{\text{liter}}} = 132 \text{ grams.}$$

Now you try this one:

How many liters of the gas NO are there in 100 grams (measured at STP)?

134 liters. **section 139**

74.7 liters. **section 151**

129

[*from section 141*]

YOUR ANSWER: To find the number of ampere-hours equivalent to 3 faradays, you should multiply 3 faradays by

$$\frac{26.8 \text{ ampere-hours}}{\text{faraday}}.$$

You are correct. This is the only answer given that will convert faradays to ampere-hours. Thus,

$$(3 \text{ faradays})\left(\frac{26.8 \text{ ampere-hours}}{\text{faraday}}\right) =$$

$$80.4 \frac{\cancel{\text{faraday}}\text{-ampere-hours}}{\cancel{\text{faraday}}} = 80.4 \text{ ampere-hours.}$$

Perhaps you wonder where we found the statement we gave you, that 26.8 ampere-hours = 1 faraday. We looked it up in a table of *conversion factors* or *equivalents*. Such tables are to be found in most of the reference handbooks of mathematical and scientific data. You will find a table of some useful equivalents in Table E of the Appendix. You will want to refer to this table from time to time.

Earlier you saw an example of how to make a conversion factor. There are just two steps: (1) Establish an equality of units. (2) Write a fraction equal to unity, using the terms of the equality as the numerator and denominator. From the equality $2a=b$, for example, we can write

$$\frac{2a}{b} = 1 = \frac{b}{2a}.$$

Both of the fractions shown are conversion factors.

There are two conversion factors for every pair of units; which factor to use in a particular problem depends upon the unit required in the answer. For example, if we asked you to find how many a's there are in 5 b's, you would write

$$5\cancel{b} \times \frac{2a}{\cancel{b}} = 10a,$$

but if we asked you to find how many b's there are in 5 a's, then you would write

$$5\cancel{a} \times \frac{b}{2\cancel{a}} = 2\tfrac{1}{2}b.$$

Now try this exercise:

Find a conversion factor relating seconds and minutes.

(Of course in this case you know the relation 60 sec = 1 min, but if you did not, you would look it up in Table E in the Appendix.

1 min = 60 sec. **section 115**

60 sec = 1 min. **section 123**

60. **section 136**

$\frac{1 \text{ min}}{60 \text{ sec}}$ or $\frac{60 \text{ sec}}{1 \text{ min}}$. **section 145**

130
[*from section 137*]

YOUR ANSWER: (b) $\frac{96{,}500 \text{ coulombs}}{6.02 \times 10^{23} \text{ electrons}}$ is not a correct conversion factor.

No, you are mistaken. The table of equivalents in the Appendix tells us:

(11) 1 faraday = 96,500 coulombs, and
(12) 1 faraday = 6.02×10^{23} electrons.

Since we know that quantities that are equal to the same thing are equal to each other, we can write

$$96{,}500 \text{ coulombs} = 6.02 \times 10^{23} \text{ electrons.}$$

From this equality, it follows that

$$\frac{96{,}500 \text{ coulombs}}{6.02 \times 10^{23} \text{ electrons}}$$

is a correct conversion factor; it is a fraction with units expressed, equal to unity.

Go back to section 137 and choose another answer.

131

[*from section 145*]

YOUR ANSWER: Either of the conversion factors, $\frac{1 \text{ min}}{60 \text{ sec}}$ or $\frac{60 \text{ sec}}{1 \text{ min}}$, could be used to convert 60 minutes to seconds.

Not quite. Let's see what happens if we choose $\frac{1 \text{ min}}{60 \text{ sec}}$.

$$(60 \text{ min})\left(\frac{1 \text{ min}}{60 \text{ sec}}\right) = 1\,\frac{\text{min} \times \text{min}}{\text{sec}} = 1\,\frac{\text{min}^2}{\text{sec}}.$$

This comes out with a unit that is not what we want; hence this particular conversion factor is not appropriate for this application.

Return to section 145 and select another answer.

132

[*from section 125*]

YOUR ANSWER: The response to the question, "What weight of zinc . . . ?" should be expressed in terms of liters.

That was careless of you; you probably chose "liters" because that was the only unit named in the question. The real issue is: What kind of quantity are you trying to find? The question clearly asks for an answer in a unit of weight.

Think this through, then return to section 125 and try again.

133
[*from section 149*]

YOUR ANSWER: (a) is not a correct conversion factor, but (b) is correct.

You are correct.

Since the formula weight of NaOH is 40.0, ratio (a) becomes

$$\frac{1 \text{ mole of NaOH}}{36.0 \text{ grams of NaOH}} = \frac{40.0 \text{ grams}}{36.0 \text{ grams}} = 1.11,$$

which means that this ratio is *not valid* as a conversion factor, since it does not equal unity. On the other hand, the formula weight of Ag is 107.870, which we round off to 107.9, and ratio (b) becomes

$$\frac{1 \text{ mole of Ag}}{107.9 \text{ grams of Ag}} = \frac{107.9 \text{ grams}}{107.9 \text{ grams}} = 1,$$

which makes this ratio correct as a conversion factor.

CONVERSION FACTORS INVOLVING GAS VOLUMES

Let us now consider the measurement of gases. Because of their low density, it is usually more convenient to measure gases by volume than by weight. There is a very simple relation (to be developed in Chapter 5) between the volume of a gas and a mole of the gas:

One mole of any gas = 22.4 liters of the gas (measured at STP†).

As usual, when we have an equality of units such as this, we can construct a pair of reciprocally related conversion factors. Thus,

$$\frac{22.4 \text{ liters}}{1 \text{ mole}} = 1 = \frac{1 \text{ mole}}{22.4 \text{ liters}}$$
(both volumes measured at STP).

Thus, to find the number of moles of CO_2 gas in 100 liters (STP):

$$(100 \text{ liters})\left(\frac{1 \text{ mole}}{22.4 \text{ liters}}\right) = 4.56 \frac{\cancel{\text{liter}}\text{-moles}}{\cancel{\text{liter}}} = 4.56 \text{ moles.}$$

† Standard temperature and pressure. This will be explained farther along in this book.

Now you try this one:
How many liters will be occupied by 5 moles of H_2, at STP?

112 liters. **section 128**

0.223 liters. **section 146**

134
[*from section 111*]

YOUR ANSWER: There is a mistake in equation (d):

$$(38 \text{ calories/gram})(14 \text{ grams}) = 504 \text{ calories.}$$

You are correct. The answer given *is* wrong. Here is a correct version of the equation:

$$\left(38 \frac{\text{calories}}{\text{gram}}\right)(14 \text{ grams}) = 532 \frac{\text{calorie-}\cancel{\text{grams}}}{\cancel{\text{gram}}} = 532 \text{ calories.}$$

The answer "504 calories" is not correct. With all our emphasis on units, don't overlook the fact that the numerical part of an answer must be right, too!

You are coming along nicely now. Notice that you can handle units, multiplying and dividing them, just as you can the literal numbers (letters) in an algebra problem. You can carry out arithmetic operations on units as you do on letters—for instance, $(3a)(4b) = 12ab$.

CONVERSION FACTORS

Let us now apply this knowledge to the problem of converting from one unit to another. When dealing with units with which we are familiar, we can convert easily and quickly. To convert 4 feet to inches, we just remember that there are 12 inches in every foot, and state immediately that 4 feet are equal to 48 inches. What we really do is use a *conversion factor,* as follows:

(1) Start with what we are given (4 feet).
(2) Remember the relation 12 inches = 1 foot.
(3) Use this relation to make a fraction that is equal to *one* (unity):

$$\frac{12 \text{ inches}}{1 \text{ foot}} = 1.$$

This fraction is our conversion factor; it equals unity because both numerator and denominator have the same value.

(4) Multiply our "given" quantity by this conversion factor (fraction):

$$(4 \text{ feet})(12 \text{ inches/foot}) = 48 \text{ inches}.$$

Remember that multiplying by *one* cannot change any value, though it may change the form of the expression.

Suppose we want to convert 3 hours to minutes. What conversion factor should we choose to multiply by?

60. **section 112**

60 minutes. **section 118**

$\frac{60 \text{ minutes}}{\text{hour}}$. **section 141**

135

[*from section 141*]

YOUR ANSWER: To find the number of ampere-hours equivalent to 3 faradays, you should divide 3 faradays by $\frac{26.8 \text{ ampere-hours}}{\text{faraday}}$.

No, this is not correct.

$$(3 \text{ faradays}) \div \left(\frac{26.8 \text{ amp-hrs}}{\text{faraday}}\right) =$$

$$(3 \text{ faradays}) \left(\frac{\text{faraday}}{26.8 \text{ amp-hrs}}\right) = 0.112 \frac{(\text{faraday})^2}{\text{amp-hr}}.$$

But we want the answer in ampere-hours; the unit *faraday²/amp-hr* tells us that we have gone far astray.

Return to section 134 and restudy this.

136

[*from section 129*]

YOUR ANSWER: "60" is the required conversion factor relating seconds and minutes.

No! Remember that a conversion factor is always a *fraction* with *units* expressed, and is always *equal to unity*. "60" does not fulfill any of these requirements.

Apparently you have not mastered the essential ideas of the last section. Turn back to section 116 and start reviewing at that point.

137

[*from section 145*]

YOUR ANSWER: $\frac{60 \text{ sec}}{1 \text{ min}}$ is the conversion factor that should be used to convert 60 minutes to seconds.

You are correct.

$$(60 \text{ min})\left(\frac{60 \text{ sec}}{1 \text{ min}}\right) = 3600 \frac{\cancel{\text{min}}\text{-sec}}{\cancel{\text{min}}} = 3600 \text{ sec.}$$

The units are correct, so we know we used the right conversion factor. Notice how easy it is to make up a conversion factor when we have an equality, and also how easy it is to determine which side up the factor should be.

Study the conversion factors listed below. Refer to the table of equivalents in the Appendix, and see whether any of these factors is *incorrect*.

(a) $\frac{1 \text{ atmosphere}}{15 \text{ lbs/in}^2}$.

(b) $\frac{96{,}500 \text{ coulombs}}{6.02 \times 10^{23} \text{ electrons}}$.

(c) $\frac{760 \text{ mm of Hg}}{15 \text{ lbs/in}^2}$.

(a) is not a correct conversion factor. **section 121**

(b) is not a correct conversion factor. **section 130**

(c) is not a correct conversion factor. **section 143**

They are all correct conversion factors. **section 149**

138
[*from section 149*]

YOUR ANSWER: Both (a) and (b) are wrong as conversion factors.

No, not quite. Let's check factor (b):

$$\frac{1 \text{ mole of Ag}}{107.9 \text{ grams of Ag}}$$

From the table of atomic weights we find that the atomic weight of Ag is 107.870, which we round off to 107.9. This is also the formula weight of Ag. Thus 1 mole of Ag weighs 107.9 grams, and

$$\frac{1 \text{ mole of Ag}}{107.9 \text{ grams of Ag}} = \frac{107.9 \text{ grams}}{107.9 \text{ grams}} = 1.$$

Hence (b) is indeed a correct conversion factor, since it is a fraction with units expressed and equal to unity. But this makes your choice of answer wrong.

Return to section 149 and choose another answer.

139
[*from section 128*]

YOUR ANSWER: One hundred grams of NO at STP will occupy 134 liters.

No, you have inverted the ratio. You must have calculated as follows:

$$(100 \text{ grams})\left(\frac{30 \text{ grams}}{22.4 \text{ liters}}\right) = 134\,\frac{\text{grams}^2}{\text{liter}}.$$

Then you got cold feet and used the unit you knew should be there, liters. Whenever the unit is wrong, this fact should be a loud and clear warning to you that you have made a mistake!

Go back to section 128 and try again.

140
[*from section 111*]

YOUR ANSWER: There is a mistake in statement (e): (12 liter-atmospheres) (4 grams/liter) = 48 gram-atmospheres.

No, there is no error in this statement.

$$(12 \text{ liter-atm})\left(4\,\frac{\text{grams}}{\text{liter}}\right) = 48\,\frac{\cancel{\text{liter}}\text{-atm-grams}}{\cancel{\text{liter}}}$$

$$= 48 \text{ atm-grams} = 48 \text{ gram-atms.}$$

Return to section 111 and try again.

141
[*from section 134*]

YOUR ANSWER: To convert 3 hours to minutes, we should multiply by $\frac{60 \text{ minutes}}{\text{hour}}$.

You are correct.

$$(3 \text{ hrs})\left(\frac{60 \text{ min}}{\text{hr}}\right) = 180\,\frac{\text{min-}\cancel{\text{hrs}}}{\cancel{\text{hr}}} = 180 \text{ minutes.}$$

You may think that these examples are so easy that there is no need to do them this way. Well, let's try another problem, in which you may *not* be familiar with the units.

Given the statement that 26.8 ampere-hours = 1 faraday, how would you determine how many ampere-hours there are in 3 faradays?

Multiply 3 faradays by 26.8. **section 120**

Multiply 3 faradays by $\frac{26.8 \text{ ampere-hours}}{\text{faraday}}$. **section 129**

Divide 3 faradays by $\frac{26.8 \text{ ampere-hours}}{\text{faraday}}$. section 135

Multiply 3 faradays by $\frac{26.8 \text{ faradays}}{\text{ampere-hour}}$. section 147

142

[*from section 116*]

YOUR ANSWER: $30 \frac{\text{lbs}}{\text{ft}^2} \times 10 \text{ ft} = 300 \text{ ft/lb}$.

No, this is not correct. You have inverted a fraction or ratio without justification. All you need to do, besides multiplying 30×10, is one multiplication and one simple cancellation of units.

Return to section 116 and try again.

143

[*from section 137*]

YOUR ANSWER: (c) $\frac{760 \text{ mm of Hg}}{15 \text{ lbs/in}^2}$ is not a correct conversion factor.

No, you are mistaken. The table of equivalents in the Appendix tells us:

(7) 1 atmosphere = 760 mm of Hg, and
(10) 1 atmosphere = 15 lbs/in^2.

Since we know that quantities that are equal to the same thing are equal to each other, we can write

$$760 \text{ mm of Hg} = 15 \text{ lbs/in}^2.$$

From this equality, it follows that

$$\frac{760 \text{ mm of Hg}}{15 \text{ lbs/in}^2}$$

is a correct conversion factor; it is a fraction with units expressed, equal to unity.

Go back to section 137 and choose another answer.

144

[*from section 149*]

YOUR ANSWER: I forget how to figure out how many grams I need.

No one expects you to remember the atomic weights of the elements; if that is your trouble, turn to the atomic weight table and solve the problem.

If your trouble is deeper than this, you will have to do some reviewing.

We usually use the term "mole" to represent one gram-molecular weight (or one gram-formula weight) of a substance.

Let's find the weight of one mole of NaCl.

(1) We find the formula weight of a compound by finding the *sum* of the atomic weights of all the elements:

atomic weight of Na =	23.00
atomic weight of Cl =	35.45
formula weight of NaCl =	58.45

(2) We express the formula weight in grams to find the weight of one mole. So one gram-formula weight or one mole of NaCl equals 58.45 grams.

Now return to section 149 and try again.

145

[*from section 129*]

YOUR ANSWER: Either $\frac{1 \text{ min}}{60 \text{ sec}}$ or $\frac{60 \text{ sec}}{1 \text{ min}}$ represents a conversion factor relating seconds and minutes.

You are correct.
Since 1 min = 60 sec,

$$\frac{1 \text{ min}}{60 \text{ sec}} = 1 = \frac{60 \text{ sec}}{1 \text{ min}}.$$

There are thus *two* equally correct conversion factors relating seconds and minutes. Let's carry it a step further.
Which of the two conversion factors above should you use to convert 60 minutes to seconds?

Either one could be used, since they are equal. **section 131**

$\frac{60 \text{ sec}}{1 \text{ min}}$ is the only one to use. **section 137**

$\frac{1 \text{ min}}{60 \text{ sec}}$ is the only one to use. **section 150**

146

[*from section 133*]

YOUR ANSWER: Five moles of H_2 (at STP) will occupy 0.223 liters.

No, not right. Let's check it.
To get this answer, you must have calculated as follows:

$$(5 \text{ moles})\left(\frac{1 \text{ mole}}{22.4 \text{ liters}}\right) = \frac{5}{22.4} = 0.223$$

Then, since you knew the answer had to be in liters, you "tacked" this word onto your answer. If you had carried your calculations through with units, however, you would have found units of moles²/liter, which is obviously wrong.

Now turn back to section 133 and try again.

147

[*from section 141*]

YOUR ANSWER: To find the number of ampere-hours equivalent to 3 faradays, you should multiply 3 faradays by $\dfrac{26.8 \text{ faradays}}{\text{ampere-hour}}$.

No, this is not right.

$$(3 \text{ faradays})\left(\frac{26.8 \text{ faradays}}{\text{ampere-hour}}\right) =$$

$$\frac{80.4 \text{ faradays} \times \text{faradays}}{\text{ampere-hours}} = 80.4 \frac{\text{faraday}^2}{\text{ampere-hour}}.$$

But you were asked how to find the number of ampere-hours; this must be an incorrect answer since the unit is wrong.

Turn back to section 134 and restudy this material.

148

[*from section 111*]

YOUR ANSWER: I don't understand the question.

If you don't understand this, it will be necessary for you to go back to section 116, or even to the beginning of the chapter, and review. But first notice this:

In algebra:

$$(3a)\left(16\frac{b}{a}\right) = \frac{3 \times 16 \times \cancel{a} \times b}{\cancel{a}} = 48b.$$

In a chemical problem:

$$(3 \text{ grams})\left(16\frac{\text{liters}}{\text{gram}}\right) = \frac{3 \times 16 \times \cancel{\text{grams}} \times \text{liters}}{\cancel{\text{grams}}} = 48 \text{ liters}.$$

The pattern and logic of the cancellation process are the same in both cases. You can handle units algebraically, just as you can the letters a and b.

Now turn back to section 116 and restudy the material from there.

149

[*from section 137*]

YOUR ANSWER: The three ratios given are all correct conversion factors.

You are correct. You're doing fine! Undoubtedly you noticed that both factors (b) and (c) require the use of *two* entries from the table in the Appendix, coupled with the principle that quantities that are equal to the same thing are equal to each other. The procedure to use in such cases is spelled out in the responses to wrong choices in sections 130, 143, and 148; if you are at all uncertain about this, read those sections.

CONVERSION FACTORS INVOLVING MOLES

Now let us turn to a unit that is particularly important in chemistry, the *mole*. The mole is the "package" that chemists find it convenient to work with.

Whether we are using a formula in an equation to represent a molecule of an ionic compound or an elementary substance, a mole always represents 6.02×10^{23} units, and *the weight of one mole is always the formula weight expressed in grams*. Thus:

H_2 = one mole of H_2 = 2.0 grams of these molecules
NaCl = one mole of NaCl = 58.5 grams of this ionic compound
Cu = one mole of Cu = 63.5 grams of this element
Na^+ = one mole of Na^+ = 23.0 grams of sodium ions
Remember: Formulas represent moles.

Since a mole of any definite species can be equated with a certain definite number of grams, we can easily form a conversion factor to convert into moles any specific weight of a chemical substance for which we know the formula weight, or vice versa.

Use the atomic weight table to check the two sets of conversion factors given below:

$$\text{(a)}\quad \frac{\text{1 mole of NaOH}}{\text{36.0 grams of NaOH}} = 1 = \frac{\text{36.0 grams of NaOH}}{\text{1 mole of NaOH}}.$$

$$\text{(b)}\quad \frac{\text{1 mole of Ag}}{\text{107.9 grams of Ag}} = 1 = \frac{\text{107.9 grams of Ag}}{\text{1 mole of Ag}}.$$

Both (a) and (b) are correct. **section 113**

(a) is correct but (b) is wrong. **section 124**

(a) is wrong but (b) is correct. **section 133**

Both (a) and (b) are wrong. **section 138**

I forget how to figure out how many grams I need. **section 144**

150

[*from section 145*]

YOUR ANSWER: $\frac{\text{1 min}}{\text{60 sec}}$ is the conversion factor that should be used to convert 60 minutes to seconds.

No. To show why this is wrong, let's try using it and see what happens.

$$(\text{60 min})\left(\frac{\text{1 min}}{\text{60 sec}}\right) = 1\,\frac{\text{min} \times \text{min}}{\text{sec}} = 1\,\frac{\text{min}^2}{\text{sec}}.$$

This comes out with units that are not what we want. Hence this conversion factor is not appropriate for this application.

Return to section 145 and select another answer.

[*from section 128*]

YOUR ANSWER: One hundred grams of NO at STP will occupy 74.7 liters.

You are correct.

$$(100 \text{ grams})\left(\frac{22.4 \text{ liters}}{30.0 \text{ grams}}\right) = 74.7 \frac{\text{liters} \times \cancel{\text{grams}}}{\cancel{\text{grams}}} = 74.7 \text{ liters.}$$

This material on units, dimensions, and conversion factors is basic to all study of chemistry (and other sciences as well). You will need to use these methods throughout the rest of this TutorText* course. Go on with section 152.

* Trademark registered in U. S. Patent Office by U. S. Industries, Inc.

[*from section 151*]

CHAPTER 4—UNITS AND DIMENSIONS—SUMMARY

Every numerical answer to a chemistry problem has a *unit* included. Although sometimes the unit is understood and not expressed, it always helps to avoid misunderstanding and confusion to state explicitly the unit involved.

The metric system is used in almost all scientific and chemical work. The four basic units of importance to us are:

Grams: unit of mass (weight), answers the question, "How heavy?"

Meters: unit of length, answers the question, "How long a distance?"

Seconds: unit of time, answers the question, "How long a time?"

Liters: unit of volume, answers the question, "How large a size?"

A subunit one-thousandth as large as each of these units bears the prefix *milli-*, and a superunit one thousand times larger takes the prefix *kilo-*. Examples are:

1000 milliliters = 1 liter
1000 grams = 1 kilogram

These units, like literal coefficients in algebra, can be added, subtracted, multiplied, and divided, just as any numerical value can be. An answer, if the unit is wrong, must be considered as a wrong answer, even though the numerical value may be correct.

To convert one unit to another without changing the value, we multiply by a *conversion factor*, a fraction equal to one, which has different units in numerator and denominator. Examples of conversion factors are:

$$\frac{1 \text{ liter}}{1000 \text{ milliliters}}$$

$$\frac{1000 \text{ grams}}{1 \text{ kilogram}}$$

$$\frac{1 \text{ kilogram}}{1000 \text{ grams}}$$

The table of relations and conversion factors given in Table E in the Appendix enables us to make conversions easily from one unit to another.

The *mole* is a unit commonly used by chemists, and represents a "package" of 6.02×10^{23} individual units. A mole is equivalent to the formula weight of any substance expressed in grams. The ability to convert moles to grams and grams to moles is required of every chemist. A formula represents a mole:

$$\text{Number of moles} = \frac{\text{Number of grams}}{\text{gram-formula weight}}$$

Now go on to the review questions, section 153.

153
[*from section 152*]

CHAPTER 4—REVIEW QUESTIONS AND PROBLEMS

1. How many seconds are there in one kilosecond?

2. Which of the following is a correct conversion factor?

$$\frac{1 \text{ second}}{60 \text{ minutes}} \qquad \frac{1 \text{ minute}}{60 \text{ seconds}} \qquad \frac{1 \text{ second}}{1 \text{ minute}}$$

3. What is meant by a "mole"?

4. A particular molecule has a diameter of 50 A. (50 angstroms). What is this distance expressed in centimeters? in inches? (Refer to Table E in the Appendix.)

5. From Table E (Appendix), determine the charge in coulombs carried by a single electron.

6. What does a formula represent?

Turn to section 547 for the answers, then go on to section 154.

Chapter 5

THE EMPIRICAL GAS LAWS

In general, chemical substances are either liquids, solids, or gases. Solids and liquids are easily measured by means of their weight, but this is not convenient for gases. Gases are best measured by volume, but the volume of a gas is meaningful only if its temperature and pressure are specified. The relations between the volume, pressure, and temperature (V, P, and T) are easily expressed in terms of algebra.

BOYLE'S LAW

The first relation we shall examine is called *Boyle's law*. It relates volume and pressure, under the condition that the temperature is held constant. Let us test your intuitive knowledge of this relation.

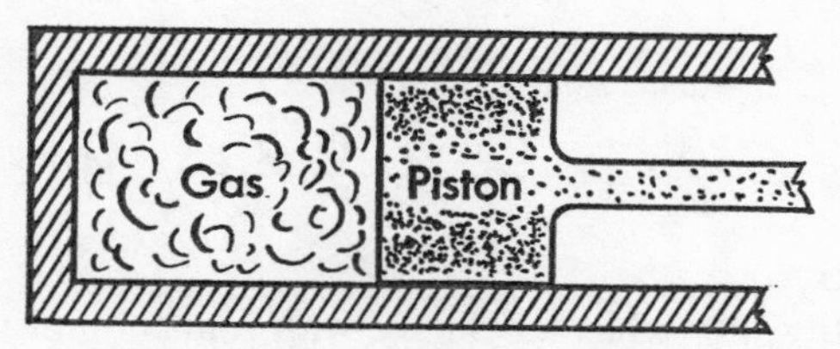

Figure 20. Gas cylinder with piston.

Suppose you have a sample of air (or any other gas) trapped in a cylinder that is provided with a movable piston (see figure above). If you push the piston *in*, so that the volume of the gas is diminished, what will happen to the pressure of the gas?

The pressure will remain constant. **section 159**

The pressure will increase. **section 165**

The pressure will decrease. **section 171**

155

[*from section 165*]

YOUR ANSWER: The correct statement of Boyle's law is either $PV = k$ or $V = k(1/P)$.

Yes; both of these statements are correct. These equations represent an *inverse* relationship: as P goes up, V must go down, and vice versa, if k is to be truly a constant.

Now to illustrate the use of this relation, let us consider a numerical example. Suppose we compress 500 cubic feet of helium gas (measured at a pressure of 1 atm) into a steel cylinder that has an internal volume of 2 cubic feet. What will be the pressure of the compressed gas?

Solution: Since $PV = k$, we can write

$$P_1V_1 = P_2V_2$$

where the subscript "$_1$" refers to the initial conditions and "$_2$" to the final conditions for the same sample of gas. In the present case,

$$P_1 = 1 \text{ atm},$$
$$V_1 = 500 \text{ ft}^3,$$
$$V_2 = 2 \text{ ft}^3.$$

Therefore,

$$P_2 = \frac{P_1V_1}{V_2} = \frac{(1 \text{ atm})(500 \text{ ft}^3)}{2 \text{ ft}^3} = 250 \text{ atm}.$$

Now you try one.

A certain tire pump has a cylinder with a maximum volume of 1.5 liters. When the plunger is completely depressed, the volume is reduced to 25 milliliters. If the contained air is at atmospheric pressure (1 atm) initially, what will be its pressure finally? (Assume that no air leaves the cylinder as the plunger is depressed.)

60 atm. **section 161**

16.7 atm. **section 174**

0.06 atm. **section 180**

156
[*from section 161*]

YOUR ANSWER: The pressure inside the balloon will increase when the balloon is warmed.

No, not appreciably. Remember we said the balloon was only *partially* inflated. This means that the rubber is not stretched, and so cannot exert any appreciable pressure.

Read section 161 again and select the correct answer.

157
[*from section 183*]

YOUR ANSWER: The correct statement of Charles's law is either $VT = k$ or $V = k(1/T)$.

These two expressions are equivalent to each other, and both are wrong. They would have you believe that as T becomes larger, V becomes smaller, the opposite of what actually happens.

Read section 183 again and then try another answer.

158
[*from section 176*]

YOUR ANSWER: The final volume of gas will be 1.42 liters.

You are correct. $V_2 = \dfrac{(1 \text{ liter})(273° + 100°)}{(273° - 10°)} = 1.42$ liters.

THE COMBINED GAS LAW

Now, since V and P are related (Boyle's law) and V and T are related (Charles's law), there is no reason why the two laws should not be combined into a single expression.

Given the two relations

$$PV = k' \qquad \text{and} \qquad V = k''T$$

(where the two constants, k' and k'', are in general not the same), we can write a single expression relating the pressure, volume, and temperature of a gas.

Which of the following expressions is a correct statement of the *combined gas law?*

$\dfrac{PV}{T} = k.$ **section 167**

$PVT = k$ or $\dfrac{PT}{V} = k.$ **section 177**

None of the above. **section 195**

159

[from section 154]

YOUR ANSWER: When the piston is pushed in, the pressure of the gas will remain constant.

No. There is a quantity of air trapped in the cylinder. When you push the piston in, this air is *compressed*—i.e., it is squeezed into a smaller space. At the same time, the pressure of the trapped air is increased.

In pushing the piston in, you do work—i.e., you expend energy. Most of this energy is stored up in the compressed gas, ready to be released again in pushing the piston back out. This is familiar to anyone who has ever used a bicycle tire pump. And this contradicts your answer.

Return to section 154 and try again.

160

[from section 167]

YOUR ANSWER: The volume of the balloon will become 25,900 cubic yards.

No. Check your work again; it looks as though you have interchanged T_1 and T_2.

Return to section 167 and try again.

161
[*from section 155*]

YOUR ANSWER: The final pressure of the air in the tire pump will be 60 atm.

You are correct. $P_2 = \frac{P_1 V_1}{V_2} = 60$ atm.

CHARLES'S LAW

Now let us go one step further. In all of the foregoing, we have assumed the temperature to be kept constant. But we can also explore the relation between the volume of a gas and its temperature under the restriction that the pressure is maintained at a constant value. This relation is known as *Charles's law.*

You know that most substances expand when heated and contract when cooled. Gases are no exception. Suppose we *partially* inflate a toy rubber balloon, then place it in the direct sunlight so that it warms up appreciably. What will happen to it?

The pressure inside will increase. **section 156**

Nothing, other than getting warm. **section 169**

It will become larger. **section 183**

162

[*from section 209*]

YOUR ANSWER: The density of chlorine at STP is 71.0 g/l.

No. That would be pretty heavy chlorine! Actually this figure, 71.0, is the molecular weight. You may have obtained it by inserting 22.4 liters for V in the equation. The correct value to use for V is 1, because you are trying to find the weight of 1 liter.

Return to section 209 and try again.

163

[*from section 203*]

YOUR ANSWER: The molecular weight of the gas is 5.62.

No. This is the answer you would get if you neglected to convert the temperature to the absolute scale. This must not be overlooked.

Return to section 203 and choose another answer.

164

[*from section 183*]

YOUR ANSWER: The correct statement of Charles's law is either $V = kT$ or $V/T = k$.

You are correct. These statements are equivalent to each other, and both are correct.

TEMPERATURE SCALES

Before we tackle a numerical example, we must consider the nature of the centigrade* (or Fahrenheit) temperature scales. In the expression as written above ($V = kT$), it is readily apparent that we will get into difficulty if we let the temperature become zero or less than zero. Actually it has been found by repeated careful experiment that any volume of gas at zero centigrade (0°C) decreases in volume by one part in 273.1 for a 1° lowering of the temperature. For a 2° lowering, the contraction is 2/273.1; for 10°, 10/273.1, and so on. If this trend continues, a decrease of 273.1°C will mean a contraction of 273.1/273.1, or the entire volume: the volume will be reduced to nothing! This temperature, 273.1°C below zero, represents a theoretical lower limit of temperature, and is known as *absolute zero.* (Actually all gases become liquids before absolute zero is reached.)

A special temperature scale has been established, based on this absolute zero, and this scale *must* be used in any calculations involving gas volumes. This is called the *absolute* or *Kelvin* scale, and its symbol or abbreviation is °K. Thus $T°K = t°C + 273°$ (we will round off 273.1 to 273 in this work).

The relation between the absolute and centigrade scales is displayed for you by the accompanying diagram. If you study this diagram you will see that whatever the centigrade temperature is, one must *add* 273° to find the absolute temperature. Similarly, of course, one finds the centigrade temperature by subtracting 273° from the absolute temperature.

* The centigrade scale is also called the Celsius scale after its inventor. The abbreviation °C holds with either name.

°C	°K
100	373
50	323
0	273
−50	223
−100	173
−150	123
−200	73
−250	23
−273	0

What is the absolute temperature that is equivalent to 25°C?

248°K. **section 170**

298°K. **section 176**

25°K. **section 185**

165

[*from section 154*]

YOUR ANSWER: When the piston is pushed in, the pressure will increase.

You are correct. In fact if the volume is reduced to half its initial value, the pressure will be doubled; if the volume is cut to one-third, the pressure will triple, and so on. This can be expressed in a simple mathematical equation, using V for volume, P for pressure, and k for a constant of proportionality. (A constant of proportionality is simply a number with a constant value. The actual value of this number is determined by the units in which pressure and volume are measured.)

Choose the pair of expressions below that is a correct statement of the relation between pressure and volume as described above.

$PV = k$ or $V = k\left(\frac{1}{P}\right)$ **section 155**

$V = kP$ or $P = kV$ **section 173**

166

[*from section 176*]

YOUR ANSWER: The final volume of gas will be 10 liters.

No, this is not right. Apparently you forgot to convert your temperatures to the absolute scale. Absolute temperatures must be used in gas problems dealing with volume, temperature, and pressure.

Return to section 176 and try again.

167

[*from section 158*]

YOUR ANSWER: A correct expression for the combined gas law is

$$\frac{PV}{T} = k.$$

You are correct. This equation indicates a *direct* relation between volume and temperature and an *inverse* relation between volume and pressure, consistent with our previous statements of Charles's and Boyle's laws.

The combined law can also be expressed in another manner. If the quantity PV/T is constant for a particular sample of gas, then we can write

$$\frac{P_1V_1}{T_1} = \frac{P_2V_2}{T_2},$$

where the subscripts "$_1$" and "$_2$" refer to the initial and final conditions, respectively. This is a convenient form for the equation when some *one* of the six quantities is to be determined from known values of the other five. Here is an example.

2000 cubic feet of oxygen gas at 0°C and 1 atmosphere pressure is compressed into a steel cylinder which has a volume of 10 cubic feet. What will be the internal pressure at a temperature of 30°C?

Solution:

(1) Tabulate the initial and final conditions:

Initial Conditions	Final Conditions
$V_1 = 2000$ cu ft	$V_2 = 10$ cu ft
$T_1 = 0°C = 273°K$	$T_2 = 30°C = 303°K$
$P_1 = 1$ atm	P_2 to be determined

(2) Solve the gas law equation for P_2:

$$P_2 = P_1\left(\frac{T_2}{T_1}\right)\left(\frac{V_1}{V_2}\right)$$

(3) Insert known values and compute the result:

$$P_2 = \frac{(1 \text{ atm})(303°K)(2000 \text{ ft}^3)}{(273°K)(10 \text{ ft}^3)} = 222 \text{ atm.}$$

Here is a problem to be worked in a similar fashion. A stratosphere balloon contains 1000 cubic yards of helium at the surface of the earth (1 atm pressure, 27°C temperature). What will be the volume of the gas at such a height that the pressure is only 0.05 atm and the temperature is −40°C?

25,900 cubic yards. **section 160**

15,500 cubic yards. **section 175**

38.75 cubic yards. **section 184**

29,600 cubic yards. **section 192**

168

[*from section 175*]

YOUR ANSWER: The volume of the gas would be 4.85 liters at STP.

Not quite. To get this answer you must have inverted one of the ratios, either the ratio of pressures or of temperatures (we will leave it to you to decide which!).

Return to section 175 and try again.

169

[*from section 161*]

YOUR ANSWER: Nothing will happen when the balloon is warmed.

How can that be? We have said that gases are no exception to the general rule that substances expand when heated and contract when cooled.

Read section 161 again and then select the correct answer.

170

[*from section 164*]

YOUR ANSWER: 25°C = 248°K.

Wrong. You performed the wrong operation; you subtracted where you should have added. To change a centigrade temperature to the corresponding absolute temperature, you should add 273°.

Return to section 164 and try another answer.

171
[*from section 154*]

YOUR ANSWER: When the piston is pushed in, the pressure of the gas will decrease.

Wrong. A quantity of gas is trapped in the cylinder. When you push the piston in, this gas is squeezed into a smaller space—that is, it is *compressed*. When a gas is compressed in this way, its pressure increases. The increased pressure of the gas tends to push the piston back out to its original position.

If the pressure of the gas decreased as you pushed the piston in, this would exert an added inward pull, or suction, on the piston. Actually, the farther *in* the piston is moved, the greater becomes the resistance to further motion in the same direction. This is familiar to anyone who has ever used a bicycle tire pump.

Return to section 154 and try again.

172
[*from section 194*]

YOUR ANSWER: The molecular weight of the gas is 2.19.

Wrong. To obtain this answer, you must have taken M/w as the number of moles, whereas it should be w/M. Furthermore, you should realize that a number such as 2.19 is pretty small for a molecular weight.

Study section 194 again and then work through the problem with care to get the right answer.

173
[*from section 165*]

YOUR ANSWER: The correct statement of Boyle's law is either $V = kP$ or $P = kV$.

Wrong. Suppose we pursue the numerical relations mentioned in section 165: "If the volume is reduced to half its initial value, the pressure will be doubled; if the volume is cut to one-third, the pressure will triple, and so on." Let us assume that the initial volume was 100 cubic centimeters (100 cm^3) and that the gas was originally at atmospheric pressure (1 atm)—i.e., $V = 100$ cm^3; $P = 1$ atm. Now if the answer $V = kP$ were correct, we could write:

$$100 = (k)(1) \quad \text{or} \quad k = 100.$$

After cutting the volume to 50 cm^3, we know that the pressure is doubled, becoming twice atmospheric (2 atm). Then,

$$50 = (k)(2) \quad \text{or} \quad k = 25.$$

This makes the constant change from 100 to 25, strange behavior for a *constant!* (If you selected the answer $P = kV$, the value of k would be inverted, and show a change from 1/100 to 1/25; same comment.)

The relation between P and V should be *inverse,* rather than direct. Now return to section 165 and choose the correct answer.

174

[*from section 155*]

YOUR ANSWER: The final pressure of the air in the tire pump will be 16.7 atm.

No. You have apparently made two mistakes that partially compensate each other, so that the answer, though wrong, does not seem absurd. Your answer could only result from dividing 25 by 1.5; this means that you have used an incorrect equation, $P_2 = P_1(V_2/V_1)$, in place of the correct $P_2 = P_1(V_1/V_2)$. But in addition to this, you have overlooked the fact that the original volume was given in *liters,* the final volume in *milliliters;* 1 liter = 1000 milliliters.

Return to section 155 and study it carefully before choosing another answer.

175

[*from section 167*]

YOUR ANSWER: The volume of the balloon will become 15,500 cubic yards.

You are correct.

$$V_2 = V_1\left(\frac{P_1}{P_2}\right)\left(\frac{T_2}{T_1}\right) = \frac{(1000)(1)(233)}{(0.05)(300)} = 15{,}500 \text{ cubic yards.}$$

STANDARD TEMPERATURE AND PRESSURE

Because of the dependence of volumes of gases on their pressures and temperatures, it is necessary to specify carefully the conditions of P and T corresponding to any measurement of volume. For convenience a particular set of conditions has been chosen as the standard of reference, namely $P = 1$ atm, and $T = 0°C$. This set of conditions is often referred to as "STP" (Standard T and P) or "NTP" (Normal T and P).

The "atmosphere" (atm) as a unit of measurement is defined as that pressure which will support a barometric column of mercury 760 mm in height. Thus, a pressure of 1 atm is equal to a pressure of 760 mm of Hg.

Try another problem, this time with pressure expressed in millimeters of mercury:

A sample of nitrogen measures 5.37 liters at a temperature of 29°C and a pressure of 620 mm of Hg. What would its volume be at STP?

4.85 liters. **section 168**

5.95 liters. **section 182**

3.96 liters. **section 190**

I don't know how to start. **section 198**

176

[*from section 164*]

YOUR ANSWER: 25°C = 298°K.

You are correct. 25°C = (25° + 273°) = 298°K. Now let us try some calculations based on Charles's law.

A 10-liter volume of a gas, initially at 20°C, is heated until its volume becomes 11 liters. The pressure, meanwhile, is adjusted so that it remains constant at its initial value. What is the final temperature?

Solution: Use the expression $\frac{V}{T} = k$. From the initial conditions, we find k to be

$$k = \frac{V_1}{T_1} = \frac{10}{293},$$

where the subscript "$_1$" indicates initial conditions. (Note that we have converted 20°C to its equivalent, 293°K.) Since k is constant, we can write

$$k = \frac{V_2}{T_2}, \text{ or better, } T_2 = \frac{V_2}{k}.$$

Subscript "$_2$" indicates the final conditions. Hence, by algebraic substitution,

$$T_2 = V_2\left(\frac{T_1}{V_1}\right), \text{ or } T_2 = T_1\left(\frac{V_2}{V_1}\right).$$

Numerically, $T_2 = \frac{(293°K)(11 \text{ liters})}{10 \text{ liters}} = 322°K = 49°C.$

Now one for you:

What volume would be attained by heating one liter of gas at constant pressure from its initial temperature of −10°C to a final temperature of 100°C?

1.42 liters. **section 158**

10 liters. **section 166**

0.70 liter. **section 189**

177

[*from section 158*]

YOUR ANSWER: A correct statement of the combined gas law is either $PVT = k$ or $\frac{PT}{V} = k$.

Incorrect.

Look at it this way: For a fixed quantity (weight) of gas, the volume varies *directly* with changes in temperature; it varies *inversely* with changes in pressure.

To show that volume varies inversely with pressure, we can write Boyle's law:

$$PV = k'.$$

To keep k' constant in this equation, P must increase if V decreases and vice versa.

To show the direct relation between volume and temperature, we can write Charles's law:

$$V = k''T \quad \text{or} \quad \frac{V}{T} = k''.$$

Either equation shows that to keep k'' constant, an increase in T must be accompanied by a decrease in V, and vice versa.

The combined gas law states both of these relations at once: it is written

$$\frac{PV}{T} = k.$$

Check this equation to see whether both Boyle's and Charles's laws are obeyed. Then return to section 158 and try again.

178

[*from section 207*]

YOUR ANSWER: The partial pressures of the components of the fuel gas are $P_{H_2} = 0.50$ atm, $P_{CO} = 8.60$ atm, $P_{N_2} = 0.90$ atm.

No, these are not correct, though they do add up to a total pressure of 10 atm, as they should. You have failed to include the molecular weights of the gases in your computations.

Return to section 207 and try again.

179

[*from section 209*]

YOUR ANSWER: The density of chlorine at STP is 0.317 g/l.

No, this is not right. You apparently have the problem set up correctly, but you have made a slip in the position of your decimal point. Check carefully through your arithmetic (or logarithms) before selecting another answer in section 209.

180
[*from section 155*]

YOUR ANSWER: The final pressure of the air in the tire pump will be 0.06 atm.

No. Apparently you set the problem up correctly, but failed to observe that the original volume was given in *liters,* the final in *milliliters*. The units *must* be consistent. Furthermore, you should realize that the answer must be *greater* than one atmosphere, not less.

Since there are 1000 milliliters in 1 liter, it is clear that your answer must be in error by a factor of 1000. Return to section 155 and try again.

181
[*from section 208*]

YOUR ANSWER: 5.48 liters of oxygen, measured at 720 mm of Hg and 21°C, could be obtained from 20.0 grams of $KClO_3$.

No. This figure indicates that you are on the right track but have not completed the problem. Return to section 208, read the question carefully, complete the problem, and select another answer.

182
[*from section 175*]

YOUR ANSWER: The volume of the gas would be 5.95 liters at STP.

Not quite. To get this answer you must have inverted one of the ratios, either the ratio of pressures or of temperatures (we will leave it to you to decide which!).

Return to section 175 and try again.

183

[*from section 161*]

YOUR ANSWER: The balloon will become enlarged when warmed.

You are correct. The gas inside expands when its temperature rises.

Now let us look into the quantitative relations that apply here. As we have already pointed out, the volume of a gas will increase if the temperature increases, and decrease if the temperature decreases (if we always maintain a constant pressure).

If we let T represent the temperature and V the volume, then which of the following pairs of expressions is correct? (k is again a proportionality constant.)

$VT = k$ or $V = k\left(\frac{1}{T}\right)$. **section 157**

$V = kT$ or $\frac{V}{T} = k$. **section 164**

184

[*from section 167*]

YOUR ANSWER: The volume of the balloon will become 38.75 cubic yards.

Hardly! This is much smaller than the original volume, when it should have expanded considerably. It looks as though you may have interchanged P_1 and P_2.

Return to section 167 and try again.

185

[*from section 164*]

YOUR ANSWER: $25°C = 25°K$.

This cannot be true, for the two scales are *never* equal. A temperature on the absolute scale is numerically 273° higher than the same temperature on the centigrade scale.

Return to section 164 and try again.

186

[*from section 207*]

YOUR ANSWER: The partial pressures of the components of the fuel gas are $P_{H_2} = 0.04$ atm, $P_{CO} = 9.02$ atm, $P_{N_2} = 0.94$ atm.

No, these are not correct, though they do add up to a total pressure of 10 atm, as they should. In order to arrive at these figures, you must have *multiplied* the stated percentages by the respective molecular weights. This isn't right; think it over.

Return to section 207 and try again.

187

[*from section 208*]

YOUR ANSWER: 4.82 liters of oxygen, measured at 720 mm of Hg and 21°C, could be obtained from 20.0 grams of $KClO_3$.

No. You have inverted certain of the factors in applying the gas law. Study this through again. Then return to section 208 and select another answer.

188
[*from section 203*]

YOUR ANSWER: The molecular weight of the gas is 15.6.

No. You must have divided when you should have multiplied. Return to section 203, check your arithmetic carefully, and try another answer.

189
[*from section 176*]

YOUR ANSWER: The final volume of gas will be 0.70 liter.

Wrong. You got your figures mixed up. You should have caught this yourself on the basis that the answer has to be *larger* than the initial 1 liter.

Go back to section 176 and try again.

190
[*from section 175*]

YOUR ANSWER: The volume of the gas would be 3.96 liters at STP.

You are correct.

$$V_{STP} = (5.37)\left(\frac{237}{302}\right)\left(\frac{620}{760}\right) = 3.96 \text{ liters.}$$

Note that in this example, in taking the gas to STP, you are cooling it and increasing its pressure. Both of these actions tend to reduce the volume, so you should expect the answer to be somewhat (but not drastically) smaller than the original 5.37 liters, and such is the case. You should establish the habit of checking your answers in all problems (not just gas law problems, indeed not just *chemistry* problems) to see whether they look plausible.

THE MOLAR VOLUME

Many years ago it was discovered by Avogadro that equal volumes of gases measured under similar conditions contain equal numbers of molecules. By repeated experiments, it has been found that one mole of any gas, measured at STP, occupies a volume of 22.4 liters (a little less than 1 cubic foot). This relation is extremely useful, as it provides a simple method of experimentally determining molecular weights. This quantity, 22.4 liters, is called the *molar volume.*

Suppose, for example, we find that 1 liter of a gas (corrected to STP) weighs 3.74 grams. We know that this must be 1/22.4 of a mole. Hence 1 mole of the gas weighs $(22.4)(3.74) = 83.80$ grams, and therefore 83.80 is the molecular weight of the gas.

Here's a problem for you:

What is the molecular weight of a gas of which 5.00 grams occupies a volume of 3.25 liters at STP?

7.26. **section 200**

1.38. **section 205**

34.5. **section 209**

191

[*from section 208*]

YOUR ANSWER: 6:23 liters of oxygen, measured at 720 mm of Hg and 21°C, could be obtained from 20.0 grams of $KClO_3$.

You are correct. The equation $2KClO_3 \longrightarrow 2KCl + 3O_2$ shows that 2 moles of $KClO_3$ produce 3 moles of O_2. But 20 grams is only 20/122.6 of one mole of $KClO_3$; hence we can expect (20/122.6)(3/2) mole of oxygen. Each mole (at STP) will occupy 22.4 liters, therefore:

$$\frac{(20 \text{ grams})(3 \text{ moles})(22.4 \text{ liters/mole})}{(122.6 \text{ grams/mole})(2 \text{ moles})} = 5.48 \text{ liters.}$$

To convert this to the stated conditions of temperature and pressure, we must multiply by two ratios:

$$(5.48 \text{ liters})\left(\frac{294}{273}\right)\left(\frac{760}{720}\right) = 6.23 \text{ liters.}$$

Now let's try another problem with one further complicating factor. Consider the reaction of barium carbonate, $BaCO_3$, with sulfuric acid to produce barium sulfate, carbon dioxide, and water:

$$BaCO_3 + H_2SO_4 \longrightarrow BaSO_4 + CO_2 + H_2O.$$

If this is carried out in the presence of excess sulfuric acid, the carbon dioxide produced will be essentially insoluble in the solution.

Suppose ten liters of CO_2 saturated with water vapor are collected at 25°C and at a total (barometric) pressure of 750 mm of mercury. Calculate the amount of $BaCO_3$ that must have reacted. (First you should calculate the number of moles of CO_2 formed, and from this the weight of $BaCO_3$ consumed.)

84.2 grams. **section 196**

76.9 grams. **section 201**

82.0 grams. **section 206**

8.74 grams. **section 210**

192

[*from section 167*]

YOUR ANSWER: The volume of the balloon will become 29,600 cubic yards.

No. To get this answer, you must have used the centigrade temperatures instead of their equivalents on the absolute scale.

Return to section 167 and try again.

193

[*from section 209*]

YOUR ANSWER: The density of chlorine at STP is 31.7 g/l.

No, this is not right. You apparently have the problem set up correctly, but you have made a slip in the position of your decimal point. Check carefully through your arithmetic (or logarithms) before selecting another answer in section 209.

194

[*from section 207*]

YOUR ANSWER: The partial pressures of the components of the fuel gas are $P_{H_2} = 4.24$ atm, $P_{CO} = 5.21$ atm, $P_{N_2} = 0.54$ atm.

You are correct. You have divided the percentages by the respective molecular weights to get the numbers of moles of the three gases (which total to 5.89 moles); then you have taken the ratio of the number of moles of hydrogen (for example) to the total number of moles (2.50/5.89) and multiplied this by the total pressure (10 atm) to obtain the answers as given above.

One situation in which Dalton's law is often required arises in the collection of a gas over water. It is frequently desired in the chemistry laboratory to produce small quantities of gases by chemical reaction. An example is the production of oxygen by heating potassium chlorate. The usual apparatus is shown in Figure 21.

The gas evolved from the heated solid is led through a rubber tube into the neck of an inverted, water-filled bottle. The gas bubbles up through the water, displacing it and filling the bottle. A gas collected in this way is necessarily saturated with water vapor, and in any calculation of the quantity of gas, this must be taken into account.

The collected gas is treated as a mixture of the principal substance with water vapor. The total pressure is ordinarily the prevailing atmospheric pressure as measured with a barometer, and the partial pressure of water vapor is obtainable from handbook tables, where it is usually listed as "vapor pressure of water at various tempera-

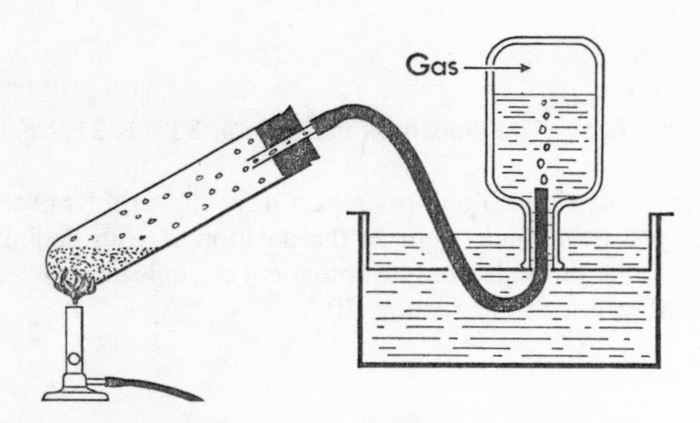

Figure 21. Collection of gas by displacement of water.

tures." An abbreviated table (Table F) will be found in the Appendix of this book.

Example: Suppose you collected 250 milliliters (ml) of oxygen over water at 25°C on a day when the barometer read 752 mm of Hg. What would the volume have been if the gas had been collected dry and at standard conditions (STP)?

Solution: First, find the partial pressure of the oxygen. For the vapor pressure of water at 25°C, the table gives 23.8 mm of Hg. This we will round off to 24 mm, because the barometric pressure is given only to the nearest millimeter. The partial pressure of oxygen must be the total pressure minus the partial pressure of water vapor, or $752 - 24 = 728$ mm of Hg.

Now we can apply the combined gas law to find the volume of oxygen at STP:

$$V_{\mathrm{STP}} = (250)\left(\frac{728}{760}\right)\left(\frac{273}{298}\right) = 220 \text{ ml.}$$

The student should verify this equation. Note that both the required pressure change (728 to 760 mm of Hg) and the required temperature change (298 to 273°K) are in the direction to result in a reduction of the volume; hence both ratios in the equation must be smaller than unity.

Now you try one:

A quantity of a solid material weighing 25.0 grams was heated in a test tube connected as shown in the figure in this section. After evolution of gas ceased, the contents of the tube weighed 14.0 grams.

The evolved gas, collected over water at 27°C and 1.00 atm pressure, occupied a volume of 6.38 liters. What is the molecular weight of the gas? (You may assume that the gas is not appreciably soluble in water.)

2.19. **section 172**

3.96. **section 199**

44.0. **section 208**

195
[*from section 158*]

YOUR ANSWER: None of the expressions given for the combined gas law is correct.

Not so; one of them is perfectly valid. Look at it this way: For a fixed quantity (weight) of gas, the volume varies *directly* with changes in temperature and varies *inversely* with pressure. This represents the word statements of Charles's and Boyle's laws. Now think this over, and try to formulate a single algebraic statement that will combine both laws.

Return to section 158 and select an answer.

196
[*from section 191*]

YOUR ANSWER: 84.2 grams of $BaCO_3$ must have reacted with sulfuric acid to give 10 liters of CO_2 (saturated with water vapor).

No, this is not right. To get this answer, you must have made a mistake in handling the pressures in your gas law calculation. Check this over carefully, then return to section 191 and choose another answer.

197
[*from section 203*]

YOUR ANSWER: The molecular weight of the gas is 0.0821.

No; an answer like this, a small decimal fraction, is of course absurd for a molecular weight. It is possible, however, that you might get this result from your calculation. If so, it indicates that you are uncertain about the units used for pressure measurement.

It was stated a few pages back that the atmosphere (atm) as a unit of measurement is defined as that pressure which will support a barometric column of mercury 760 mm in height. Pressures are often expressed in terms of millimeters of mercury (mm of Hg), but when one uses the gas constant R, with the value 0.0821 liter-atmospheres per mole per degree, then the pressure *must* be in atmospheres.

In the present problem, the pressure was stated to be 600 mm of Hg, which you must realize is the same as 600/760 of an atmosphere. The answer that directed you to this page must have been obtained by using the "600," but omitting the "760." (This answer and the value of R are the same numerically simply because the other figures conveniently cancel out in this problem; this would not generally be so.)

Return to section 203, work the problem through again to reach the correct answer.

198
[*from section 175*]

YOUR ANSWER: I don't know how to start.

What is troubling you? This problem is worked the same way as the previous one (about the stratosphere balloon). The only difference is that the pressures are given in terms of millimeters of mercury rather than atmospheres.

Tabulate the known values, as follows:

Initial Conditions	Final Conditions
$V_1 = 5.37$ liters	V_2 to be calculated
$T_1 = 29°C = 302°K$	$T_2 = 0°C = 273°K$ } STP
$P_1 = 630$ mm of Hg	$P_2 = 760$ mm of Hg } STP

Now try again to apply the combined gas law; then return to section 175 and choose an answer.

199

[from section 194]

YOUR ANSWER: The molecular weight of the gas is 3.96.

Wrong. Are you sure that you converted centigrade to absolute temperatures in the correct way?

Return to section 194 and try again.

200

[from section 190]

YOUR ANSWER: The molecular weight of the gas is 7.26.

No. You have multiplied where you should have divided and divided where you should have multiplied.

Study section 190 again, and work through the problem one logical step at a time to come up with the right answer.

201

[from section 191]

YOUR ANSWER: 76.9 grams of $BaCO_3$ must have reacted with sulfuric acid to give 10 liters of CO_2 (saturated with water vapor).

You are correct. First the volume of gas must be corrected to what it would have been dry and at STP:

$$V_{std} = V\left(\frac{T_{std}}{T_{obs}}\right)\left(\frac{P_{obs} - P_{H_2O}}{P_{std}}\right) \qquad \left[\begin{array}{l}\text{obs} = \text{observed} \\ \text{std} = \text{at STP}\end{array}\right]$$

$$= (10)\left(\frac{273}{298}\right)\left(\frac{750 - 24}{760}\right) = 8.74 \text{ liters.}$$

This value, divided by the molar volume, gives the number of moles of CO_2 evolved:

$$\frac{8.74}{22.4} = 0.390 \text{ mole.}$$

The equation for the reaction shows that the number of moles of $BaCO_3$ used up is the same as the number of moles of CO_2 produced. The formula weight of $BaCO_3$ is 197, so the number of grams used must be:

$$(0.390)(197) = 76.9 \text{ grams.}$$

A lot of steps, and you are to be congratulated if you went through them correctly the first time.

This covers the principal types of calculations that depend upon the gas laws. There can, of course, be a large number of minor variations; but if you have mastered the general methods you have studied, these variations should give no further trouble. This completes Chapter 5. Go on now to section 211 for a summary.

202

[*from section 207*]

YOUR ANSWER: I don't know how to work this.

An honest answer, at least, though perhaps a lazy one!

Since the partial pressures of gases in a mixture are in the same ratio as the numbers of moles, we must first find the numbers of moles. To find the number of moles of each gas in 100 grams of mixture, we divide the given percentages by the molecular weights of the respective gases. When we have done this, we add the individual numbers of moles to obtain the total number of moles of all the gases in 100 grams of mixture.

The partial pressure of any one of the gases is the ratio of the number of moles of that gas to the total number of moles, times 10 (because the total pressure is 10 atm).

You try it now. Return to section 207 and keep working until you get a true numerical answer.

203
[from section 209]

YOUR ANSWER: The density of chlorine at STP is 3.17 g/l.

You are correct. Density is defined as weight per unit volume, or w/V. Solving the gas law equation for this quantity, we have:

$$\text{Density} = \frac{w}{V} = \frac{PM}{RT} = \frac{(1)(71.0)}{(0.0821)(273)} = 3.17 \text{ grams/liter.}$$

This equation will give the density of a gas at *any* temperature and pressure, not solely at STP, even though the constant R was evaluated through considerations of gases at STP. Thus the density of chlorine at a pressure of 3/4 of an atmosphere and at 27°C (300°K) would be

$$\text{Density} = \frac{w}{V} = \frac{PM}{RT} = \frac{(0.750)(71.0)}{(0.0821)(300)} = 2.16 \text{ grams/liter.}$$

Try another problem:

What is the molecular weight of a gas if its density is 2.00 grams/liter, measured at 27°C and 600 mm of Hg?

5.62. **section 163**

15.6. **section 188**

0.0821. **section 197**

62.4. **section 207**

204
[*from section 208*]

YOUR ANSWER: None of the figures given is the correct answer to the problem.

No, you are mistaken; one of them *is* correct. In a problem such as this, of course, there are many points at which it is possible to go astray. You may have made a careless mistake in arithmetic; you may have inverted one of the factors (pressure or temperature) in applying the gas law; you may have forgotten to change centigrade temperatures to Kelvin temperatures; you may have run into trouble in figuring the moles-to-grams relations; and so on.

Check your work carefully. If you need to refresh your memory on the combined gas law, refer to section 158.

If you wish to continue, return to section 208 and choose the correct answer.

205
[*from section 190*]

YOUR ANSWER: The molecular weight of the gas is 1.38.

No. If you will look at this answer carefully, you will realize that it couldn't possibly be the molecular weight of anything; nothing can have a molecular weight less than that of H_2, which has a value of 2.0 (excepting only so-called "atomic hydrogen," which has the formula H). You must have divided where you should have multiplied.

Study section 190 again, and work through the problem one logical step at a time to find the correct answer.

206

[*from section 191*]

YOUR ANSWER: 82.0 grams of $BaCO_3$ must have reacted with sulfuric acid to give 10 liters of CO_2 (saturated with water vapor).

No, this is wrong. To get this answer, you must have made a mistake in handling the vapor pressure of water and applying Dalton's law. Check this over carefully, return to section 191, and try again.

207

[*from section 203*]

YOUR ANSWER: The molecular weight of the gas is 62.4.

You are correct. $M = \dfrac{wRT}{VP} = \dfrac{(2)(0.0821)(300)}{(1)(600/760)} = 62.4.$

It is to be hoped that you saved yourself some work here by noticing that 2×300 cancels exactly with 600.

PARTIAL PRESSURES

Another topic to be considered in connection with the laws for handling gas volumes has to do with mixtures of two or more gases. Suppose we write the combined gas law three times, with subscripts "A" and "B" referring to the two mixed gases taken separately, and "S" referring to the mixture:

$$P_AV_A = n_ART_A;\ P_BV_B = n_BRT_B;\ P_SV_S = n_SRT_S.$$

Now T_A, T_B, and T_S must all be the same (all the gases in a mixture are at the same temperature), also V_A and V_B are the same as V_S, since all gases occupy the whole volume of the container. The pressures P_A and P_B, however, are not necessarily equal. The *sum* of P_A and P_B must, however, equal the total pressure P_S, and similarly the numbers of moles are additive:

$$P_A + P_B = P_S; \text{ and } n_A + n_B = n_S.$$

So we can write further:

$$P_AV = n_ART; \; P_BV = n_BRT; \; P_SV = n_SRT;$$

or,

$$\frac{P_A}{n_A} = \frac{RT}{V}; \frac{P_B}{n_B} = \frac{RT}{V}; \frac{P_S}{n_S} = \frac{RT}{V}$$

and therefore

$$\frac{RT}{V} = \frac{P_A}{n_A} = \frac{P_B}{n_B} = \frac{P_S}{n_S}.$$

Thus we can state: In a mixture of gases, each gas exerts its own pressure, called its *partial pressure,* which bears the same relation to the total pressure that the number of moles of that gas bears to the total number of moles. Furthermore, the sum of the partial pressures of all gases in the mixture equals the total pressure. This is called *Dalton's Law of Partial Pressures.*

A particular fuel gas is shown by chemical analysis to contain 5.0 per cent by weight of hydrogen, 86.0 per cent carbon monoxide (CO), and the remainder nitrogen. Calculate the partial pressure of each, assuming the total pressure is 10.0 atmospheres.

P_{H_2}	P_{CO}	P_{N_2}	
0.50 atm	8.60 atm	0.90 atm	**section 178**
0.04 atm	9.02 atm	0.94 atm	**section 186**
4.24 atm	5.21 atm	0.54 atm	**section 194**

I don't know how to work this. **section 202**

[*from section 194*]

YOUR ANSWER: The molecular weight of the gas is 44.0.

You are correct. There are two ways in which you may have worked this problem. (1) You may have converted the volume to STP (dry), then compared the volume to the molar volume, 22.4 liters. (2) On the other hand, you may have used the equation $PV = (w/M)\ RT$, solving for M:

$$M = \frac{wRT}{PV} = \frac{(11)(0.0821)(300)}{(760-27)(6.38)} = 44.0.$$

Actually these two procedures for finding M are equivalent to each other. Let us proceed.

THE CHEMICAL EQUATION

We have introduced you to symbols for atoms, ions, and compounds. We have stressed that to a chemist these formulas stand for moles, 6.02×10^{23} particles, of the groups involved.

To indicate the changes that take place in reactions between such groups the chemist uses the chemical equation. A simple example:

	Ag	+	S	$\longrightarrow$	AgS
Qualitatively:	silver	+	sulfur	yields	silver sulfide
Quantitatively:	1 mole of silver atom		1 mole of sulfur atom	yields	1 mole of silver sulfide

The qualitative aspects are obvious and are implied by the quantitative aspects; we will concentrate on the quantitative aspects.

We have seen previously that the chlorine molecule is represented by the formula Cl_2; sodium by the formula Na. From the positions these elements occupy in the Periodic Table we know they combine to form NaCl. Therefore we can write:

1. word equation: sodium plus chlorine yields sodium chloride.
2. skeleton equation: $Na + Cl_2 \longrightarrow NaCl$
   (*unbalanced*)
   (Observe above we have *two* moles of chlorine atoms on left and only *one* mole of chlorine atoms on right.)
3. chemical equation:
   (*balanced*)

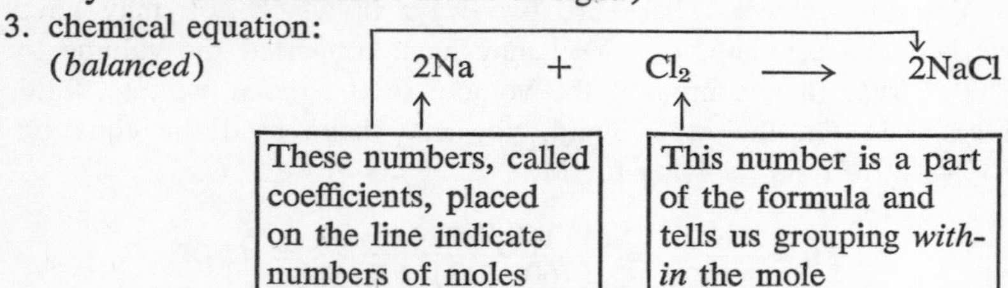

Three other examples of balanced equations:

1. $2\ KClO_3 \quad + \quad 2\ KCl \longrightarrow 3\ O_2$
   2 moles $KClO_3$ 2 moles KCl   3 moles O_2

2. $BaCO_3 \quad + \quad H_2SO_4 \longrightarrow BaSO_4 + H_2O + CO_2$
   1 mole   1 mole   1 mole   1 mole   1 mole
   (Note that we do *not* need to indicate 1 as the coefficient; it is always so understood unless indicated otherwise.)

3. $2\ Al \quad + \quad 3\ H_2SO_4 \longrightarrow Al_2(SO_4)_3 + 3\ H_2$
   2 moles   3 moles   1 mole   3 moles

Perhaps the easiest way to understand the *use* of equations is *not* to drill on the techniques of equation writing and balancing but to use them in actual work.

Remember two points about balanced chemical equations:

(1) Same number of atoms (and charges) on each side of the arrow. That's why we say it is balanced.
(2) Coefficients represent numbers of moles of formulas as written; if no coefficient is written, it is understood to be one.

Now let's proceed to use this knowledge by applying it to

WEIGHT-VOLUME PROBLEMS

Another type of calculation permits us to relate gas volumes directly with either weights or moles of nongaseous substances in a chemical equation.

For example, consider the equation

$$2Al + 3H_2SO_4 \longrightarrow Al_2(SO_4)_3 + 3H_2.$$

It is possible to produce 5.55 moles (11.10 grams) of hydrogen from 100.0 grams of aluminum. Since each mole of hydrogen occupies 22.4 liters at STP, this means that we can get

$$5.55 \times 22.4 = 124.3 \text{ liters of hydrogen}$$

at STP from 100 grams of aluminum.

Now let's try a similar problem with the additional requirement that you must take into account differences in pressure and temperature. Consider the production of oxygen gas by heating potassium chlorate:

$$2KClO_3 \xrightarrow{\text{(heat)}} 2KCl + 3O_2.$$

Suppose that this is carried out so that the oxygen is collected in a balloon (so as to avoid the need for water-vapor corrections).

What volume of gas can be obtained from 20.0 grams of $KClO_3$ if the pressure is 720 mm of Hg and the temperature is 21°C?

5.48 liters. **section 181**

4.82 liters. **section 187**

6.23 liters. **section 191**

None of these is correct. **section 204**

209

[*from section 190*]

YOUR ANSWER: The molecular weight of the gas is 34.5.

You are correct. $(5.00)\left(\frac{22.4}{3.25}\right) = 34.5.$

We are now in a position to restate the combined gas law in the form in which it is most useful in more advanced phases of chemistry. As we wrote the law earlier in this chapter, $PV/T = k$. Now we shall merely replace k by the product of two symbols, nR, and introduce the molar volume as V. We shall let n represent the number of moles of gas in the sample under consideration, and R be a general constant, known as the *universal gas constant*. Thus,

$$\frac{PV}{T} = nR, \qquad \text{or} \qquad PV = nRT.$$

To evaluate R, we can rewrite this equation solving for R, and insert known values for the other letters:

$$R = \frac{PV}{nT} = \frac{(1 \text{ atm})(22.4 \text{ liters})}{(1 \text{ mole})(273°\text{K})} = 0.0821.$$

The unit in which R is expressed here is "liter-atmospheres per mole per degree Kelvin." R will have a different numerical value and a different unit if the pressure is given in other units (such as millimeters of mercury, or pounds per square inch) or if the volume is in other units (such as milliliters, cubic feet, etc.).

Here is a slightly different type of problem:

What is the density (expressed in grams per liter) of chlorine gas (Cl_2) at STP? Note that n, the number of moles, is equal to w/M, where w is the weight of a given sample and M is the molecular weight.

71.0 g/l. **section 162**

0.317 g/l. **section 179**

31.7 g/l. **section 193**

3.17 g/l. **section 203**

[*from section 191*]

YOUR ANSWER: 8.74 grams of $BaCO_3$ must have reacted with sulfuric acid to give 10 liters of CO_2 (saturated with water vapor).

No, this is not right. It looks as though you have performed only half the problem. 8.74 is the correct figure for an intermediate step in the solution. Think through your work again and complete the problem; then turn to section 191 and select the correct answer.

211
[*from section 201*]

CHAPTER 5—THE EMPIRICAL GAS LAWS—SUMMARY

For all confined gases, *Boyle's law* applies: If the temperature is kept constant, the product of the pressure and volume is a constant.

$$PV = k \quad \text{hence} \quad P_1V_1 = P_2V_2$$

where the subscript "$_1$" refers to initial conditions and "$_2$" refers to final conditions.

Charles's law also applies: If the pressure is kept constant, the ratio of the volume to temperature is constant.

$$\frac{V}{T} = k \quad \text{hence} \quad \frac{V_1}{T_1} = \frac{V_2}{T_2}$$

In applying Charles's law, the temperature must always be measured on the *Kelvin* (*absolute*) *scale*. Figure 22 shows the relationship between the three common temperature scales. To make conversions, the following formulas can be used:

$$°K = °C - 273$$
$$°C = °K + 273$$
$$°F = (9/5)°C + 32$$
$$°C = (°F - 32)(5/9)$$

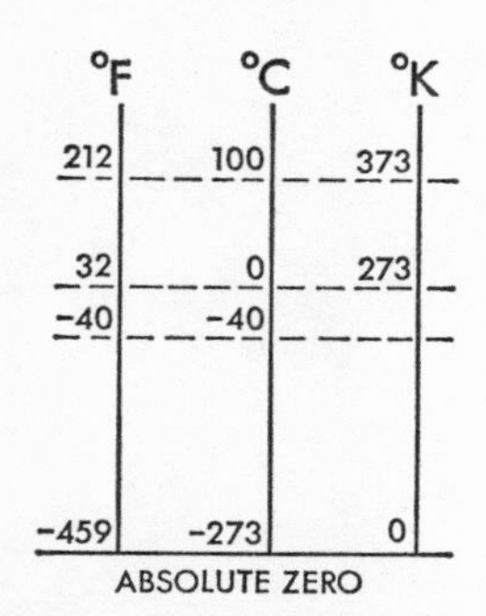

Figure 22. Relationship between the three temperature scales.

The two gas laws can be written together to give the *combined gas law:*

$$\frac{PV}{T} = k \quad \text{hence} \quad \frac{P_1V_1}{T_1} = \frac{P_2V_2}{T_2}$$

The volume of a gas is thus seen to depend on both temperature and pressure. At equal conditions of temperature and pressure, *Avogadro's hypothesis* is useful: Equal volumes of gases contain equal numbers of molecules. When measured at 0°C and normal atmospheric pressure (760 mm of mercury), one mole of any gas (which contains 6.02×10^{23} molecules) occupies a volume of 22.4 liters. This volume (22.4 liters) is called the *molar volume*. The number of molecules (6.02×10^{23}) is called *Avogadro's number*. The conditions under which the molar volume is measured, 0°C and 1 atmosphere, are called *Standard* (or *Normal*) *Temperature and Pressure,* and designated by the letters *STP* (or *NTP*).

Since the volume of a gas is related to the numbers of molecules, a generalized form of the combined gas law is often convenient:

$$PV = nRT$$

where n represents the number of moles of the gas, and the letters P, V, and T have their usual significance (T must be measured in °K); R represents a mathematical constant of proportionality, and is called the *universal gas constant,* or simply the *gas constant.*

The units of the gas constant are determined by the units selected for pressure and volume; when the volume is measured in liters and the pressure in atmospheres, then

$$R = 0.0821 \frac{\text{liter-atmospheres}}{\text{mole-degree}}$$

One can also write the law in the form

$$PV = (w/M)RT$$

where w is the weight in grams of a particular sample of gas, and M is its molecular weight.

Density is defined as the weight of a substance per unit volume, or w/V. The density of a gas can therefore be found by means of the gas law written in the form:

$$\frac{w}{V} = \frac{PM}{RT}$$

For mixtures of gases, *Dalton's law* applies: In a mixture, each gas exerts its own *partial pressure,* and the sum of the partial pressures is equal to the total pressure. This is required in calculations involving gases collected over water which contains water vapor.

Go on to the review questions, section 212.

CHAPTER 5—REVIEW QUESTIONS AND PROBLEMS

1. Convert the following temperature readings to Kelvin temperatures: 32°F, 140°C, −40°C, 22°C, 100°C.

2. Calculate the volume at STP for each of the following gases:
(a) 0.29 liters of chlorine at 30°C and 800 mm of Hg pressure.
(b) 22.4 liters of oxygen at 22°C and 760 mm of Hg.
(c) 10 liters of nitrogen at 10°C and 10 atm pressure.

3. A sample of gas occupies a volume of 52 liters at STP, and weighs 65 grams. Calculate its molecular weight.

4. Calculate the molecular weight of a gas of which 39.7 liters measured at 27°C and 700 mm of Hg weighs 66 grams.

5. Calculate the density (in grams per liter) of each of the following gases (at STP): H_2, He, CO_2, CO, UF_6.

6. Fifty milliliters of H_2 is collected over water at 24°C and 750 mm of Hg. Calculate the volume of H_2 (dry) corrected to STP. What would be the weight of this amount of H_2? (Refer to Table F in the Appendix.)

Turn to section 548 for the answers, then go on to section 213.

213
[*from section 212*]

Chapter 6

THE CALCULATION OF SOLUTION CONCENTRATIONS

Chemists work with chemicals in all three of the common physical states: gas, liquid, and solid. Solids are commonly measured by weight by means of a balance or scale. Gases are more conveniently measured by volume, but since the volume of a gas varies with the temperature and pressure, we must observe these factors (and consider them in our calculations) when we measure gases by volume. Liquids are also measured by volume. Since liquids contract and expand very little with temperature and pressure changes, we may usually neglect these two factors when measuring the volume of a liquid.

UNITS OF LIQUID MEASURE

Many of the measurements that a chemist makes are done by measuring the volume of liquid. The standard unit of volume is usually the metric unit, the liter. A liter is very nearly equal to 1.06 quarts.

Five liters of water is *about* equal to how many quarts of water?

We cannot say, since we do not know the temperature and pressure factors. **section 218**

Five liters of water is *about* equal to 5.3 quarts of water. **section 224**

Five liters of water is *about* equal to 4.71 quarts of water. **section 230**

214

[*from section 224*]

YOUR ANSWER: The conversion factor to change liters to milliliters is $\frac{1 \text{ liter}}{1000 \text{ milliliters}}$.

Well, let's check your answer. Multiply 1 liter by the conversion factor you chose:

$$(1 \text{ liter})\left(\frac{1 \text{ liter}}{1000 \text{ milliliters}}\right) = \frac{1}{1000}\left(\frac{\text{liter}^2}{\text{milliliters}}\right).$$

Since the unit is wrong, we know that the conversion factor was wrong, and the answer entirely wrong.

Return to section 224, restudy the page, and try again.

215

[*from section 239*]

YOUR ANSWER: One gram of NaOH is required to make one liter of a 1 M solution.

You are wrong.

Your trouble seems to be that you are careless about using units. To make one liter of a 1 M solution, 1 mole of NaOH is required; but 1 gram of NaOH *is not* the same as 1 mole of NaOH.

Return to section 239, restudy, and then tackle the question again.

216

[from section 232]

YOUR ANSWER: A solution consisting of 6 moles of $NaNO_3$ dissolved in enough water to make 4 liters of solution has a molarity of 1.5.

You are correct. From our definition, molarity = moles/liter. In this problem,

$$\text{molarity} = \frac{6 \text{ moles}}{4 \text{ liters}} = 1.5 \frac{\text{moles}}{\text{liter}}.$$

Hence the molarity is 1.5, and the solution is said to be a 1.5 molar solution. This is often abbreviated 1.5 M. (A capital M is understood to mean molarity.)

We can also work this kind of problem in the reverse direction. Suppose we are asked how many moles of solute there are in 5 liters of a 3.2 M solution. Since molarity = moles/liter, we can write

$$3.2 \text{ M} = \frac{3.2 \text{ moles}}{\text{liter}}.$$

We then multiply this by the 5 liters:

$$(5 \cancel{\text{liters}})\left(\frac{3.2 \text{ moles}}{\cancel{\text{liter}}}\right) = 16 \text{ moles}.$$

Now you try this one:

How many moles of $BaCl_2$ would there be in half a liter of a 0.24 M solution?

0.24 mole. **section 226**

0.5 mole. **section 234**

0.12 mole. **section 239**

YOUR ANSWER: A solution that contains 71.0 grams of Na_2SO_4 in 750 ml of solution is 0.667 molar.

You are correct. Your method should have been *approximately* like this (but could have varied in the order in which you considered the details):

We know:

(1) The solute is Na_2SO_4, and from the atomic-weight table we compute the formula weight of Na_2SO_4 as 142. Hence our conversion factor is

$$\frac{1 \text{ mole of } Na_2SO_4}{142 \text{ grams of } Na_2SO_4}.$$

(2) The amount of solute is 71 grams.

(3) The volume of the solution is 750 ml or 0.750 liter.

(4) The molarity (moles/liter) of the solution is our *unknown*.

The answer is then given by the relation

$$\frac{(71 \text{ grams of } Na_2SO_4)\left(\dfrac{1 \text{ mole of } Na_2SO_4}{142 \text{ grams of } Na_2SO_4}\right)}{(0.750 \text{ liter of solution})} =$$

$$\frac{(71)}{(142)(0.750)}\left(\frac{\text{moles of } Na_2SO_4}{\text{liters of solution}}\right) = 0.667\,\frac{\text{moles of } Na_2SO_4}{\text{liter}}.$$

Therefore, the solution is 0.667 molar.

CALCULATIONS INVOLVING WEIGHTS AND VOLUMES

Since chemical reactions are so often carried out in water solution, it would be convenient for chemists to be able to make calculations of relative amounts of solutes based on measurements of solution volumes. It turns out that this can readily be done by a suitable combination of the concept of moles as related to weights (Chapter 4) and as related to volumes of solution (this chapter).

Let us look at a weight-weight problem. Consider the reaction

$$3AgNO_3 + Na_3PO_4 \longrightarrow 3NaNO_3 + Ag_3PO_4.$$

Suppose we want to know how many grams of $AgNO_3$ will be required to produce 83.8 grams of Ag_3PO_4. How do we proceed? First we determine the formula weights of these two compounds; that of $AgNO_3$ is 170, and that of Ag_3PO_4 is 419. Then we determine how many moles we have of the substance whose weight is specified (Ag_3PO_4). This is done with a conversion factor:

$$\text{number of moles of } Ag_3PO_4 = \frac{83.8 \text{ grams}}{419 \text{ grams/mole}} = 0.2 \text{ mole.}$$

Next we note that according to the equation for the reaction, each mole of Ag_3PO_4 corresponds to 3 moles of $AgNO_3$. Therefore we must have 3×0.2 moles of $AgNO_3 = 0.6$ moles of $AgNO_3$, or

$$(0.6 \text{ moles})(170 \text{ grams of } AgNO_3\text{/mole}) = 102 \text{ grams of } AgNO_3.$$

This is the required weight of $AgNO_3$.

Now, suppose we are concerned with the same process brought about by mixing solutions of $AgNO_3$ and Na_3PO_4. If the two solutions before mixing are both 1 molar, what volume of $AgNO_3$ solution will be needed to react exactly with 25 ml of Na_3PO_4 solution?

The first step will certainly be to write the balanced equation for the process:

$$3AgNO_3 + Na_3PO_4 \longrightarrow 3NaNO_3 + Ag_3PO_4.$$

What do you think the next step should be?

Determine the formula weights of $AgNO_3$ and Na_3PO_4. **section 223**

Determine the number of moles of Na_3PO_4 in 25 ml of solution. **section 242**

Determine the weight of Na_3PO_4 in 25 ml of solution. **section 252**

218
[*from section 213*]

YOUR ANSWER: We cannot say, since we do not know the temperature and pressure factors.

Sorry, you are wrong, and wrong for two reasons.

First: temperature and pressure factors have practically no effect on the volume of a liquid, and chemists usually neglect these factors in their work.

Second: the word *about,* which was italicized in the question, tells you that an approximate answer is satisfactory. (This is a point well worth remembering; *don't* make chemistry unduly hard for yourself by seeking exact answers where the question, as here, specifies approximate answers.)

Now, restudy section 213 and choose another answer.

219
[*from section 224*]

YOUR ANSWER: The conversion factor to change liters to milliliters is $\frac{1000 \text{ milliliters}}{1 \text{ liter}}$.

You are correct. Multiply 1 liter by the conversion factor:

$$(1 \text{ liter})\left(\frac{1000 \text{ milliliters}}{1 \text{ liter}}\right) = 1000 \text{ milliliters.}$$

Since the unit is correct, you may feel confident that your method is correct. (Of course there is still the possibility of making an error in your arithmetic.)

Your answer was correct. Very good!

MOLARITY OF SOLUTIONS

Since it is so very convenient to measure chemicals in the form of liquids, chemists often take solids and dissolve them in a liquid. If the solution is made up carefully and exactly, the chemist will be able to measure a precise amount (weight) of the solid by using a precise volume of the solution.

A very convenient and useful method of expressing the concentration of a solution is in terms of *moles of dissolved substance per liter of solution.* If a solution has *1 mole* of dissolved substance* *per liter of solution,* the solution is a *1 molar* solution, i.e., the *molarity* of the solution is *1;* hence, molarity equals the number of moles of solute per liter of solution.

Suppose you take 58.5 grams of sodium chloride (NaCl) and dissolve it in enough water to make exactly 1 liter of solution. What is the molarity of the solution?

The molarity of the solution is 58.5. **section 225**

The molarity of the solution is 1. **section 232**

I don't understand how to handle this. **section 237**

* The dissolved substance is called the "solute"; the liquid in which it is dissolved is called the "solvent."

220

[*from section 242*]

YOUR ANSWER: There are 2.5 moles of Na_3PO_4 in 25 ml of a 1 molar solution.

No. You have made an arithmetic mistake that you could have avoided easily if you had made proper use of the system of units and dimensions. Don't overlook the identity

$$\frac{1000 \text{ ml}}{1 \text{ liter}} = 1 = \frac{1 \text{ liter}}{1000 \text{ ml}}.$$

This should give you a hint; it is up to you to decide what to do with it.

Return to section 242 and try again.

YOUR ANSWER: Forty grams of NaOH are required to make one liter of a 1 M solution.

You are correct. Did you solve the problem in a logical fashion? We know:

(1) Molarity of solution = 1 mole/liter.
(2) Volume of solution = 1 liter.
(3) Our solute is NaOH.
(4) One mole of NaOH weighs 40 grams (calculated from the atomic-weight table).
(5) Our answer is to be in *grams*.

Therefore,

$$\left(1\ \frac{\text{mole}}{\cancel{\text{liter}}}\right)(1\ \cancel{\text{liter}}) = 1\ \text{mole (of NaOH)}.$$

Since 1 mole of NaOH weighs 40 grams, the correct answer is 40 grams of NaOH.

Now try this:

How many grams of KOH are required to prepare 700 milliliters of 0.35 M KOH? ("0.35 M KOH" is shorthand for "a 0.35 M solution of KOH.")

13,800 grams of KOH are required. **section 227**

1380 grams of KOH are required. **section 233**

13.8 grams of KOH are required. **section 241**

222
[*from section 232*]

YOUR ANSWER: A solution consisting of 6 moles of $NaNO_3$ dissolved in enough water to make 4 liters of solution has a molarity of 4.

You are wrong.

It is true that we made up 4 liters of solution, but the concentration depends not only on the amount of solution we make up but also on the amount of material dissolved.

$$\text{Remember: molarity} = \frac{\text{moles of solute}}{\text{liters of solution}}.$$

Now turn back to section 232, restudy, and then apply this formula to the question. Do a better job this time!

223
[*from section 217*]

YOUR ANSWER: The next step should be to determine the formula weights of $AgNO_3$ and Na_3PO_4.

No. This has already been done in fixing the molarity of the solutions, and you don't need to do it again. This is one of the chief advantages of expressing concentrations in terms of molarity.

Return to section 217 and choose another answer.

224
[*from section 213*]

YOUR ANSWER: Five liters of water is about equal to 5.3 quarts of water.

You are correct. Five liters times the conversion factor $\frac{1.06 \text{ quarts}}{\text{liter}}$ gives us $(5 \text{ liters})\left(\frac{1.06 \text{ quarts}}{\text{liter}}\right) = 5.3 \text{ quarts}$.

As chemists we don't usually have any need to change metric units to English units, but it is useful to keep in mind that a liter is just a little larger than a quart.

The liquid measures most commonly used by chemists are the *liter* (l), which is the STANDARD UNIT, and the *milliliter* (ml), which is 1/1000 of a liter. Thus, 1 liter = 1000 milliliters.

What is the proper conversion factor to change liters to milliliters?

$\dfrac{1 \text{ liter}}{1000 \text{ milliliters}}$. **section 214**

$\dfrac{1000 \text{ milliliters}}{1 \text{ liter}}$. **section 219**

225

[*from section 219*]

YOUR ANSWER: A solution of 58.5 grams of NaCl in enough water to make 1 liter has a molarity of 58.5.

You are wrong.

The problem mentioned that the solution contains 58.5 grams of NaCl; there is no reason to suppose that 58.5 grams of NaCl = 58.5 moles of NaCl. Your answer is incorrect because you have confused the unit *grams* with the unit *moles*.

Restudy section 219 and choose another answer.

226

[*from section 216*]

YOUR ANSWER: Half a liter of a 0.24 M solution contains 0.24 mole of $BaCl_2$.

No. You say the concentration of the solution is 0.24 M, which means that we have 0.24 mole of solute in every liter of solution. But *in this problem* we have only one-half liter of solution, so we have less than 0.24 mole. So your answer is wrong.

To solve the problem, think in terms of units. First, make an inventory of what you know:

(1) Molarity of solution = 0.24 mole/liter.
(2) Volume of solution = 0.5 liter.
(3) Our answer is to be in the unit *moles.*

Then determine what mathematical operations will give the required units. In this case, multiplying *moles/liter* by *liters* will give *moles:* hence,

$$\left(0.24\ \frac{\text{mole}}{\text{liter}}\right)(0.5\ \text{liter}) = ?\ \text{moles}.$$

Now return to section 216, restudy the page, and choose another answer.

227
[*from section 221*]

YOUR ANSWER: 13,800 grams of KOH are required to prepare 700 milliliters of 0.35 M KOH.

Sorry, you are wrong. It is rather obvious where you slipped up. The problem said 700 *milliliters,* but you carelessly read 700 *liters.*
Now, think back; how do you change milliliters to liters?
Return to section 221 and try again.

228
[*from section 254*]

YOUR ANSWER: 0.075 ml of 1 molar $AgNO_3$ solution contains 0.075 mole of $AgNO_3$.

No. Remember that according to the definition of molarity, a 1 molar solution contains *1 mole in 1 liter* (*not* 1 mole in 1 milliliter!).
Return to section 254 and try again.

[*from section 242*]

YOUR ANSWER: There is 0.25 mole of Na_3PO_4 in 25 ml of a 1 molar solution.

No. You have made an arithmetic mistake that you could have avoided easily if you had made proper use of the system of units and dimensions. Don't overlook the identity

$$\frac{1000 \text{ ml}}{1 \text{ liter}} = 1 = \frac{1 \text{ liter}}{1000 \text{ ml}}.$$

This should give you a hint; it is up to you to decide what to do with it.

Return to section 242 and try again.

230

[*from section 213*]

YOUR ANSWER: Five liters of water is about equal to 4.71 quarts of water.

Sorry, your answer is wrong.

In the first place, you were told 1 liter is about equal to 1.06 quarts; therefore, 5 liters is certain to be equal to more than 5 quarts. So your answer does not make good sense.

In the second place, any conversion from one unit to another should be done by means of a conversion factor. (See Chapter 4, Units and Dimensions.) Since 1 liter = 1.06 quarts,

$$\frac{1 \text{ liter}}{1.06 \text{ quarts}} = 1 = \frac{1.06 \text{ quarts}}{1 \text{ liter}}.$$

Apparently you used the wrong conversion factor, obtaining this expression:

$$\left(\frac{1 \text{ liter}}{1.06 \text{ quarts}}\right)(5 \text{ liters}) = 4.71.$$

Then you forgot about dimensional units; if you had worked out the units, you would have obtained an answer of

$$4.71 \frac{(\text{liters})^2}{\text{quart}}.$$

You were seeking an answer in quarts. By using the wrong one of the two conversion factors, you obtained an answer in liters²/quart. YOU WOULD HAVE CAUGHT THIS ERROR HAD YOU REMEMBERED TO CHECK UNITS. ALWAYS CHECK UNITS!

Now return to section 213 and choose another answer.

231

[*from section 249*]

YOUR ANSWER: The HCl solution is 0.4 molar if 30 ml of it will react exactly with 20 ml of 0.3 molar Na_2CO_3 solution.

You are correct. The number of moles of Na_2CO_3 is given by

$$(20\ \cancel{\text{ml}})\left(\frac{1\ \cancel{\text{liter}}}{1000\ \cancel{\text{ml}}}\right)\left(\frac{0.3\ \text{mole}}{\cancel{\text{liter}}}\right) = 0.006\ \text{mole;}$$

then the equation $Na_2CO_3 + 2HCl \longrightarrow 2NaCl + CO_2 + H_2O$ shows that you need 0.012 mole of HCl. The molarity is then

$$\left(\frac{0.012\ \text{mole}}{30\ \text{ml}}\right)\left(\frac{1000\ \text{ml}}{1\ \text{liter}}\right) = 0.4\ \text{mole/liter}$$
$$= 0.4\ \text{molar.}$$

Now let's try another sort of problem, one that involves both volumes and weights. This can be solved by a procedure essentially identical with the methods we have just been studying.

Consider the reaction

$$2Al + 2NaOH + 2H_2O \longrightarrow 2NaAlO_2 + 3H_2.$$

What volume of 4 molar NaOH would be needed to dissolve 13.5 grams of aluminum, according to this equation?

2000 ml. **section 240** 250 ml. **section 251**

500 ml. **section 247** 125 ml. **section 255**

232

[*from section 219*]

YOUR ANSWER: A solution of 58.5 grams of NaCl in enough water to make 1 liter of solution has a molarity of 1.

You are correct. According to the atomic-weight table,

$$\begin{aligned} \text{atomic weight of Na} &= 23.0 \\ \text{atomic weight of Cl} &= \underline{35.5} \\ \text{formula weight of NaCl} &= 58.5 \end{aligned}$$

and hence, 58.5 grams of NaCl = 1 mole of NaCl. One mole of NaCl per liter of solution means we have a *1 molar* solution, or we have a solution whose *molarity* is 1. Remember: moles/liter = molarity.

Suppose we dissolve 6 moles of $NaNO_3$ in enough water to make 4 liters of solution. What is the molarity of the solution?

The molarity is 1.5. **section 216**

The molarity is 4. **section 222**

The molarity is 6. **section 246**

233

[*from section 221*]

YOUR ANSWER: 1380 grams of KOH are required to prepare 700 milliliters of 0.35 M KOH.

Sorry, your answer is wrong.

You recognized that the problem stated the volume in *milliliters* and that you should convert to *liters*. But you made a mistake in the relationship between liters and milliliters: any *milli-* unit is *one-thousandth* as much as the unit. Hence, 1000 milliliters = 1 liter, and our conversion factor is

$$\frac{1 \text{ liter}}{1000 \text{ milliliters}}.$$

Now return to section 224, review it, and then return to section 221 and work out the problem again.

234
[*from section 216*]

YOUR ANSWER: Half a liter of a 0.24 M solution contains 0.5 mole of $BaCl_2$.

No. It is true that we have 0.5 liter, but 0.5 liter *does not equal* 0.5 mole, and your answer does not make good sense.

The way to solve the problem is to think in terms of units. First, make an inventory of what you know:

(1) Molarity of solution = 0.24 mole/liter.
(2) Volume of solution = 0.5 liter.
(3) Our answer is to be in the unit *moles.*

Then determine what mathematical operations will give the correct unit. In this case, multiplying *mole/liter* by *liters* will give *moles:* hence,

$$\left(0.24 \frac{\text{mole}}{\text{liter}}\right)(0.5 \text{ liter}) = ? \text{ moles.}$$

Now return to section 216, restudy the page, and choose another answer.

235
[*from section 241*]

YOUR ANSWER: A solution that contains 71.0 grams of Na_2SO_4 in 750 milliliters of solution is 0.750 molar.

Sorry, your answer is wrong.

Apparently you assumed that since there were 750 milliliters of solution the molarity was 0.750. *This is a very bad mistake,* for there is no relationship between volume and molarity unless other factors that you completely forgot about are taken into consideration.

Now return to section 241, think through the problem carefully, and try another answer.

236
[*from section 254*]

YOUR ANSWER: 1.33 ml of 1 molar $AgNO_3$ solution contains 0.075 mole of $AgNO_3$.

No. You have divided where you should have multiplied. You would not have made this mistake if you had been following the method of units and dimensions.

Return to section 254 and try again.

237
[*from section 219*]

YOUR ANSWER: I don't understand how to handle this.

Well, first we must calculate how many moles of NaCl there are in 58.5 grams of NaCl. One mole of a substance is one *gram-formula-weight* of the substance. From the table of atomic weights:

$$\begin{aligned} \text{atomic weight of Na} &= 23.0 \\ \text{atomic weight of Cl} &= \underline{35.5} \\ \text{formula weight of NaCl} &= 58.5 \end{aligned}$$

Hence one mole of NaCl = 58.5 grams of NaCl.

If this point is not completely clear, section 149 (Chapter 4) should be thoroughly restudied.

Then return to section 219, restudy it, and see whether you can find the correct answer to this problem.

238
[*from section 249*]

YOUR ANSWER: The HCl solution is 0.36 molar if 30 ml of it will react exactly with 20 ml of 0.3 molar Na_2CO_3 solution.

No. You have multiplied where you should have divided. Return to section 249 and try again. Be sure to apply the method of units and dimensions to help keep you out of trouble.

239
[*from section 216*]

YOUR ANSWER: Half a liter of a 0.24 M solution contains 0.12 mole of $BaCl_2$.

You are correct. A good way to solve problems of this type, and many others, is to follow this kind of logical process:

Make an inventory of what you know:

(1) Molarity of solution = 0.24 mole/liter.
(2) Volume of solution = 0.5 liters.
(3) Our answer is to be in the unit *moles*.

Then perform the operations required to make the result have the correct unit:

$$(0.24 \text{ mole/liter})(0.5 \text{ liter}) = 0.12 \text{ mole}.$$

Now try this problem:

How many grams of NaOH are required to make one liter of a 1 M solution?

One gram of NaOH. **section 215**

Forty grams of NaOH. **section 221**

One mole of NaOH. **section 245**

240

[*from section 231*]

YOUR ANSWER: 2000 ml of 4 molar NaOH would be needed to dissolve 13.5 grams of aluminum.

No. You have inverted one of the factors. Stick with the method of units and dimensions and you will avoid difficulties of this kind. Return to section 231 and try again.

241

[*from section 221*]

YOUR ANSWER: 13.8 grams of KOH are required to prepare 700 milliliters of 0.35 M KOH.

You are correct. Good. Did you solve it in the following way? We know:

(1) Volume = 700 milliliters or 0.700 liter.
(2) Molarity = 0.35 mole/liter.
(3) The solute is KOH. Calculated from the atomic-weight table, 1 mole of KOH = 56.0 grams of KOH.
(4) The question asks for the number of grams of KOH required to prepare the specified solution.

To solve, find the number of moles of KOH required, and then convert moles to grams:

$$\text{Number of moles} = (0.700 \text{ liter})\left(\frac{0.35 \text{ mole}}{\text{liter}}\right) = 0.245 \text{ mole of KOH.}$$

Since 1 mole of KOH = 56.0 grams of KOH,

$$(0.245 \text{ mole of KOH})\left(\frac{56.0 \text{ grams of KOH}}{1 \text{ mole of KOH}}\right) = 13.8 \text{ grams of KOH.}$$

Now try this problem:

A solution of Na_2SO_4 contains 71.0 grams of Na_2SO_4 in 750 milliliters of solution. What is the molarity of the solution?

Molarity = 0.667. **section 217**

Molarity = 0.750. **section 235**

Molarity = 2.67. **section 248**

242

[*from section 217*]

YOUR ANSWER: The next step should be to determine the number of moles of Na_3PO_4 in 25 ml of the 1 molar solution.

You are correct. Since the molarity tells you the relation between moles and volume, the number of moles is easily determined.

How many moles of Na_3PO_4 are there in 25 ml of a 1 molar solution?

2.5 moles. **section 220**

0.25 mole. **section 229**

0.04 mole. **section 250**

0.025 mole. **section 254**

243

[*from section 254*]

YOUR ANSWER: 7.5 ml of 1 molar $AgNO_3$ solution contains 0.075 mole of $AgNO_3$.

No. You have made a mistake in positioning your decimal point. You would not have made this mistake if you had been following the method of units and dimensions.

Return to section 254 and try again.

244

[*from section 249*]

YOUR ANSWER: The HCl solution is 0.012 molar if 30 ml of it will react exactly with 20 ml of 0.3 molar Na_2CO_3 solution.

No. You have not finished the problem. It is true that 0.012 mole of HCl is exactly the amount required, but the question did not ask, "How many moles?" but rather, "What is the molarity?" You must answer the question you were asked! The fact that you have the figure 0.012 indicates that you are on the right track.

Return to section 249 and select another answer.

245

[*from section 239*]

YOUR ANSWER: One mole of NaOH is required to make one liter of a 1 M solution.

Your statement is correct, *but* it does not answer the question. You were asked the question "How many grams?" and your answer must be in grams.

Return to section 239 and try again.

246

[*from section 232*]

YOUR ANSWER: A solution consisting of six moles of $NaNO_3$ dissolved in enough water to make 4 liters of solution has a molarity of 6.

You are wrong. It is true that we dissolved 6 moles of $NaNO_3$, but the concentration depends not only on the amount of material we dissolve but also on the amount of solution formed.

$$\text{Remember: molarity} = \frac{\text{moles of solute}}{\text{liters of solution}}.$$

Now turn back to section 232, restudy, and then apply this formula to the question. Do a better job this time!

247

[*from section 231*]

YOUR ANSWER: 500 ml of 4 molar NaOH would be needed to dissolve 13.5 grams of aluminum.

No. You have inverted one of the factors. Stick with the method of units and dimensions and you will avoid difficulties of this kind.

Return to section 231 and try again.

248
[*from section 241*]

YOUR ANSWER: A solution that contains 71.0 grams of Na_2SO_4 in 750 milliliters of solution is 2.67 molar.

Sorry, you are wrong.

Apparently your mistake occurred when you tried to convert grams of Na_2SO_4 to moles of Na_2SO_4.

1 mole of Na_2SO_4 = 142 grams of Na_2SO_4 (from the atomic-weight table); hence, our conversion factor should be

$$\frac{1 \text{ mole of } Na_2SO_4}{142 \text{ grams of } Na_2SO_4}.$$

Applying this factor, we obtain

$$\left(\frac{1 \text{ mole of } Na_2SO_4}{142 \text{ grams of } Na_2SO_4}\right)(71.0 \text{ grams of } Na_2SO_4) = 0.5 \text{ mole of } Na_2SO_4.$$

Now return to section 241 and reconsider the question.

249
[*from section 254*]

YOUR ANSWER: 75 ml of 1 molar $AgNO_3$ solution contains 0.075 mole of $AgNO_3$.

You are correct.

$$(0.075 \text{ mole})\left(1 \frac{\text{liter}}{\text{mole}}\right)\left(1000 \frac{\text{ml}}{\text{liter}}\right) = 75 \text{ ml}.$$

We have thus shown that 25 ml of 1 molar Na_3PO_4 requires 75 ml of 1 molar $AgNO_3$ for complete reaction.

Now another problem. Consider the equation:

$$Na_2CO_3 + 2HCl \longrightarrow 2NaCl + H_2O + CO_2.$$

What is the molarity of a solution of HCl if 30 ml of the solution react exactly with 20 ml of a 0.3 molar solution of Na_2CO_3?

The HCl solution is 0.4 molar. **section 231**

The HCl solution is 0.36 molar. **section 238**

The HCl solution is 0.012 molar. **section 244**

The HCl solution is 0.2 molar. **section 253**

250

[*from section 242*]

YOUR ANSWER: There is 0.04 mole of Na_3PO_4 in 25 ml of a 1 molar solution.

No. You have divided where you should have multiplied, a mistake you could easily have avoided by proper use of the system of units and dimensions.

Return to section 242 and try again.

251

[*from section 231*]

YOUR ANSWER: 250 ml of 4 molar NaOH would be needed to dissolve 13.5 grams of aluminum.

No. In order to get this answer, you have probably made a mistake in the number of moles of NaOH required. Be sure to stick with the method of units and dimensions. Notice also that, according to the equation, the ratio of moles of NaOH to moles of Al is 2 : 2 which is the same as 1 : 1.

Now return to section 231 and try again.

252
[*from section 217*]

YOUR ANSWER: The next step should be to determine the weight of Na_3PO_4 in 25 ml of solution.

No. This is not necessary, because you have already done this in fixing the molarity of the solutions, and you don't need to do it again.
Return to section 217 and choose another answer.

253
[*from section 249*]

YOUR ANSWER: The HCl solution is 0.2 molar if 30 ml of it will react exactly with 20 ml of 0.3 molar Na_2CO_3 solution.

No. It looks as though you forgot an essential step. Go back to the problem that starts in section 217 and follow through the entire problem up to its correct answer in section 249. Then rework the present problem (section 249) and select another answer.

254
[*from section 242*]

YOUR ANSWER: There is 0.025 mole of Na_3PO_4 in 25 ml of a 1 molar solution.

You are correct.

$$(25\ \cancel{\text{ml}})\left(\frac{1\ \cancel{\text{liter}}}{1000\ \cancel{\text{ml}}}\right)\left(1\,\frac{\text{mole}}{\cancel{\text{liter}}}\right) = 0.025 \text{ mole.}$$

We have now determined the number of moles of one reactant, Na_3PO_4, in the equation

$$\underset{}{3AgNO_3} + \underset{(0.025 \text{ mole})}{Na_3PO_4} \longrightarrow 3NaNO_3 + Ag_3PO_4.$$

The next step to be taken is identical with the corresponding step in the weight-weight problem. Since the equation tells us that 3 moles of $AgNO_3$ are needed for each mole of Na_3PO_4, we deduce immediately that we need (3)(0.025) = 0.075 mole of $AgNO_3$ for our particular quantity of phosphate.

What volume of 1 molar $AgNO_3$ solution contains 0.075 mole of $AgNO_3$?

0.075 ml. **section 228**

1.33 ml. **section 236**

7.5 ml. **section 243**

75 ml. **section 249**

255

[*from section 231*]

YOUR ANSWER: 125 ml of 4 molar NaOH would be needed to dissolve 13.5 grams of aluminum.

You are correct. The steps to achieve this answer are as follows:

Moles of Al: $(13.5 \text{ grams})\left(\dfrac{1 \text{ mole}}{27 \text{ grams}}\right) = 0.5 \text{ mole.}$

Ratio of NaOH to Al is 2 : 2, which is the same as 1 : 1.
Since our solution of NaOH is 4.0 molar, we have

$$\frac{4 \text{ moles}}{\text{liter}} = 1 = \frac{1 \text{ liter}}{4 \text{ moles}}.$$

Volume of NaOH solution:

$$(0.5 \text{ mole})\left(\frac{1 \text{ liter}}{4 \text{ moles}}\right)\left(\frac{1000 \text{ ml}}{\text{liter}}\right) = 125 \text{ ml.}$$

This completes the material of Chapter 6. You should now be able to carry out any type of calculations involving quantities of materials, either as solids, as liquid solutions, or as gases.

Go on to section 256 for the summary.

CHAPTER 6—THE CALCULATION OF SOLUTION CONCENTRATIONS—SUMMARY

The *liter* (l) and its submultiple the *milliliter* (ml) are the units of volume commonly used in chemistry. It is convenient to remember that a liter is just slightly larger than a quart.

The concentration of a solution is often indicated in terms of *molarity* (M):

$$\text{Molarity} = \frac{\text{Moles of solute}}{\text{Liters of solution}}.$$

Remember that a *solute* dissolved in a *solvent* makes a *solution.*

The molarity (M) of a solution times the volume of the solution in liters (l) gives us the number of moles of dissolved material contained in the solution:

$$\text{Moles of solvent} = \text{Molarity (liters of solution)}.$$

257
[*from section 256*]

CHAPTER 6—REVIEW QUESTIONS AND PROBLEMS

1. (a) How many milliliters are there in one liter?
(b) How many quarts are there in a liter (approximately)?
(c) How many moles of solute are there in 1 liter of a 1 M solution?
(d) How many moles of solute are there in 3 liters of a 2 M solution?
(e) How many moles of solute are there in 0.5 liter of a 0.4 M solution?
(f) How many moles of solute are there in 400 ml of a 0.6 M solution?

2. What is the molarity of each of the following solutions?
(a) 6 moles of NaOH dissolved in enough water to make 8 liters of solution.
(b) 0.5 mole of $AgNO_3$ dissolved in 3 liters of solution.
(c) 0.1 mole of KCl dissolved in 250 ml of solution.
(d) 3 moles of $Al(NO_3)_3$ dissolved in 10 liters of solution.

3. (a) How many grams of $BaCl_2$ are required to make 1 liter of 1 M solution?
(b) How many grams of KNO_3 are required to make 300 ml of a 0.2 M solution?
(c) How many grams of LiCl are contained in 3.4 liters of a 0.25 M solution?

4. Given the equation: $2AgNO_3 + BaCl_2 \longrightarrow 2AgCl + Ba(NO_3)_2$:
(a) What is the molar ratio of $AgNO_3$ to $BaCl_2$?
(b) How many moles of $BaCl_2$ are there in 50 ml of a 1 M solution of $BaCl_2$?
(c) How many moles of $AgNO_3$ would react with this much $BaCl_2$?
(d) How many milliliters of a 1 M solution of $AgNO_3$ would be required to react with this much $BaCl_2$?

(e) What volume of a 0.2 M solution of $BaCl_2$ would be required to react with 200 ml of 0.4 M solution of $AgNO_3$?

(f) What would be the molarity of a $BaCl_2$ solution, if 50 ml of it are required to react exactly with 48 ml of a 0.75 M solution of $AgNO_3$?

5. What volume of a 6 M solution of HCl will be needed to dissolve 32.7 grams of zinc metal according to the reaction:

$$Zn + 2HCl \longrightarrow ZnCl_2 + H_2?$$

Turn to section 549 for the answers, then go on to section 258.

[*from section 257*]

Chapter 7

ENERGY CONSIDERATIONS

When a chemist is working in the laboratory, he is often concerned with what substances are formed and what substances are required. Any chemical equation should be understood as a statement that under specified conditions,

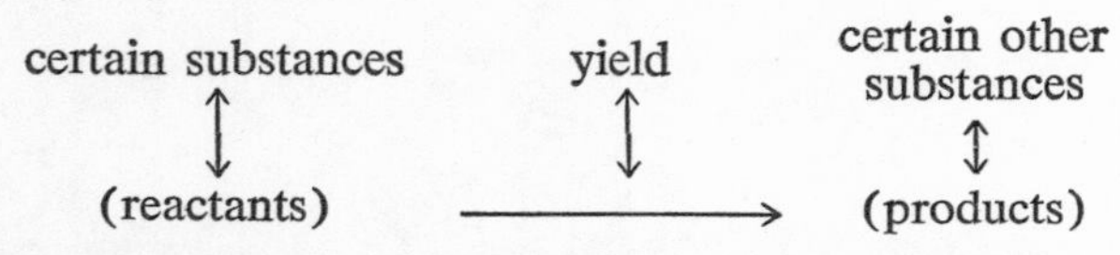

Such a reaction is to be read from left to right, and the items on the left are always called the *reactants,* and those on the right the *products.**

ENERGY IN CHEMICAL REACTIONS

A chemical reaction always involves energy. Sometimes this energy must be supplied to make a reaction take place, and sometimes energy is released during the course of the reaction. We can indicate this by including an energy term in the equation. Let us do this, using Q as a symbol to stand for energy.

In the equation $C + O_2 \longrightarrow CO_2 + Q$, should the energy term be considered a reactant or a product?

The energy term is a reactant. **section 263**

The energy term is a product. **section 275**

* Sometimes it is desired to indicate that a reaction is reversible, and to do this a double arrow ($\rightleftarrows$) is used; but even in this case, the substances on the left are referred to as the reactants, and those on the right as the products. Reversible reactions will be discussed in more detail in Chapter 9.

259
[*from section 275*]

YOUR ANSWER: The reaction

$$P_4 + 5O_2 \longrightarrow P_4O_{10} + Q$$

is exoergic.

You are correct. Q on the right side of the arrow means that Q is a product, which means that the reaction is exoergic.

Is the reaction that takes place inside a flashlight battery when it is in use endoergic or exoergic?

Endoergic. **section 265**

Exoergic. **section 271**

Neither. **section 280**

I can't tell. **section 287**

260
[*from section 271*]

YOUR ANSWER: A negative value of ΔH signifies that the reaction is endoergic.

You did not read the question and preceding text very carefully. If a positive ΔH means that the reaction is endoergic, a negative value could hardly mean the same thing.

Restudy section 271 carefully, and choose another answer.

261

[*from section 289*]

YOUR ANSWER: The equation

$$N_2 + O_2 \longrightarrow 2NO;\ \Delta H = +43.2 \text{ Kcal}$$

is equivalent to

$$N_2 + O_2 \longrightarrow 2NO - 43.2 \text{ Kcal.}$$

No! Reread the material in section 275, then return to section 289 and select another answer.

262

[*from section 279*]

YOUR ANSWER: A reaction is exoergic (its ΔH is negative) if the reactants have a lower energy content than the products.

Wrong, since a higher energy level for the products means that we must use energy to go up to the level of the products, just as we must use energy to climb up a hill.

Return to section 279, read again from the beginning, and study the graphs carefully.

263

[*from section 258*]

YOUR ANSWER: The energy term in the equation

$$C + O_2 \longrightarrow CO_2 + Q$$

is a reactant.

A careless answer! This is really a very simple question; the answer depends only on being able to tell which is the right side and which the left side of an equation.

Return to section 258, restudy it, and answer the question again.

264

[*from section 273*]

YOUR ANSWER: $\Delta H = +126.3$ Kcal for the reaction

$$H_2O_{(liq,\ 25^\circ)} \longrightarrow H_2O_{(g,\ 25)}.$$

No. You realized correctly that you must combine equations 1 and 2, *but* it is necessary to reverse one of them before adding. Reversing a reaction, as we have seen, changes the sign of the corresponding ΔH.

Return to section 273 and try again.

265

[*from section 259*]

YOUR ANSWER: The reaction in a flashlight battery is endoergic.

No. While there is no appreciable direct heat effect in the flashlight battery, energy must be produced from it in order to light up the bulb. Remember, electricity is a form of energy. Also, keep in mind carefully the meanings of the words endoergic and exoergic.

Return to section 259 and select another answer.

266

[*from section 282*]

YOUR ANSWER: The heat of formation of water (liq, 25°) is +68.4 Kcal/mole.

No. The previously written equation—

$$H_2O_{(liq,\ 25^\circ)} \longrightarrow H_{2\ (g,\ 25^\circ)} + \tfrac{1}{2}O_{2\ (g,\ 25^\circ)};\ \Delta H = +68.4 \text{ Kcal}$$

—has a value of $\Delta H = +68.4$ Kcal. Remember that a positive ΔH means heat is *absorbed*. If heat is absorbed when H_2O is decomposed into its elements, what would you expect to happen when the elements combine to form water?

Think this over, return to section 282, and try again.

267

[*from section 272*]

YOUR ANSWER: The heat of formation of NO is

$$\Delta H = +43.2 \text{ Kcal/mole.}$$

No, you are mistaken. ΔH for the reaction that involved two moles of NO is 43.2 Kcal. So the heat of formation of *one* mole of NO cannot be 43.2 Kcal.

Return to section 272, restudy carefully, and choose another answer.

268

[*from section 276*]

YOUR ANSWER: The heat of reaction for the combustion of graphite is $\Delta H = +96.5$ Kcal.

No. You have not kept in mind the meaning of the sign of the ΔH value.

Return to section 276 and restudy carefully the examples given there. Then choose the correct answer.

YOUR ANSWER: $\Delta H = +10.5$ Kcal for the reaction

$$H_2O_{\text{(liq, 25°)}} \longrightarrow H_2O_{\text{(g, 25°)}}$$

You are correct. Very good. This process can be visualized as the sum of two steps, which can be written separately, then added along with the ΔH values:

$$H_2O_{\text{(liq, 25°)}} \longrightarrow H_{2\text{ (g, 25°)}} + \tfrac{1}{2}O_{\text{(g, 25°)}};\ \Delta H = +68.4 \text{ Kcal}$$

add:

$$H_{2\text{ (g, 25°)}} + \tfrac{1}{2}O_{\text{(g, 25°)}} \longrightarrow H_2O_{\text{(g, 25°)}};\ \Delta H = -57.9 \text{ Kcal}$$

$$H_2O_{\text{(liq, 25°)}} + H_{2\text{ (g, 25°)}} + \tfrac{1}{2}O_{2\text{ (g, 25°)}} \longrightarrow H_2O_{\text{(g, 25°)}} + H_{2\text{ (g, 25°)}} + \tfrac{1}{2}O_{2\text{ (g, 25°)}};\ \Delta H = 68.4 + (-57.9) \text{ Kcal}$$

or, as a net reaction,

$$H_2O_{\text{(liq, 25°)}} \longrightarrow H_2O_{\text{(g, 25°)}};\ \Delta H = +10.5 \text{ Kcal.}$$

Note that the first equation stated above is the reverse of Equation 2 from section 273, and that the sign of ΔH is changed.

In working the following problem, remember that ΔH for the process of heating liquid water is always equal to the temperature interval (°C) multiplied by 18, the molecular weight. (This is valid for water because the calorie is defined in terms of water; for any other substance, an additional factor would be required, the *heat capacity* of the substance.)

Which of the following items of information, in addition to those in section 273, would enable you to find ΔH for the reaction

$$H_2O_{\text{(liq, 0°)}} \longrightarrow H_2O_{\text{(g, 100°)}}?$$

ΔH for the process $H_2O_{\text{(g, 0°)}} \rightarrow H_2O_{\text{(g, 100°)}}$. **section 278**

ΔH for the process $H_2O_{\text{(liq, 0°)}} \rightarrow H_2O_{\text{(g, 0°)}}$. **section 285**

ΔH for the process $H_2O_{\text{(g, 25°)}} \rightarrow H_2O_{\text{(g, 100°)}}$. **section 290**

ΔH for the process $H_2O_{\text{(liq, 100°)}} \rightarrow H_2O_{\text{(g, 100°)}}$. **section 290**

270
[*from section 275*]

YOUR ANSWER: The reaction

$$P_4 + 5O_2 \longrightarrow P_4O_{10} + Q$$

is endoergic.

No. Be more careful. Is the Q term in this reaction a product or a reactant? What is the meaning of "endoergic"?

Return to section 275, restudy it, and answer the question again.

271
[*from section 259*]

YOUR ANSWER: The reaction taking place in a flashlight battery is exoergic.

You are correct. The electrical energy that lights up the lamp bulb must be a product of the battery reaction; hence the reaction is exoergic.

HEAT OF REACTION

The energy involved in any reaction is usually called the *heat of reaction,* even though it may be electrical in nature. The heat of reaction is given the symbol ΔH.†

When a reaction is endoergic, ΔH represents the amount of energy required; when the reaction is exoergic, ΔH represents the amount of energy released. For an endoergic reaction, we label the ΔH value as positive; conversely a positive ΔH tells us that the reaction is endoergic. The sign of ΔH, however, is not necessarily always positive, differing in this respect from the Q value.

† Δ (delta) is the capital D in the Greek alphabet, and stands for the word "difference." The symbol ΔH is read "delta H."

What meaning would you suppose a negative ΔH has?

The reaction is endoergic. **section 260**

The reaction is exoergic. **section 276**

I don't know. **section 283**

272

[*from section 279*]

YOUR ANSWER: A reaction is endoergic (its ΔH is positive) if the reactants have a lower energy content than the products.

You are correct. Both parts of this answer mean exactly the same thing. A lower level of energy for the reactants than for the products means we will have to supply energy to make the reaction take place, just as we must supply energy to climb up a hill.

The ΔH value for any reaction can always be referred to as the *heat of the reaction.* If the reaction is a combustion reaction, we sometimes call it a *heat of combustion;* if the reaction is one in which a compound is formed from its elements we can refer to this as the *heat of formation.* Consider:

$$2H_2 + O_2 \longrightarrow 2H_2O + 115.6 \text{ Kcal}$$

or

$$2H_2 + O_2 \longrightarrow 2H_2O; \Delta H = -115.6 \text{ Kcal.}$$

Now, the heat of reaction is the heat released (since ΔH has a negative value) when 2 moles of H_2 (gas) combine with 1 mole of O_2 (gas) to form 2 moles of H_2O (gas).

The heat of combustion of H_2 (gas) is -57.8 Kcal/mole and the heat of formation of water is -57.8 Kcal/mole since heat of combustion and heat of formation in this case are the same thing, and are always expressed *per mole of the substance concerned.* The ΔH

for any reaction is *always* given for the reaction *as written,* reading from left to right.

Now let's refer back to the equation for the formation of nitric oxide given in section 289:

$$N_2 + O_2 \longrightarrow 2NO; \ \Delta H = +43.2 \text{ Kcal.}$$

What is the heat of formation of NO?

+43.2 Kcal/mole. **section 267**

−43.2 Kcal/mole. **section 277**

+21.6 Kcal/mole. **section 282**

−21.6 Kcal/mole. **section 288**

273

[*from section 282*]

YOUR ANSWER: The heat of formation of $H_2O_{\text{(liq, 25°)}}$ is −68.4 Kcal/mole.

You are correct. If 68.4 Kcal is *absorbed* (ΔH positive) when one mole of water is decomposed, clearly 68.4 Kcal will be *liberated* (ΔH negative) in the reverse process, the combination of oxygen and hydrogen to give one mole of water.

Let us now summarize the heat effects for those processes concerning water that we have studied so far.

(Eq. 1) $H_{2\,\text{(g, 25°)}} + \frac{1}{2}O_{2\,\text{(g, 25°)}} \longrightarrow H_2O_{\text{(g, 25°)}};$

$\Delta H = -57.9$ Kcal

(Eq. 2) $H_{2\,\text{(g, 25°)}} + \frac{1}{2}O_{2\,\text{(g, 25°)}} \longrightarrow H_2O_{\text{(liq, 25°)}};$

$\Delta H = -68.4$ Kcal

(Eq. 3) $H_2O_{\text{(liq, 0°)}} \longrightarrow H_2O_{\text{(liq, 100°)}};$ $\Delta H = +1.8$ Kcal

What is ΔH for the reaction

$$H_2O_{\text{(liq, 25°)}} \longrightarrow H_2O_{\text{(g, 25°)}}?$$

$\Delta H = +126.3$ Kcal. **section 264**

$\Delta H = +10.5$ Kcal. **section 269**

$\Delta H = -10.5$ Kcal. **section 281**

$\Delta H = -126.3$ Kcal. **section 286**

274
[*from section 289*]

YOUR ANSWER: The equation

$$N_2 + O_2 \longrightarrow 2NO;\ \Delta H = +43.2 \text{ Kcal}$$

is equivalent to

$$N_2 + O_2 - 43.2 \text{ Kcal} \longrightarrow 2NO.$$

No! Reread the material in section 275, especially about the sign of Q. Then turn again to section 289 and select another answer.

275
[*from section 258*]

YOUR ANSWER: The energy term in the equation

$$C + O_2 \longrightarrow CO_2 + Q$$

is a product.

You are correct. Since Q appears on the right side of the arrow it is to be considered a product.

We will decide arbitrarily that Q is always to be taken as a *positive* quantity, and hence when it is written in an equation, it should always have a + sign.

For example, we can decompose water into its elements by electrolysis. The equation is

$$2H_2O \longrightarrow 2H_2 + O_2.$$

To make this happen, we have to supply electrical energy; we indicate this by writing

$$2H_2O + Q \longrightarrow 2H_2 + O_2,$$

which shows us that energy is supplied as a reactant.

The reverse reaction, the combination of hydrogen and oxygen to produce water, releases energy, so we write

$$2H_2 + O_2 \longrightarrow 2H_2O + Q.$$

The quantitative value of Q in these two reactions will *of necessity* be exactly the same, because each reaction is the reverse of the other.

A chemical reaction that yields energy is called an *exoergic* (or *exothermic*) reaction, while a reaction that requires energy is called *endoergic* (or *endothermic*).

Does the following equation represent an exoergic or an endoergic reaction?

$$P_4 + 5O_2 \longrightarrow P_4O_{10} + Q$$

Exoergic. **section 259**

Endoergic. **section 270**

276

[*from section 271*]

YOUR ANSWER: A negative value of ΔH signifies that the reaction is exoergic.

You are correct. If a positive value of ΔH means that the reaction is endoergic, then a negative value signifies an exoergic reaction.

The Q value of a reaction is *always* written as part of the equation itself; when we write the ΔH for a reaction, we *never* write it in the equation as a reactant or product. For example,

$$C + O_2 \longrightarrow CO_2;\ \Delta H = \text{a negative quantity.}$$

The negative ΔH tells us that the reaction is exoergic, hence we can also write

$$C + O_2 \longrightarrow CO_2 + Q.$$

As another example, consider the reaction

$$H_2 + I_2 \longrightarrow 2HI;\ \Delta H = \text{a positive quantity.}$$

The positive ΔH tells us that the reaction is endoergic, hence we can also write

$$H_2 + I_2 + Q \longrightarrow 2HI.$$

Energy can be expressed in many different units. Calories, ergs, joules, kilowatt-hours, and electron-volts are just a few of the more common units. Since all of these measure energy, they can be converted into each other by means of conversion factors, as discussed in Chapter 4. The units we will use in this chapter are the calorie (cal) and the kilocalorie (Kcal).

A calorie is defined as the amount of energy required to raise the temperature of one gram of water one degree centigrade. This means that it is also the amount of energy released when the temperature of one gram of water decreases one degree centigrade. The kilocalorie is equal to 1000 calories. Both Q values and ΔH values are expressible in either of these units.

When graphite (a form of carbon) is burned in oxygen, the reaction is

$$C + O_2 \longrightarrow CO_2 + 96.5\ \text{Kcal}.$$

What is the value of ΔH for this reaction?

$\Delta H = +96.5$ Kcal. **section 268**

$\Delta H = -96.5$ Kcal. **section 289**

277

[*from section 272*]

YOUR ANSWER: The heat of formation of NO is

$$\Delta H = -43.2\ \text{Kcal/mole.}$$

Well, let's see. The given reaction–

$$N_2 + O_2 \longrightarrow 2NO; \ \Delta H = +43.2 \text{ Kcal}$$

–involves *two* moles of NO. The heat of reaction for two moles ($\Delta H = +43.2$ Kcal) cannot possibly be the same as the heat of formation of NO, because this means the heat of formation of *one* mole of NO.

Return to section 272, study it carefully, and choose another answer.

278
[*from section 269*]

YOUR ANSWER: To find ΔH for

$$H_2O_{\text{(liq, 0°)}} \longrightarrow H_2O_{\text{(g, 100°)}},$$

I would need to know ΔH for the process

$$H_2O_{\text{(g, 0°)}} \longrightarrow H_2O_{\text{(g, 100°)}}.$$

No. This wouldn't help, because you would still need ΔH for the $H_2O_{\text{(liq, 0°)}} \longrightarrow H_2O_{\text{(g, 0°)}}$ step, which you don't know.

Return to section 273 followed by section 269. Study the material on these pages, then select another answer.

279
[*from section 289*]

YOUR ANSWER: The equation

$$N_2 + O_2 \longrightarrow 2NO; \ \Delta H = +43.2 \text{ Kcal}$$

is equivalent to

$$N_2 + O_2 + 43.2 \text{ Kcal} \longrightarrow 2NO.$$

You are correct. Your equation is endoergic, and that is exactly what "$\Delta H = +43.2$ Kcal" means.

The ΔH for any reaction represents the difference in energy between the products and the reactants. Let us use a simple graph to represent this idea visually:

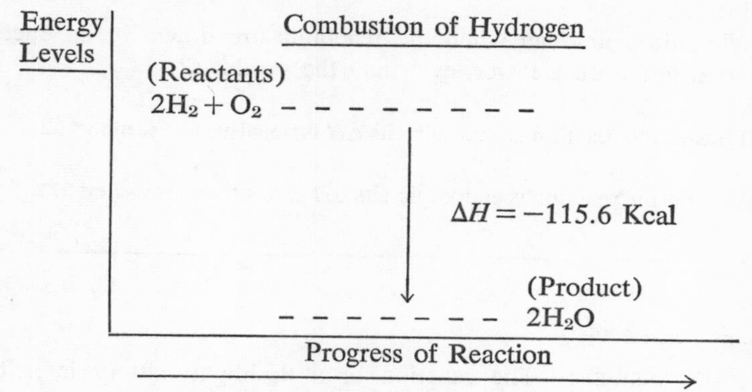

Figure 23. Energy levels, combustion of H_2.

The difference between the energy levels of the product and reactants is exactly what is meant by ΔH (see footnote, section 271). A negative value for ΔH means that the reactants contain more energy than the products, and that in going from reactants to products energy is given off, hence the reaction is exoergic.

Let us consider the reaction that is the reverse of the combustion of hydrogen, namely the electrolysis of water.

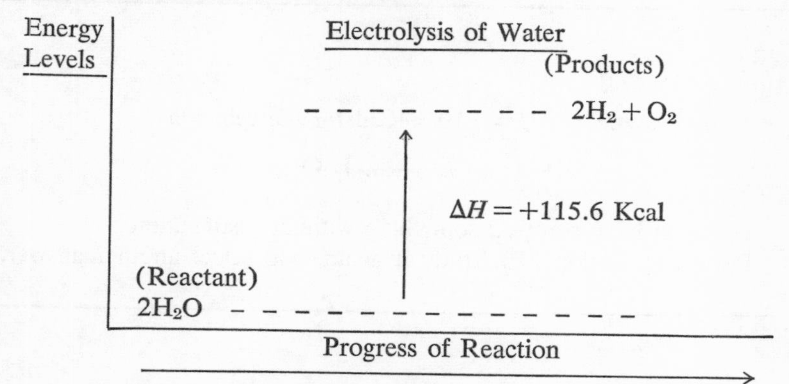

Figure 24. Energy levels, electrolysis of water.

As before, ΔH is the difference between the energy levels of the reactant and the products. A positive value for ΔH means that the products have more energy than the reactants, that in going from reactants to products energy is consumed, and hence the reaction is endoergic.

What does it mean when the reactants are drawn in an energy-reaction graph on a lower level than the products?

It means the reaction is exoergic (its ΔH is negative). **section 262**

It means the reaction is endoergic (its ΔH is positive). **section 272**

280

[*from section 259*]

YOUR ANSWER: The reaction in a flashlight battery is neither endoergic nor exoergic.

No, you are mistaken. Perhaps you chose this answer because you know that a flashlight battery does not warm up appreciably, nor cool off, in operation. But remember that the electricity that lights the bulb is a form of energy.

With this in mind, return to section 259 and choose another answer.

281

[*from section 273*]

YOUR ANSWER: $\Delta H = -10.5$ Kcal for the reaction

$$H_2O_{(liq,\ 25°)} \longrightarrow H_2O_{(g,\ 25°)}.$$

No. You have reversed something without justification.

Return to section 273, study it again, and select another answer.

YOUR ANSWER: The heat of formation of NO is

$$\Delta H = +21.6 \text{ Kcal/mole.}$$

You are correct. The ΔH value as given, +43.2 Kcal, was for *two* moles of NO, so the value of the heat of formation of *one* mole of NO would, of course, be +21.6 Kcal/mole. Furthermore, the positive sign for the ΔH means that energy is required to make the reaction proceed; in other words the production of NO is an endoergic reaction.

It takes energy to raise the temperature of a substance. For example, we can write

$$H_2O_{\text{(liq, 0°C)}} \longrightarrow H_2O_{\text{(liq, 100°C)}}; \quad \Delta H = 1800 \text{ cal} = 1.80 \text{ Kcal}‡.$$

(Note that this value of ΔH is consistent with the definition of the calorie, since the formula weight of water is 18.) This, of course, is a *physical* rather than a chemical change, but energy is involved in both physical and chemical changes. The amount of energy involved in chemical changes is *usually much greater* than that in physical changes, for the same quantity of material. For example, contrast the 1.8 Kcal for the above reaction with 68.4 Kcal for the electrolysis of 1 mole of water:

$$H_2O_{\text{(liq, 25°)}} \longrightarrow H_{2\,\text{(g, 25°)}} + \tfrac{1}{2}O_{2\,\text{(g, 25°)}}; \quad \Delta H = 68.4 \text{ Kcal.}$$

It is possible to combine heats of successive reactions or processes in various ways to obtain over-all heat changes. In order to do this, it is sometimes necessary to reverse an equation. For example, suppose we wish to know the heat of formation of water (liquid at 25°) when the only information we have at hand is that given with the last equation written above.

Consider the equation below:

$$H_{2\,\text{(g, 25°)}} + \tfrac{1}{2}O_{2\,\text{(g, 25°)}} \longrightarrow H_2O_{\text{(liq, 25°)}}$$

‡The abbreviations in parentheses indicate the physical state of each substance: g for gas, liq for liquid, and the temperature in degrees centigrade.

What is the value of ΔH per mole of H_2O?

$\Delta H = +68.4$ Kcal. **section 266**

$\Delta H = -68.4$ Kcal. **section 273**

283

[*from section 271*]

YOUR ANSWER: I don't know the significance of a negative ΔH.

Think a minute! "+" and "−" are algebraic symbols. They are frequently used to indicate concepts that are opposites of each other. If distance *up* is taken as "+," then "−" means distance *downward;* if *credits* are taken as "+," then "−" indicates *debits;* if time *after* an event is "+," then "−" means time *before* the event.

In chemistry, we use algebraic symbols and operations as tools. We try to find a chemical interpretation of these ideas.

Now return to section 271, restudy it, and select another answer.

284

[*from section 289*]

YOUR ANSWER: The equation

$$N_2 + O_2 \longrightarrow 2NO;\ \Delta H = +43.2 \text{ Kcal}$$

is equivalent to

$$N_2 + O_2 \longrightarrow 2NO + 43.2 \text{ Kcal.}$$

No, you are wrong; you have listed the energy as a product. That would mean the reaction is exoergic. *But,* "$\Delta H = +43.2$ Kcal" means that the reaction is *endoergic.*

Return to section 289 and select another answer.

285
[*from section 269*]

YOUR ANSWER: To find ΔH for

$$H_2O_{(liq,\ 0°)} \longrightarrow H_2O_{(g,\ 100°)},$$

I would need to know ΔH for the process

$$H_2O_{(liq,\ 0°)} \longrightarrow H_2O_{(g,\ 0°)}.$$

No. This wouldn't solve your problem, because you would still need ΔH for $H_2O_{(g,\ 0°)} \longrightarrow H_2O_{(g,\ 100°)}$, which you don't know.

Return to section 273, followed by section 269. Study the material on these pages, then select another answer.

286
[*from section 273*]

YOUR ANSWER: $\Delta H = -126.3$ Kcal for the reaction

$$H_2O_{(liq,\ 25°)} \longrightarrow H_2O_{(g,\ 25°)}.$$

No. You realized correctly that you must combine equations 1 and 2, *but* it is necessary to reverse *one* of them before adding. This, as we have seen, changes the corresponding sign of ΔH.

Return to section 273 and try again.

287

[from section 259]

YOUR ANSWER: I can't tell whether the reaction in a flashlight battery is endoergic or exoergic.

You should be able to tell. Where does the energy that lights up the bulb come from? Remember that electricity is a form of energy, just as much as heat is. Think this over.

Return to section 259 and select another answer.

288

[from section 272]

YOUR ANSWER: The heat of formation of NO is

$$\Delta H = -21.6 \text{ Kcal/mole.}$$

The reaction given–

$$N_2 + O_2 \longrightarrow 2NO; \ \Delta H = +43.2 \text{ Kcal}$$

–involves *two* moles of NO, so you were correct in dividing the ΔH value by two. But think, what does a positive value of ΔH for this reaction mean? Should the sign of ΔH be positive or negative? Think!

Return to section 272, restudy it, and choose another answer.

289
[*from section 276*]

YOUR ANSWER: The heat of reaction for the combustion of graphite is $\Delta H = -96.5$ Kcal.

You are correct. A negative sign for the ΔH value tells us that the reaction is exoergic, hence the Q value (which is always positive) belongs on the product side of the equation. Since that is exactly the equation we started with–

$$C + O_2 \longrightarrow CO_2 + 96.5 \text{ Kcal}$$

–your answer was indeed correct.

Let's try another example.

$$N_2 + O_2 \longrightarrow 2NO; \ \Delta H = +43.2 \text{ Kcal.}$$

How would this equation be written if we wanted to include a Q term in the equation?

$N_2 + O_2 \rightarrow 2NO - 43.2$ Kcal. **section 261**

$N_2 + O_2 - 43.2 \text{ Kcal} \rightarrow 2NO$. **section 274**

$N_2 + O_2 + 43.2 \text{ Kcal} \rightarrow 2NO$. **section 279**

$N_2 + O_2 \rightarrow 2NO + 43.2$ Kcal. **section 284**

290
[*from section 269*]

YOUR ANSWER: To find ΔH for

$$H_2O_{\text{(liq, 0°)}} \longrightarrow H_2O_{\text{(g, 100°)}},$$

I would need to know ΔH for either of the following two processes:

$$H_2O_{\text{(g, 25°)}} \longrightarrow H_2O_{\text{(g, 100°)}}; \ \Delta H = 0.57 \text{ Kcal.}$$

$$H_2O_{\text{(liq, 100°)}} \longrightarrow H_2O_{\text{(g, 100°)}}; \ \Delta H = 9.72 \text{ Kcal.}$$

You are correct, whichever of these responses you chose, because there are two equally valid approaches to the problem:

(1)

$$H_2O_{\text{(liq, 0°)}} \longrightarrow H_2O_{\text{(liq, 25°)}}; \quad \Delta H = 0.45 \text{ Kcal}$$
$$H_2O_{\text{(liq, 25°)}} \longrightarrow H_2O_{\text{(g, 25°)}}; \quad \Delta H = 10.50 \text{ Kcal}$$
$$H_2O_{\text{(g, 25°)}} \longrightarrow H_2O_{\text{(g, 100°)}}; \quad \Delta H = 0.57 \text{ Kcal}$$

(add)

$$H_2O_{\text{(liq, 0°)}} \longrightarrow H_2O_{\text{(g, 100°)}}; \quad \Delta H = 11.52 \text{ Kcal}$$

(2)

$$H_2O_{\text{(liq, 0°)}} \longrightarrow H_2O_{\text{(liq, 100°)}}; \quad \Delta H = 1.80 \text{ Kcal}$$
$$H_2O_{\text{(liq, 100°,}} \longrightarrow H_2O_{\text{(g, 100°)}}; \quad \Delta H = 9.72 \text{ Kcal}$$

(add)

$$H_2O_{\text{(liq, 0°)}} \longrightarrow H_2O_{\text{(g, 100°)}}; \quad \Delta H = 11.52 \text{ Kcal}$$

These relations may be clarified by Figure 25.

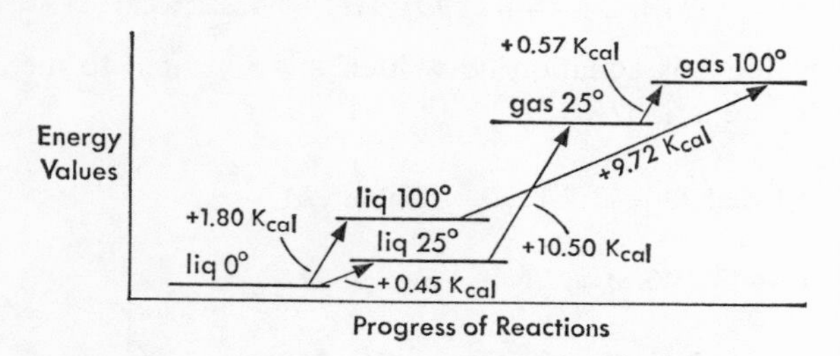

Figure 25. Energy transformation for H_2O.

You have now completed the detailed study of energy relations of Chapter 7. Go to the next section for a summary.

CHAPTER 7—ENERGY CONSIDERATIONS—SUMMARY

In any chemical reaction, *reactants give products.* In an equation representing that reaction, the reactants are always written on the *left,* the products on the *right:*

$$\text{reactants} \longrightarrow \text{products}$$

The energy involved in a chemical reaction may be indicated generally by the letter "Q."

For an *exoergic* reaction:

$$\text{reactants} \longrightarrow \text{products} + Q$$

For an *endoergic* reaction:

$$\text{reactants} + Q \longrightarrow \text{products}$$

The value of Q is always *positive.*

The energy produced or required by a reaction may also be indicated separately from the equation as a ΔH value, called the *heat of reaction.* ΔH is numerically equal to Q, and is by convention given a *positive* sign if Q is on the *left* in the equation, *negative* if on the *right.*

The *heat of combustion* or *of reaction* for a particular substance may be written in a similar fashion, as a ΔH value, but in these cases it always applies to *one mole* of the substance named, rather than to an equation as written.

Q values are always written in *energy units,* e.g., calories or kilocalories, but ΔH values are written in energy units for the reaction as written, involving a particular amount of reactants, or energy units per mole, e.g., calories per gram or calories per mole, of a stated substance.

When dealing with equations in which energy units are stated, or in dealing with ΔH values, it is often necessary to specify the temperature, pressure, and state of aggregation of the substances involved, since energy values will differ for the same chemical reaction under different conditions.

Try the review questions in section 292.

CHAPTER 7—REVIEW QUESTIONS AND PROBLEMS

1. Classify the following statements as True or False:
(a) In a chemical reaction, products are written on the left.
(b) In a chemical reaction, reactants are written on the left.
(c) In the equation for an exoergic reaction, Q is on the left.
(d) Q never has a negative sign or a negative value.
(e) ΔH never has a negative sign or a negative value.
(f) A positive value for ΔH means an exoergic reaction.
(g) A positive value for ΔH means that Q is on the right.
(h) A positive value for ΔH means that Q is a "reactant."
(i) If Q is a "product," then ΔH has a negative value.
(j) Q written on the left means that the reaction is endoergic.

2. Given the reaction: $CS_2 + 2O_2 \longrightarrow SO_2 + CO_2 + 10{,}850$ cals,
(a) Is the reaction exoergic or endoergic?
(b) What is the Q-value?
(c) What is the value of ΔH?
(d) What is the heat of combustion of CS_2 in cals/mole?
(e) What is the heat of reaction per mole of oxygen?

3. Given the reaction: $2CO + O_2 \longrightarrow 2CO_2$, $\Delta H = -68$ Kcals,
(a) Is the reaction exoergic or endoergic?
(b) Rewrite the equation to include a Q-value.
(c) What is the heat of combustion of CO?
(d) What is heat of reaction per mole of oxygen consumed?

4. Given the reactions:

$$C + O_2 \longrightarrow CO_2, \qquad \Delta H = -94 \text{ Kcals};$$
$$2CO + O_2 \longrightarrow 2CO_2, \quad \Delta H = -136 \text{ Kcals};$$

(a) Is the reaction $2C + O_2 \longrightarrow 2CO$ exoergic or endoergic?
(b) Write this equation to include a Q-value.
(c) What is the value of ΔH for this reaction?
(d) What is the heat of formation of CO in Kcals per mole?

Turn to section 550 for the answers, then go on to section 293.

293
[from section 292]

Chapter 8

NUCLEAR REACTIONS AND EQUATIONS

Chemists are often concerned with radioactivity and other changes that involve the nucleus. In this chapter we will focus our attention on these nuclear changes rather than on the chemical and physical changes that always accompany them. Nuclear changes are very much more energetic than chemical changes, just as chemical changes are usually more energetic than physical changes. For a *very crude* comparison we may remember that the energy involved in nuclear events is *about* 1000 times as great as the energy involved in chemical events; also, the energy involved in chemical events is about 100 times as great as that in physical changes, when equal amounts of matter are involved.

THE NUCLEUS

The atomic number of an element tells us a very fundamental fact about the element: it tells us the number of protons in the nucleus of that element.

How many protons are there in the nucleus of an oxygen atom?

There are 8 protons in an oxygen nucleus. **section 298**

There are 16 protons in an oxygen nucleus. **section 304**

294
[from section 312]

YOUR ANSWER: $_{47}Ag^{108}$ has 47 neutrons.

You are wrong. The $_{47}$ tells us the number of protons, not the number of neutrons.

Restudy section 312 and choose another answer.

295
[*from section 300*]

YOUR ANSWER: The three nuclei

$$_{92}U^{238},\ _{92}U^{234},\ \text{and}\ _{92}U^{235}$$

all have the same mass number.

Well, let's consider: the only difference between these nuclei is in the numbers written above, which are the mass numbers; so your answer is wrong.

Restudy section 300 carefully and choose another answer.

296
[*from section 316*]

YOUR ANSWER: The complete equation is

$$_{88}Ra^{226} \longrightarrow {_2He^4} + \boxed{_{88}Ra^{222}}$$

Well, let's see:

Key *A:* $226 = 4 + 222$ So 222 is the correct new *A* number.
Key *Z:* $88 \neq^* 2 + 88$ So 88 is *not* the correct *new* *Z* number.

Restudy the *reasoning* in section 316 and continue on.

* $\neq$ is a commonly used symbol and is read "does not equal."

297
[*from section 331*]

YOUR ANSWER: The correct equation is

$$_{83}Bi^{211} \longrightarrow {_{-1}\beta^0} + {_{84}Po^{211}}.$$

No, this is not correct. The question asked what the equation would be if bismuth (mass 211) gave off an *alpha* particle. Your answer tells what would happen if it gave off a *beta* particle.

Turn back to section 331 and make a more careful choice.

298

[*from section 293*]

YOUR ANSWER: There are 8 protons in the nucleus of an oxygen atom.

You are correct. All you had to do was look up the atomic number for oxygen, since the atomic number equals the number of protons in the nucleus. Let's try the reverse of this problem.

What element has a nucleus containing 19 protons?

A fluorine nucleus has 19 protons. **section 305**

A potassium nucleus has 19 protons. **section 312**

299

[*from section 328*]

YOUR ANSWER:

$$_{82}Pb^{210} + {}_{-1}\beta^0 \longrightarrow {}_0\gamma^0 + {}_{81}Tl^{210}$$

is the correct equation for the simultaneous emission of beta and gamma radiation from $_{82}Pb^{210}$.

No, you are mistaken. It is true that the equation you have chosen *does* meet the tests of the two Nuclear Keys, but it is wrong in that the beta particle is written on the left, which implies that it is a reactant, whereas the statement of the problem says it is *emitted,* i.e., it is a *product*.

Return to section 328 and choose another answer.

YOUR ANSWER: $_{47}Ag^{108}$ has 61 neutrons.

You are correct.

$$\begin{array}{rl} 108 = & \text{the number of protons and neutrons} \\ \text{minus } \underline{47} = & \text{the number of protons} \\ 61 = & \text{the number of neutrons} \end{array}$$

The number of protons and neutrons in a nucleus is often referred to as the *mass number* and is given the symbol A; the number of protons is called the *atomic number* and is given the symbol Z. Notice and remember that *both* the mass number, A, *and* the atomic number, Z, are positive integers (whole numbers). As in the above example, the difference between A and Z, that is, A minus Z, equals the number of neutrons, and is given the symbol N. N, like A and Z, is always an integer. N is called the *neutron number*. Hence, using algebraic equations:

$$Z + N = A$$

$$Z = A - N$$

$$N = A - Z$$

These three equations are different ways of saying one and the same thing.

Now, look carefully at the nuclear symbols listed below:

$$_{92}U^{238} \quad _{92}U^{234} \quad _{92}U^{235}$$

How are these three nuclei alike?

They all have the same mass number. **section 295**

They all have the same number of neutrons. **section 310**

They all have the same number of protons. **section 321**

301
[*from section 321*]

YOUR ANSWER:

$$_8O^{16} + {}_1p^1 \longrightarrow {}_7N^{13} + {}_2He^4$$

is a correct equation.

You are correct. This question is best answered in three steps:

(1) Apply Key *A:* $16+1=13+4$
(2) Apply Key *Z:* $8+1= 7+2$
(3) Check atomic numbers against atomic symbols:

Oxygen: atomic number = 8
Proton: atomic number = 1
Nitrogen: atomic number = 7
Helium: atomic number = 2

And we see that the equation is correct and that you chose the right answer. That's fine! Keep these Nuclear Keys in mind and this next problem should be easy.

Is this nuclear equation formally correct?

$$_{13}Al^{27} + {}_0n^1 \longrightarrow {}_{11}Na^{24} + {}_2He^4$$

No, it is not correct. **section 307**

Yes, it is correct. **section 316**

302
[*from section 317*]

YOUR ANSWER:

$$_{83}Bi^{211} \longrightarrow {}_{-1}e^0 + {}_{82}Pb^{211}.$$

You handled the *A* numbers correctly, but look what you did with the *Z* numbers:

$$83 \neq -1 + 82$$

Either you were careless or you don't understand the use of negative numbers.

In either case, turn back to section 322 and proceed from there.

303

[from section 318]

YOUR ANSWER:

$$_4Be^9 \ (p, \alpha) \ _3Li^6$$

is the simplified equation corresponding to

$$_4Be^9 + {_1p^1} \longrightarrow {_3Li^6} + {_2\alpha^4}.$$

You are correct. The symbol first written inside the parentheses is the particle that reacts with the starting material; that written second within the parentheses is the particle (or ray) that is emitted along with the heavy product.

Let's try another equation.

Write the complete nuclear equation that corresponds to the simplified equation

$$_3Li^7 \ (p, \gamma) \ _4Be^8.$$

$_3Li^7 + {_1p^1} \rightarrow {_4Be^8}$. **section 309**

$_3Li^7 + {_0\gamma^0} \rightarrow {_4Be^8} + {_1p^1}$. **section 326**

$_3Li^7 + {_1p^1} \rightarrow {_4Be^8} + {_0\gamma^0}$. **section 332**

304

[from section 293]

YOUR ANSWER: There are 16 protons in an oxygen nucleus.

Sorry, your answer is wrong. You must have looked up the atomic weight.

Return to section 293, reread the information, and try again.

305
[from section 298]

YOUR ANSWER: A fluorine nucleus has 19 protons.

Come now. Let's be more careful. Nineteen is *not* the atomic number of fluorine.

Recheck the question (review section 298) and try another answer.

306
[from section 322]

YOUR ANSWER: That "−1" *does* bother me; I need help here.

O.K. It is good to recognize when you need help.

Our basic Key *A* still holds good:

$$A \text{ numbers on left} = A \text{ numbers on right.}$$
$$88 = -1 + X$$

This is a simple algebraic equation. What value must X have to make it a true statement? 89, of course! So 89 is our new A number.

Now, turn back to section 322 and proceed to a correct answer.

307
[from section 301]

YOUR ANSWER: The equation

$$_{13}Al^{27} + {_0n^1} \longrightarrow {_{11}Na^{24}} + {_2He^4}$$

is not correct.

You are wrong! It is your job to find out why you are wrong and do a better job. Here are three possible reasons for your error:

(1) Perhaps you were lazy and just took a chance that since the last two answers were right, this one would be wrong. If so, learn right now that work, not guessing, is the pathway to

success in chemistry. If you *just guessed,* turn back to section 301, restudy it, and go on.

(2) Perhaps you were careless in adding the numbers in the equation. If so, learn right now that you *cannot* succeed in any science if you are careless in simple arithmetic. If you were careless, turn back to section 301, recheck the example, and *verify to your own satisfaction* that it is correct, then proceed.

(3) Perhaps you do not understand the *Nu-clear Keys* and to you they are just *Un-clear Keys.* If so, let's master this right now.

Reviewing:

$$\mathrm{Al}^{27}_{13}$$

27 ← Numbers *here* are *A* numbers (*mass* numbers).

13 ← Numbers *here* are *Z* numbers (*atomic* numbers).

Z numbers tell us how many protons we have.

A numbers tell us how many *protons and neutrons* we have in all.

And now, the Nuclear Keys:

Key *A:* The sum of the *A* numbers on the left equals the sum of the *A* numbers on the right.

Key *Z:* The sum of the *Z* numbers on the left equals the sum of the *Z* numbers on the right.

These keys apply to *all nuclear reactions.*

Now, turn back to section 321 and start rereading and restudying at that point.

308

[*from section 316*]

YOUR ANSWER: The complete equation is

$$_{88}\mathrm{Ra}^{226} \longrightarrow {}_{2}\mathrm{He}^{4} + \boxed{_{86}\mathrm{Rn}^{226}}$$

Let's apply our Nuclear Keys:

Key *Z:* $88 = 2 + 86$ So 86 *is* the new *Z* number.

Key *A:* $226 \neq$† $4 + 226$ So 226 *cannot be* the new *A* number.

† $\neq$ is a commonly used symbol and is read "does not equal."

Return to section 316, restudy the *reasoning* on that page, and then continue with your progress.

309

[*from section 303*]

YOUR ANSWER:

$$_{3}Li^{7} + {}_{1}p^{1} \longrightarrow {}_{4}Be^{8}$$

is the equation corresponding to

$$_{3}Li^{7}\ (p, \gamma)\ {}_{4}Be^{8}.$$

You were all right *as far as you went;* however, the simplified equation specified that gamma radiation was emitted, and the complete equation *must* contain all the information in the simplified equation.

Return to section 303 and consider the question again.

310

[*from section 300*]

YOUR ANSWER: The three nuclei

$$_{92}U^{238},\ {}_{92}U^{234},\ \text{and}\ {}_{92}U^{235}$$

all have the same number of neutrons.

Well, let's consider: In each nucleus,

$$A - Z = \text{the number of neutrons.}$$
$$\text{In } {}_{92}U^{238},\ 238 - 92 = 146.$$
$$\text{In } {}_{92}U^{234},\ 234 - 92 = 142.$$
$$\text{In } {}_{92}U^{235},\ 235 - 92 = 143.$$

It is evident that the nuclei all have different numbers of neutrons, and that your answer is wrong.

Restudy section 300 carefully and choose another answer.

311

[*from section 328*]

YOUR ANSWER: $_{82}Pb^{210} + _{0}\gamma^{0} \longrightarrow _{-1}\beta^{0} + _{83}Bi^{210}$ is the correct equation for the simultaneous emission of beta and gamma radiation from $_{82}Pb^{210}$.

No, you are mistaken. It is true that the equation you have chosen *does* meet the test of the two Nuclear Keys, but it is wrong in that the gamma ray is written on the left, which implies that it is a reactant, whereas the statement of the problem says it is *emitted;* i.e., it is a *product*.

Return to section 328 and choose another answer.

312

[*from section 298*]

YOUR ANSWER: A potassium nucleus has 19 protons.

You are correct. You're doing fine. Let's move ahead.

NUCLEAR SYMBOLS

Every nucleus (except that of hydrogen) contains neutrons as well as protons in the nucleus. The subscript number written below and to the left of the symbol (*this number* $\longrightarrow {}_{1}H^{1}$) tells us how many protons there are in the nucleus. The other number, written as a superscript (*this number* $\curvearrowright {}_{1}H^{1}$) tells us the total number of *both* neutrons and protons in the nucleus. For example, the *nuclear symbol* $_{30}Zn^{65}$ indicates that the zinc nucleus has 30 protons and 35 neutrons. The 30 protons we read directly; we find the number of neutrons in the nucleus by subtracting 30 from 65: $65 - 30 = 35$.

When we write a symbol such as $_{47}Ag^{108}$ we are writing a *nuclear* symbol, and it represents *not an atom* but the *nucleus* alone.

Now look at the nuclear symbol ${}_{47}Ag^{108}$ and decide how many neutrons it has.

${}_{47}Ag^{108}$ has 47 neutrons. **section 294**

${}_{47}Ag^{108}$ has 61 neutrons. **section 300**

${}_{47}Ag^{108}$ has 108 neutrons. **section 319**

313
[*from section 322*]

YOUR ANSWER: The complete equation is

$${}_{88}Ra^{225} \longrightarrow {}_{-1}e^{0} + \boxed{{}_{87}Fr^{225}}$$

Let's check this by applying Key *A* and Key *Z:*

$$\text{Key } A\text{: } 225 = 0 + 225. \quad \text{O.K.}$$
$$\text{Key } Z\text{: } 88 \neq^{\dagger} -1 + 87,$$
$$\text{since } -1 + 87 = 86,$$

and your answer was wrong!

Turn to section 322 (which tells about negative numbers) and carry on from there.

† $\neq$ is a commonly used symbol and is read "does not equal."

314
[*from section 321*]

YOUR ANSWER:

$${}_{8}O^{16} + {}_{1}p^{1} \longrightarrow {}_{7}N^{13} + {}_{2}He^{4}$$

is not a correct equation.

Well, let's check.

$$\text{Key } A\text{: } 16 + 1 = 13 + 4.$$
$$\text{Key } Z\text{: } 8 + 1 = 7 + 2.$$

Checking atomic numbers:

Oxygen: 8
Proton: 1
Nitrogen: 7
Helium: 2

And we see that the equation *is* correct and that you chose the wrong answer.

Return to section 321, restudy, *be sure* you understand the Nuclear Keys and then try again.

315
[*from section 332*]

YOUR ANSWER:

$$_{90}Th^{232}\ (n,\ 3n)\ _{53}I^{133} + {}_{37}Rb^{97}$$

represents a *fusion* reaction.

Well, let's consider. This reaction starts with a single nucleus, $_{90}Th^{232}$, and ends up with two smaller nuclei, $_{53}I^{133}$ and $_{37}Rb^{97}$, as well as with three neutrons (against the one neutron that was consumed). This does not fit the definition of fusion!

Return to section 332 and choose another answer.

316
[*from section 301*]

YOUR ANSWER: Yes, the equation

$$_{13}Al^{27} + {}_{0}n^{1} \longrightarrow {}_{11}Na^{24} + {}_{2}He^{4}$$

is correct.

You are correct. Let's check your *reasoning*.
Did you apply the Nuclear Keys?
Did you check the A numbers? $27 + 1 = 24 + 4$.
Did you check the Z numbers? $13 + 0 = 11 + 2$.
Did you check symbols against Z numbers?

13 is the atomic number for an aluminum nucleus.
0 is the atomic number for a neutron.
11 is the atomic number for a sodium nucleus.
2 is the atomic number for a helium nucleus.

If you carried out *all* of these steps you are getting along fine!

Now, you should be able to apply the Nuclear Keys to complete a nuclear equation for yourself.

Radium, mass number 226, gives off a helium nucleus of mass 4, and becomes a new nucleus in the process.

We may express this as follows:

$$_{88}Ra^{226} \longrightarrow {}_2He^4 + \boxed{?}$$

Now, apply the Nuclear Keys to discover for yourself what belongs in the box.

Choose the correct answer:

$\boxed{_{88}Ra^{222}}$ **section 296**

$\boxed{_{86}Rn^{226}}$ **section 308**

$\boxed{_{86}Rn^{222}}$ **section 322**

I don't understand. **section 330**

317

[*from section 331*]

YOUR ANSWER: The correct equation is

$$_{83}Bi^{211} \longrightarrow {}_{81}Tl^{207} + {}_2\alpha^4.$$

You are correct. We can check it by noting that

$$\begin{aligned} 211 &= 207 + 4 \\ 83 &= \ \ 81 + 2 \end{aligned}$$

and that $_2\alpha^4$ is the correct symbol for an alpha particle, and also that thallium (Tl) has atomic number 81. Notice that

$$_{83}Bi^{211} \longrightarrow {}_2\alpha^4 + {}_{81}Tl^{207}$$

is *also* correct, since the *order* in which the nuclear symbols are written on the right makes no difference.

Suppose that ${}_{83}\text{Bi}^{211}$ emits a β particle. What is the nuclear equation for this event?

${}_{83}\text{Bi}^{211} \rightarrow {}_{-1}e^0 + {}_{82}\text{Pb}^{211}$. **section 302**

${}_{83}\text{Bi}^{211} \rightarrow {}_{-1}e^0 + {}_{84}\text{Po}^{211}$. **section 328**

318

[*from section 328*]

YOUR ANSWER:

$${}_{82}\text{Pb}^{210} \longrightarrow {}_{-1}\beta^{\circ} + {}_{0}\gamma^{0} + {}_{83}\text{Bi}^{210}$$

is the correct equation for the simultaneous emission of beta and gamma radiation from ${}_{82}\text{Pb}^{210}$.

You are correct. Both ${}_{-1}\beta^0$ and ${}_{0}\gamma^0$ appear on the right side, and the Nuclear Keys show that ${}_{83}\text{Bi}^{210}$ must be the main product.

Let us summarize the kinds of nuclear reactions for which you have learned to write equations:

(1) Reactions involving a proton, ${}_{1}p^1$.
(2) Reactions involving a neutron, ${}_{0}n^1$.
(3) Reactions involving an electron, ${}_{-1}e^0$ (also called a beta particle, ${}_{-1}\beta^0$).
(4) Reactions involving a helium nucleus, ${}_{2}\text{He}^4$ (also called an alpha particle, ${}_{2}\alpha^4$).
(5) Reactions involving gamma radiation, which does *not* consist of *particles,* and has the symbol ${}_{0}\gamma^0$, often written just γ.

Other particles sometimes occur, but the rules for handling them are the same as for the above particles (which are by far the most common and important).

The rules are just our old friends, the Nuclear Keys:

Key *A:* The sum of the *A* numbers *on the left* equals the sum of the *A* numbers *on the right.*

Key *Z:* The sum of the *Z* numbers *on the left* equals the sum of the *Z* numbers *on the right.*

These rules apply to *all* nuclear reactions.

Sometimes a simplified way of writing these nuclear equations is convenient. For example:

$$_{13}Al^{27} + {_0}n^1 \longrightarrow {_{11}}Na^{24} + {_2}He^4 \text{ can be expressed}$$

$$_{13}Al^{27}\ (n, \alpha)\ {_{11}}Na^{24}$$

This tells us the large nucleus we start with. (→ $_{13}Al^{27}$)

This names the smaller particle added. (→ n)

This names the smaller particle given off. (→ α)

This tells us the large nucleus we end up with. (→ $_{11}Na^{24}$)

Subscripts are not written for the items written within the parentheses, which will usually be the familiar particles listed at the top of this section. You should be able to write a nuclear equation in this simplified form for yourself.

Write a simplified nuclear equation for

$$_4Be^9 + {_1}p^1 \longrightarrow {_3}Li^6 + {_2}\alpha^4.$$

$_4Be^9\ (p, \alpha)\ {_3}Li^6$. **section 303**

$_4Be^9\ (p, Li)\ {_2}\alpha^4$. **section 324**

$_4Be^9\ (\alpha, p)\ {_3}Li^6$. **section 329**

319

[*from section 312*]

YOUR ANSWER: $_{47}Ag^{108}$ has 108 neutrons.

Not so! The ^{108} tells us the number of protons *and* neutrons, not the number of neutrons.

Restudy section 312 and choose another answer.

320
[*from section 332*]

YOUR ANSWER:

$${}_{90}Th^{232}\ (n,\ 3n)\ {}_{53}I^{133} + {}_{37}Rb^{97}$$

represents a *fission* reaction.

You are correct. Fission means to divide, or break up into smaller parts. ${}_{90}Th^{232}$ is what we start with, and we end up with ${}_{53}I^{133}$ and ${}_{37}Rb^{97}$. This certainly fits the definition of fission.

Notice that this process uses up one neutron, but produces three neutrons! Now, under suitable conditions, each of the product neutrons can react with another ${}_{90}Th^{232}$ nucleus to produce fission, and this process can continue in many successive steps, until all the available ${}_{90}Th^{232}$ is used up. This is an example of a nuclear *chain reaction*. Similar chain reactions in ${}_{92}U^{235}$ and ${}_{94}Pu^{239}$ are employed in "atomic bombs."

Fusion reactions, such as occur in the H-bomb, will not be discussed in this text.

For your help and convenience, we list in the chapter summary the symbols you are most likely to meet in elementary considerations of nuclear reactions and equations.

Almost all other nuclear symbols you will ever meet will be nuclei, which you can identify from a periodic chart by checking the Z number of the nucleus.

Proceed to section 333 for the chapter summary and then try the review problems in section 334.

321
[*from section 300*]

YOUR ANSWER: The three nuclei

$${}_{92}U^{238},\ {}_{92}U^{234},\ \text{and}\ {}_{92}U^{235}$$

all have the same number of protons.

You are correct. All these nuclei have the same atomic number, 92. This is the Z number, which tells us how many protons there are in the nuclei.

ISOTOPES

Atoms that are alike in Z number, that is, have the same number of protons, are called *isotopes* of each other, or are said to be *isotopic* to each other. Thus, all copper atoms, since they all have atomic number 29, have 29 protons, and their nuclei are all isotopic.*

In chemical changes, nuclei are not considered, because they *do not* change. But in nuclear changes (which of course involve much greater energies than chemical changes), the number of protons or neutrons in a nucleus can change.

To represent such changes in an easy fashion we use these symbols:

p —— which stands for a proton
and
n —— which stands for a neutron.

We can write these as complete nuclear symbols as follows:

$$_{1}p^{1}$$

^{1} ⟶ Tells us p has mass number 1.
$_{1}$ ⟶ Tells us p has atomic number 1.

$$_{0}n^{1}$$

^{1} ⟶ Tells us n has mass number 1.
$_{0}$ ⟶ Tells us n has atomic number 0 (that is, it has no protons).

Now, let's consider a nuclear reaction. Let's see what we get if we add a proton to the carbon nucleus of mass 12.

	proton		carbon nucleus mass 12		
A numbers / *Z* numbers	$_{1}p^{1}$	plus	$_{6}C^{12}$	$\longrightarrow$	?

* Since the name "copper" or the symbol "Cu" *immediately* tells us that the nucleus contains 29 protons, i.e., that the atomic number is 29, some chemists write Cu^{63} instead of $_{29}Cu^{63}$. Both notations are common, and you should be able to use either form. Either symbol represents a copper nucleus having 29 protons, 34 neutrons, and a mass number of 63.

To proceed:

(1)		(2)
We add the *A* numbers to get a new *A* number:	and	We add the *Z* numbers to get a new *Z* number:
$1+12=13.$		$1+6=7.$

hence

$$ {}_{1}p^{1} + {}_{6}\mathrm{C}^{12} \longrightarrow {}_{7}?^{13} $$

and we look up (in the Periodic Table) the element whose atomic number is 7, and complete the nuclear equation thus:

$$ {}_{1}p^{1} + {}_{6}\mathrm{C}^{12} \longrightarrow {}_{7}\mathrm{N}^{13}. $$

Since ${}_{7}?^{13}$ is a nucleus with 7 protons, it must be nitrogen, whose symbol is N.

NUCLEAR KEYS

The vital points to consider are that *in every nuclear equation*

(1) The *sum* of the *A* numbers on the left equals the sum of the *A* numbers on the right.

(2) The *sum* of the *Z* numbers on the left equals the sum of the *Z* numbers on the right.

This is such a very important concept that we shall call statements (1) and (2) our *Nuclear Keys* and shall expect you to learn to apply them to nuclear reactions. We shall refer to the first part, which deals with the *A* numbers, as "Key *A*"; and the second part, which deals with the *Z* numbers, as "Key *Z*."

Now, let's apply these Nuclear Keys:

Is this nuclear equation formally correct?

$$ {}_{8}\mathrm{O}^{16} + {}_{1}p^{1} \longrightarrow {}_{7}\mathrm{N}^{13} + {}_{2}\mathrm{He}^{4} $$

It is correct. **section 301**

It is not correct. **section 314**

322

[*from section 316*]

YOUR ANSWER: The complete equation is

$$_{88}Ra^{226} \longrightarrow {}_{2}He^{4} + \boxed{_{86}Rn^{222}}$$

You are correct. You are apparently able to use the Nuclear Keys as a useful tool. That is very good.

Let's try another one of these:

$$_{88}Ra^{225} \longrightarrow {}_{-1}e^{0} + \boxed{?}$$

Don't let that "−1" bother you. Apply the Nuclear Keys and decide what belongs in the box. (The letter *e* stands for an electron.)

What belongs in the above box?

That "−1" *does* bother me; I need help here. **section 306**

$\boxed{_{87}Fr^{225}}$ **section 313**

$\boxed{_{89}Ac^{225}}$ **section 331**

323

[*from section 328*]

YOUR ANSWER: I don't know what to do with that strange symbol $_{0}\gamma^{0}$.

There is nothing especially difficult about this. The symbol $_{0}\gamma^{0}$ indictates that a gamma ray has *no* protons and *no* neutrons, i.e., both *A* and *Z* are equal to zero. This is another way of saying that gamma rays are not made up of charged particles, as alpha and beta rays are. Actually gamma rays are a form of electromagnetic radiation, similar in nature to X-rays. The presence of $_{0}\gamma^{0}$ in a nuclear equation contributes nothing to the summation of either *A* or *Z*. Apply the Nuclear Keys as usual.

Return to section 328 and choose an answer.

324
[*from section 318*]

YOUR ANSWER:

$$_4Be^9 \ (p, \text{Li}) \ _2\alpha^4$$

is the simplified equation corresponding to

$$_4Be^9 + {_1p^1} \longrightarrow {_3Li^6} + {_2\alpha^4}.$$

No, you have made a mistake.

Li ($_3Li^6$ of course) is larger than $_2\alpha^4$, and so Li should *not* be inside the parentheses.

Restudy section 318 and make another choice for your answer.

325
[*from section 331*]

YOUR ANSWER: The correct equation is

$$_{83}Bi^{211} \longrightarrow {_2\alpha^4} + {_{81}Tl^{215}}.$$

No, this is not right. Check that *A* Key again!

Return to section 331 and select another answer.

326
[*from section 303*]

YOUR ANSWER:

$$_3Li^7 + {_0\gamma^0} \longrightarrow {_4Be^8} + {_1p^1}$$

is the equation corresponding to

$$_3Li^7 \ (p, \gamma) \ _4Be^8.$$

No. You have reversed things, and the test of the Nuclear Keys should have shown you that something was wrong. In the abbreviated equation, the first item inside the parentheses is a particle that plays the part of a *reactant,* while the second is a *product.*

Think this over, return to section 303, and choose again.

327

[*from section 332*]

YOUR ANSWER:

$$_{90}Th^{232}\ (n,\ 3n)\ _{53}I^{133} + _{37}Rb^{97}$$

represents *neither* a fission nor a fusion reaction.

You are mistaken. This does fit one of the two definitions.

Study the definitions in section 332 again, and select another answer.

328

[*from section 317*]

YOUR ANSWER: $_{83}Bi^{211} \longrightarrow _{-1}e^0 + _{84}Po^{211}$.

You are correct. You are doing fine; let's proceed.

Many isotopes break up with the simultaneous emission of beta and gamma radiation. $_{82}Pb^{210}$ is an example. It produces a beta particle, $_{-1}\beta^0$, and a gamma ray, which may be represented by the symbol $_0\gamma^0$. (Notice that the symbols $_{-1}e^0$ and $_{-1}\beta^0$ are equivalent, and can be used interchangeably.)

Which of the following equations is correct?

$_{82}Pb^{210} + _{-1}\beta^0 \rightarrow _0\gamma^0 + _{81}Tl^{210}$. **section 299**

$_{82}Pb^{210} + _0\gamma^0 \rightarrow _{-1}\beta^0 + _{83}Bi^{210}$. **section 311**

$_{82}Pb^{210} \rightarrow _{-1}\beta^0 + _0\gamma^0 + _{83}Bi^{210}$. **section 318**

I can't tell, because I don't know what to do with that strange symbol $_0\gamma^0$. **section 323**

329

[*from section 318*]

YOUR ANSWER:

$$_4Be^9\ (\alpha,\ p)\ _3Li^6$$

is the simplified equation corresponding to

$$_4Be^9 + {}_1p^1 \longrightarrow {}_3Li^6 + {}_2\alpha^4.$$

You have the correct symbols outside the parentheses, but inside the parentheses you have made a mistake. $(\alpha,\ p)$ means that an alpha is added, and that a proton is given off.

Whatever appears *before* the comma inside the parentheses is added to what is in front of the parentheses.

Whatever appears *after* the comma inside the parentheses is given off along with what follows the parentheses.

Now, return to section 318, study the question carefully, and choose another answer.

330

[*from section 316*]

YOUR ANSWER: I don't understand.

Well, you have to apply the Nuclear Keys:

Key *A*: The sum of *A* numbers on the left equals the sum of *A* numbers on the right.

and

Key *Z:* The sum of *Z* numbers on the left equals the sum of *Z* numbers on the right.

Then look up in the Periodic Table the symbol for the nucleus whose atomic number equals the new *A* number.

Now, turn back to section 316, *restudy* the reasoning on this page, and proceed from there.

331

[*from section 322*]

YOUR ANSWER: The complete equation is

$$_{88}Ra^{225} \longrightarrow {}_{-1}e^{0} + \boxed{_{89}Ac^{225}}$$

You are correct. You applied the Nuclear Keys correctly:

$$\text{Key } A\text{: } 225 = 0 + 225$$
$$\text{Key } Z\text{: } 88 = -1 + 89$$

and 89 is the atomic number of actinium (Ac).

RADIOACTIVITY

Let's step ahead a bit. There are some nuclei that are inherently unstable. Such nuclei are said to be *radioactive* and are often called *radioisotopes.* When these unstable nuclei break down, they do it in one of the three ways that we have chosen as examples above.

By using our Nuclear Keys we can tell exactly what the new nucleus will be *if* we know the original nucleus and *if* we know what was emitted.

What is emitted will be:

(1) an electron, symbol $_{-1}e^{0}$ (often called a beta particle, symbol $_{-1}\beta^{0}$);
or (2) a helium nucleus, symbol $_{2}He^{4}$ (often called an alpha particle, symbol $_{2}\alpha^{4}$);
or (3) a gamma ray, symbol $_{0}\gamma^{0}$ (usually written simply as γ). The gamma ray is a powerful quantum of radiation, but it is not a material particle; it has no protons and no neutrons.

Let's suppose that we are dealing with a radioactive isotope of bismuth (mass number 211). This isotope can either emit an alpha *or* a beta particle.

Write the nuclear reaction for the decomposition of $_{83}Bi^{211}$ if it gives off an alpha particle.

$_{83}Bi^{211} \rightarrow {}_{-1}\beta^0 + {}_{84}Po^{211}$. **section 297**

$_{83}Bi^{211} \rightarrow {}_{81}Tl^{207} + {}_{2}\alpha^4$. **section 317**

$_{83}Bi^{211} \rightarrow {}_{2}\alpha^4 + {}_{81}Tl^{215}$. **section 325**

332

[*from section 303*]

YOUR ANSWER: $_3Li^7 + {}_1p^1 \longrightarrow {}_4Be^8 + {}_0\gamma^0$ is the equation corresponding to $_3Li^7$ (p, γ) $_4Be^8$.

You are correct. Let us continue.

Reactions such as the above can be carried out with many, many different nuclei and a variety of smaller particles. Hundreds of artificial nuclei have been produced by nuclear transformations. Any such reaction in which one nucleus is changed into another is called a *transmutation.*

FISSION AND FUSION

Besides such transmutations, two other kinds of nuclear reactions will be mentioned here because of their great importance. These two kinds of reactions are:

(1) *nuclear fission,* in which a large nucleus is broken up into two large fragments together with various tiny particles; and
(2) *nuclear fusion,* in which two smaller nuclei are fused together to form a single larger nucleus.

It is important to take particular care about these two words, *fission* and *fusion,* because of their similarity in both spelling and pronunciation. These are both important, because all power-producing nuclear reactions, from the large hydrogen bombs to the smallest nuclear reactor, are of one of these two types.

Is the reaction given below a fusion or a fission reaction?

$$_{90}Th^{232} + {}_0n^1 \longrightarrow {}_{53}I^{133} + {}_{37}Rb^{97} + 3({}_0n^1)$$

In simplified form, $_{90}Th^{232}$ $(n, 3n)$ $_{53}I^{133} + {}_{37}Rb^{97}$

It is a fusion reaction. **section 315**

It is a fission reaction. **section 320**

It is neither. **section 327**

CHAPTER 8—NUCLEAR REACTIONS AND EQUATIONS—SUMMARY

The symbol $_{30}\mathrm{Zn}^{65}$ represents the *nucleus* of one particular isotope of the element zinc. The number written as a subscript is the *atomic number,* while the superscript is the *mass number.*

The atomic number is often represented by the letter Z, the mass number by A, and the neutron number by N. Thus for any isotope,

$$Z+N=A.$$

Nuclear reactions usually involve some *particles* as well as atomic nuclei. Those particles required in the present study are the following:

Name	Symbols		Equivalents
electron	$_{-1}e^0$	$_{-1}\beta^0$	beta particle
neutron	$_0n^1$		
proton	$_1p^1$	$_1\mathrm{H}^1$	hydrogen nucleus ($A=1$)
alpha particle	$_2\alpha^4$	$_2\mathrm{He}^4$	helium nucleus
deuteron	$_1d^2$	$_1\mathrm{H}^2$	hydrogen nucleus ($A=2$)
positron	$_1e^0$		"positive electron"
gamma radiation	$_0\gamma^0$	γ	(not a particle)

Nuclear reactions can be checked by means of the so-called *Nuclear Keys:*

Key *A:* The sum of the *mass numbers* (A numbers) of all species appearing on the left side of the equation must equal the corresponding sum on the right.

Key *Z:* The sum of the *atomic numbers* (Z numbers) of all species appearing on the left side of the equation must equal the corresponding sum on the right.

A short method of writing nuclear equations is presented. For example the equation,

$$_{13}Al^{27} + {}_{0}n^{1} \longrightarrow {}_{11}Na^{24} + {}_{0}\gamma^{0}$$

can be written in the form,

$$_{13}Al^{27}\ (n,\ \gamma)\ {}_{11}Na^{24}.$$

The first symbol within the parentheses is the particle which initiates the reaction, the second is the particle (or ray) which is emitted.

Some nuclei are inherently unstable, and disintegrate spontaneously, emitting an alpha or beta particle or a gamma ray, or two of these simultaneously. The residual nucleus is no longer the same element (except in a few special cases). This phenomenon is *radioactivity*.

Nuclear *fission* is a nuclear reaction wherein a large nucleus, such as $_{92}U^{235}$, is broken up into two massive nuclei which share most of the mass of the starting nucleus. The fission process is initiated by collision with a neutron, and itself results in the liberation of more neutrons, so that the fission reaction can become self-sustaining, and proceed as a *chain reaction.*

Nuclear *fusion* is a process whereby two small nuclei combine or fuse together to form a larger nucleus.

Both fission and fusion reactions produce or liberate large amounts of energy, which in some cases can be applied to useful purposes.

Continue with section 334.

CHAPTER 8—REVIEW QUESTIONS AND PROBLEMS

1. Match the symbols on the right with the names on the left:

electron	$_{-1}e^0$
proton	$_1e^0$
neutron	$_1d^2$
positron	$_2He^4$
gamma ray	$_2\alpha^4$
alpha particle	$_1p^1$
deuteron	$_0\gamma^0$
	$_0n^1$
	$_1H^1$
	$_{-1}\beta^0$

2. Complete each of the following equations by correctly filling in the blank:

(a) $_1H^2 + {}_1H^2 \longrightarrow$ ________
(b) $_4Be^9 + {}_2He^4 \longrightarrow {}_6C^{12} +$ ________
(c) $_{92}U^{238} + {}_0n^1 \longrightarrow$ ________
(d) $_{92}U^{239} \longrightarrow {}_{-1}\beta^0 +$ ________
(e) $_{93}Np^{239} \longrightarrow {}_{94}Pu^{239} +$ ________
(f) $_{84}Po^{216} \longrightarrow {}_2\alpha^4 +$ ________
(g) $_4Be^9\ (\alpha, n)$ ________
(h) $_{17}Cl^{35}\ (n, \beta)$ ________
(i) $_{92}U^{235}\ (n, 3n)\ {}_{42}Mo^{102} +$ ________
(j) $_6C^{13} + {}_1p^1 \longrightarrow$ ________

3. Identify which of the equations in Question 2 represent fission reactions, and which represent fusion.

Turn to section 551 for the answers, then go on to section 335.

Chapter 9
EQUILIBRIUM PHENOMENA

When we write a chemical equation, we usually use a single arrow, like this:

$$2H_2 + O_2 \longrightarrow 2H_2O.$$

This indicates that we are concerned principally with the fact that hydrogen and oxygen can be combined or united to form water.

Of course, we could have written

$$2H_2O \longrightarrow 2H_2 + O_2.$$

Had we done this, we would have shown interest principally in the fact that water can be decomposed to yield hydrogen and oxygen.

REVERSIBLE REACTIONS

Often we wish to concern ourselves with the fact that a chemical process will occur in *both* directions. We do so by using a double arrow, like this:

$$2H_2 + O_2 \leftrightarrows 2H_2O.$$

Remember that the *reactants* are the chemical species written on the *left* of the arrow (whether it be a single arrow or a double arrow), and the *products* are the chemical species on the *right*. The double arrow reminds us that the chemical process we are considering can take place *either* from left to right *or* from right to left.

Look at this equation:

$$3Fe + 4H_2O \leftrightarrows Fe_3O_4 + 4H_2.$$

Which of the following statements is correct?

The reactants are "$Fe_3O_4 + 4H_2$." **section 340**

The reactants are "$3Fe + 4H_2O$." **section 349**

336

[*from section 356*]

YOUR ANSWER: There is an error in (a).

$$\text{If } HC_2H_3O_2 \rightleftarrows H^+ + C_2H_3O_2^-, \text{ then}$$
$$V_r \propto [HC_2H_3O_2] \text{ and } V_l \propto [H^+][C_2H_3O_2^-].$$

Sorry, (a) is entirely correct, and you are wrong. Perhaps you were bothered by the symbols for the ions H^+ and $C_2H_3O_2^-$ that appeared in the equation. Don't let this bother you; all you have to do is to write a velocity expression using the species *as they appear in the chemical equation.*

Now turn back to section 356 and hunt further for possible errors.

337

[*from section 349*]

YOUR ANSWER: No, we cannot convert 100 per cent of the H_2 and I_2 to HI.

You are correct. Very good. This is a most important point. Let's be sure you understand it fully.

EFFECT OF CONCENTRATION ON REACTION RATE

Hydrogen gas combines with iodine gas to produce hydrogen iodide gas. As a matter of fact, the greater the concentration of hydrogen gas and the greater the concentration of iodine gas, the faster will we produce hydrogen iodide.

Let's express this relationship mathematically, using the following symbols:

V_r = velocity of reaction toward the right;
$[H_{2(g)}]$ = concentration of hydrogen gas;
$[I_{2(g)}]$ = concentration of iodine gas;
$\propto$ means "is directly related to" or "is directly proportional to."

Using these symbols we can write

$$V_r \propto [H_{2(g)}][I_{2(g)}].$$

The square brackets next to each other, like this, [ ] [ ], indicate that the *concentrations* of the chemical species inside the brackets are to be multiplied together.

We will call the mathematical expression we wrote above, a velocity expression.

$$V_r \propto [H_{2(g)}][I_{2(g)}]$$

This is the velocity expression *toward the right;* we will use V_l to indicate a velocity expression toward the left.

Now, let's try another example. Consider the equation

$$N_{2(g)} + O_{2(g)} \leftrightarrows 2NO_{(g)}.$$

What is the velocity relationship (expression) for this reaction going toward the right?

$V_r \propto [N_{2(g)}] + [O_{2(g)}]$. **section 342**

$V_r = [N_{2(g)}][O_{2(g)}]$. **section 350**

$V_r \propto [N_{2(g)}][O_{2(g)}]$. **section 356**

I don't understand; I need more explanation. **section 365**

338

[*from section 362*]

YOUR ANSWER: $V_l \propto [pP]\ [qQ]\ [rR] \ldots$ is correct.

Sorry, you are wrong!

You are confusing the meaning of the capital letters and the lowercase letters used in writing the general reversible chemical equation. Consider:

$$aA + bB + cC \ldots \leftrightarrows pP + qQ + rR \ldots$$

The capital letters stand for chemical species, and when you are writing a velocity expression the *capital* letters belong inside brackets.

The *small* letters represent the coefficients of the large letters, and these *small* letters appear as powers in the velocity expression.

Now turn back to section 362, restudy the text about reversible equations, and then choose the correct answer to the question.

339

[*from section 344*]

YOUR ANSWER: The equilibrium expression for the reaction $N_2O_2 \rightleftarrows 2NO$ is

$$K = \frac{[NO]}{[N_2O_2]}.$$

No, you are not correct. It is true that the equilibrium expression does have the general form of

$$K = \frac{\text{products}}{\text{reactants}}.$$

But you forgot that the general equilibrium expression,

$$K = \frac{[P]^p[Q]^q[R]^r \ldots}{[A]^a[B]^b[C]^c \ldots}$$

has some exponents in it, and that these exponents correspond to the coefficients in the general equation

$$aA + bB + cC \ldots \rightleftarrows pP + qQ + rR \ldots.$$

Now return to section 344, restudy, and choose the correct answer this time.

340
[*from section 335*]

YOUR ANSWER: The reactants are "Fe_3O_4 and $4H_2$."

You are wrong! The reactants are *never* on the right side of the arrow. The chemical species on the right are called *products*.

Return to section 335 and restudy it, and then choose another answer.

341
[*from section 356*]

YOUR ANSWER: There is an error in (b):

$$\text{If } H_2SO_4 \rightleftarrows H^+ + HSO_4^-, \text{ then}$$
$$V_r \propto [H_2SO_4] \text{ and } V_l \propto [H^+]\,[HSO_4^-].$$

You are wrong: (b) is entirely correct.

V_l depends on the concentrations of the species on the right, and V_r depends on the concentrations of the species on the left. Do not be troubled by the fact that some of the species are ions. All that is necessary is for you to write the species exactly as they appear in the chemical equation inside the brackets that indicate concentration.

Now return to section 356 and hunt further for possible errors.

342
[*from section 337*]

YOUR ANSWER: $V_r \propto [N_{2(g)}] + [O_{2(g)}]$.

You are wrong! You do not *add* the concentrations together in writing a velocity expression.

In section 337 we wrote

$$V_r \propto [H_{2(g)}]\,[I_{2(g)}].$$

All velocity expressions are like this in that they involve a *product* of one or more concentration factors and never an *addition* of concentrations.

Turn to section 365, where you will find an analogy which may help you to understand these relations.

343
[*from section 349*]

YOUR ANSWER: Yes, we can convert 100 per cent of the H_2 and I_2 to HI.

Well, let's consider. The equation

$$H_{2(g)} + I_{2(g)} \rightleftarrows 2HI_{(g)}$$

tells us (1) that hydrogen and iodine gases will combine to form hydrogen iodide gas, *but* (2) the double arrow tells us that hydrogen iodide gas will decompose and form hydrogen gas and iodine gas.

The more hydrogen and the more iodine we start with, the more hydrogen iodide gas we will produce; but the more hydrogen iodide we have, the more will in turn decompose.

Therefore, we *can never* make this reaction *go 100 per cent to completion* toward the right side of the equation—i.e., to the production of hydrogen iodide.

Your answer was wrong; therefore, return to section 349 and consider this equation again.

344
[*from section 366*]

YOUR ANSWER: When a reversible chemical reaction is at equilibrium, no apparent change is taking place.

You are correct. Very good. At equilibrium, $V_r = V_l$, and neither of them is equal to zero. Since the rates are not zero, both chemical reactions must be taking place, but since the rates are *equal,* there is no apparent change.

EQUILIBRIUM CONSTANTS

Let us now consider the general reversible chemical equation,

$$aA + bB + cC + \ldots \rightleftarrows pP + qQ + rR + \ldots,$$

for which we have derived these expressions for V_r and V_l:

$$V_r \propto [A]^a [B]^b [C]^c \ldots \text{ and } V_l \propto [P]^p [Q]^q [R]^r \ldots$$

To change from a proportionality to an equation, we must write a constant in the expression, as follows:

$$V_r = (k_r)\ [A]^a [B]^b [C]^c \ldots \text{ and } V_l = (k_l)\ [P]^p [Q]^q [R]^r \ldots$$

Now remember that *at equilibrium,* $V_r = V_l$, so we can write

$$(k_r)\ [A]^a [B]^b [C]^c \ldots = (k_l)\ [P]^p [Q]^q [R]^r \ldots.$$

Algebraic rearrangement gives us the expression

$$\frac{k_r}{k_l} = \frac{[P]^p[Q]^q[R]^r \ldots}{[A]^a[B]^b[C]^c \ldots}.$$

Now let us give a new symbol to the ratio k_r/k_l, namely K. Then

$$K = \frac{[P]^p[Q]^q[R]^r \ldots}{[A]^a[B]^b[C]^c \ldots}.$$

K is called an *equilibrium constant* for the reversible reaction. In general every reversible reaction will have a different value for K, and this value will be different at different temperatures.

Let us apply this to the specific equation

$$N_2O_2 \rightleftarrows 2NO.$$

What is the expression for the equilibrium constant for this reaction?

$K = \dfrac{[NO]}{[N_2O_2]}$. **section 339**

$K = \dfrac{[N_2O_2]}{[NO]^2}$. **section 355**

$K = \dfrac{[NO]^2}{[N_2O_2]}$. **section 363**

345
[*from section 363*]

YOUR ANSWER: The equilibrium expression for the reaction $N_{2(g)} + 3H_{2(g)} \leftrightarrows 2NH_{3(g)}$ is

$$K = \frac{[NH_{3(g)}]}{[N_{2(g)}][H_{2(g)}]}.$$

You were careless—you forgot to take the coefficients into account. You can easily correct this; turn back to section 363 and reread; then choose a better answer.

346
[*from section 362*]

YOUR ANSWER: $V_l \propto [P]^p [Q]^q [R]^r$ is correct.

You are correct! Splendid! You seem to understand the basic idea. To summarize this process of writing a rate expression from the general chemical equation:

(1) CAPITAL letters represent CHEMICAL SPECIES and go *inside the brackets.*

(2) *Lower-case* letters represent COEFFICIENTS and appear *as powers of the species.*

(3) And, of course, the *velocity to the right* depends on the species on the *left* and, similarly, the *velocity to the left* depends on the species on the *right.*

EQUILIBRIUM

We shall now continue our study of these reversible equations. If we carry out a reversible chemical reaction in a closed vessel, eventually a point will be reached at which no further chemical action is apparent. *Apparently* the reaction will have stopped, but this will not be the case; the reaction will be continuing *in both directions,* but the *rates* in both directions will be equal.

Notice carefully: it is the *rates* of chemical change that are equal. (We did *not* say the amounts on both sides are equal, and this is not generally the case.) Let us use the symbols:

$$V_r = V_l$$

(velocity to right = velocity to left.)

When this condition exists, there is no visible chemical change taking place, and we say that the reaction is at *equilibrium*.

Which of the two statements below is correct?

When a chemical reaction is at equilibrium, the amounts of materials on both sides are the same. **section 353**

When a chemical reaction is at equilibrium, the rates for both forward and reverse processes are equal. **section 366**

347

[*from section 369*]

YOUR ANSWER: The value of K is greater than one.

You are correct. In general,

$$K = \frac{\text{products}}{\text{reactants}}.$$

Since the question stated that the concentration of the products was greater than the concentration of the reactants, the numerator of the fraction is greater than the denominator, and the value of K *must be* more than one.

Suppose that we are told that the equilibrium constant, K, for a certain reaction is a small fraction, much less than 1. What does this tell us about the concentrations of the products as compared with the concentrations of the reactants?

The concentration of the products is much larger than the concentration of the reactants. **section 360**

The concentration of the products is much smaller than the concentration of the reactants. **section 370**

YOUR ANSWER: There is an error in (c).

You are correct. There is an error in (c):

$$\text{If } 2Fe^{++} + Cl_2 \rightleftarrows 2Fe^{+++} + 2Cl^-, \text{ then}$$

$$V_l \propto [Fe^{+++}]^2 [Cl^-]^2 \text{ is correct,}$$

$$\text{but } V_r \propto [Fe^{++}]^2 [Cl]^2 \text{ is wrong.}$$

The subscript $_2$ in Cl_2 is *not* a coefficient, and hence cannot be used as a power in the velocity expression; it must appear as a part of the chemical symbol inside the brackets.

The correct expression for V_r is

$$V_r \propto [Fe^{++}]^2 [Cl_2].$$

GENERAL FORMULA FOR REVERSIBLE REACTIONS

Now, let's try to write a general expression for a reversible chemical reaction and for the V_l and V_r that are associated with it.

Every reversible chemical equation has this general structure:

$$\text{Reactant(s)} \rightleftarrows \text{Product(s)}.$$

There can be one or more chemical species on the left, and one or more on the right. Let us use A, B, C, etc., as general symbols for reactants and P, Q, R, etc., as symbols for products.

In any chemical equation there is a coefficient for each of the products and for each of the reactants. We will use a *small letter* to stand for the coefficient of each particular species. Thus, *a* is the coefficient of A, and so on. Using this symbolism, the general reversible chemical equation can be written

$$a\text{A} + b\text{B} + c\text{C} \ldots \rightleftarrows p\text{P} + q\text{Q} + r\text{R} \ldots$$

What would be the correct expression for the velocity to the right, V_r, based on the above equation?

$V_r \propto [a\text{A}][b\text{B}][c\text{C}] \ldots$ **section 354**

$V_r \propto [\text{A}]^a[\text{B}]^b[\text{C}]^c \ldots$ **section 362**

349

[*from section 335*]

YOUR ANSWER: The reactants are "$3Fe + 4H_2O$."

You are correct. Products are on the right of the arrow and reactants are on the left of the arrow.

Let's consider this matter of reversible equations a bit further: Consider the equation

$$H_{2(g)} + I_{2(g)} \rightleftarrows 2HI_{(g)}.*$$

This equation tells us that:

(1) If we mix together some pure $H_{2(g)}$ and some pure $I_{2(g)}$ they will react together to form $HI_{(g)}$.
(2) Pure $HI_{(g)}$ will decompose to form $H_{2(g)}$ and $I_{2(g)}$.
(3) *Both* these processes occur at the same time.

Let us consider this same equation further:

$$H_{2(g)} + I_{2(g)} \leftrightarrows 2HI_{(g)}.$$

If we put equal numbers of moles of $H_{2(g)}$ and $I_{2(g)}$ together, will we ever be able to get all of these substances converted to $HI_{(g)}$?

No, we cannot convert them 100 per cent. **section 337**

Yes, we can convert them 100 per cent. **section 343**

* We often want to indicate the physical state of the reactants and products. We do this by using letters written in parentheses below the chemical species involved. Thus

(g) = in the gaseous state;
(e) = in the liquid state;
(s) = in the solid state;
(aq) = dissolved in water.

350

[*from section 337*]

YOUR ANSWER: $V_r = [N_{2(g)}][O_{2(g)}]$.

You are almost right, but not quite.

The rate or velocity *depends on* the product of these concentrations, but it *does not equal* this product.

Turn to section 365, where you will find an analogy which may help you to understand these relations.

351

[*from section 358*]

YOUR ANSWER: The equilibrium expression for the reaction $2NH_{3(g)} \leftrightarrows N_{2(g)} + 3H_{2(g)}$ is

$$K = \frac{[NH_{3(g)}]^2}{[N_{2(g)}][H_{2(g)}]^3}.$$

You are wrong.

When we write an equilibrium expression, the products are always in the numerator, and the reactants in the denominator. Notice that *reversing* the role of *products and reactants* in a reversible equation has the effect of *inverting* the *equilibrium* expression.

Now return to section 358 and consider the question again.

352

[*from section 366*]

YOUR ANSWER: When a reversible chemical reaction is at equilibrium, no chemical change is taking place.

Let's consider: At equilibrium, $V_r = V_l$. We did not say $V_r = 0 = V_l$, and of course, if there is a velocity, and it is not zero, then chemical changes are taking place.

Return to section 366, restudy, and reconsider the question.

353

[*from section 346*]

YOUR ANSWER: When a chemical reaction is at equilibrium, the amounts of materials on both sides are the same.

Come on now, you are not being careful; this is exactly what we denied!

Return to section 346, reread the entire page (carefully this time), and then choose the correct answer.

354

[*from section 348*]

YOUR ANSWER: $V_r \propto [aA]\,[bB]\,[cC]\ldots$ is correct.

Sorry, you have made a mistake in interpreting the general reversible equation

$$aA + bB + cC \ldots \rightleftharpoons pP + qQ + rR \ldots$$

The *capital* letters stand for chemical species; when writing a velocity expression only these *capital* letters belong inside brackets.

The *small* letters represent the coefficients of the large letters, and these *small* letters must appear as powers (exponents) in the velocity expression.

Now turn back to section 348, restudy the text about reversible equations, and then choose another answer to the question.

355
[from section 344]

YOUR ANSWER: The equilibrium expression for the reaction $N_2O_2 \leftrightarrows 2NO$ is

$$K = \frac{[N_2O_2]}{[NO]^2}.$$

You have been careless.
Look at the general equilibrium expression,

$$K = \frac{[P]^p[Q]^q[R]^r \ldots}{[A]^a[B]^b[C]^c \ldots}.$$

Products belong in the *denominator* of the constant.
Reactants belong in the *numerator* of the constant.
You have reversed the correct procedure.
Return to section 344, restudy, and choose another answer.

356
[from section 337]

YOUR ANSWER: $V_r \propto [N_{2(g)}] [O_{2(g)}]$.

You are correct.
Let's put this into words:

V_r	means	the velocity of the reaction to the right;
$\propto$	means	"depends on" or "is proportional to";
$[N_{2(g)}]$	means	the concentration of nitrogen gas;
$[O_{2(g)}]$	means	the concentration of oxygen gas.

Or, putting it all together: The velocity of the reaction to the right depends on the concentration of nitrogen gas times the concentration of oxygen gas.

Let's look at this reaction again:

$$N_{2(g)} + O_{2(g)} \leftrightarrows 2NO_{(g)}.$$

What can we say about the velocity of the reaction *to the left?*

Notice that

$$N_{2(g)} + O_{2(g)} \rightleftarrows 2NO_{(g)}$$

means the same as

$$N_{2(g)} + O_{2(g)} \rightleftarrows NO_{(g)} + NO_{(g)}.$$

So we can write the equation for the velocity to the left (V_l) as

$$V_l = [NO_{(g)}]\,[NO_{(g)}] = [NO_{(g)}]^2.$$

Therefore, whenever a velocity expression is to be written for an equation in which one or more of the species appears with an expressed coefficient (i.e., other than *one*), this coefficient will appear in the velocity expression as a power of the corresponding concentration factor.

Example: Given the equation

$$N_{2(g)} + 3H_{2(g)} \rightleftarrows 2NH_{3(g)},$$

we can write

$$V_r \propto [N_{2(g)}]\,[H_{2(g)}]^3 \text{ and } V_l \propto [NH_{3(g)}]^2.$$

Below you will find five chemical equations and the velocity expressions related to them. Consider each set carefully and decide whether the expressions for V_r and V_l are correct or incorrect. Pick out the *only one* that is *incorrect.*

(a) If $HC_2H_3O_2 \rightleftarrows H^+ + C_2H_3O_2^-$, then
$V_r \propto [HC_2H_3O_2]$ and $V_l \propto [H^+][C_2H_3O_2^-]$. **section 336**

(b) If $H_2SO_4 \rightleftarrows H^+ + HSO_4^-$, then
$V_r \propto [H_2SO_4]$ and $V_l \propto [H^+][HSO_4^-]$. **section 341**

(c) If $2Fe^{++} + Cl_2 \rightleftarrows 2Fe^{+++} + 2Cl^-$, then
$V_r \propto [Fe^{++}]^2[Cl]^2$ and $V_l \propto [Fe^{+++}]^2[Cl^-]^2$. **section 348**

(d) If $H_2S \rightleftarrows H^+ + HS^-$, then
$V_r \propto [H_2S]$ and $V_l \propto [H^+][HS^-]$. **section 361**

(e) If $NaCl + H_2SO_4 \rightleftarrows NaHSO_4 + HCl$, then
$V_r \propto [NaCl][H_2SO_4]$ and $V_l \propto [NaHSO_4][HCl]$. **section 367**

357

[*from section 362*]

YOUR ANSWER: I don't understand this. What should I do now?

When studying a course such as this it is often well to review from time to time. If this question is not clear to you, it means the general topic is not clear either. Since it is a *very important* topic, you should learn it now; future work will require you to understand it well.

If you have been studying a long while, perhaps you should take a breather. In any event, be sure your head is clear and fresh before you do any more studying, and when you do continue your study, *turn back to the first page* of this chapter and start in again. Since you have been over this material before, it should go much easier this time.

Be sure to think through each question and each answer, and *don't* depend on what you remember from your previous reading. You should restudy the text, not just reread it. Don't let the fact that you are told to restudy worry you. Everybody has to restudy from time to time; work this through carefully, and success will follow.

Turn to section 335.

358

[*from section 363*]

YOUR ANSWER: The equilibrium expression for the reaction $N_{2(g)} + 3H_{2(g)} \leftrightarrows 2NH_{3(g)}$ is

$$K = \frac{[NH_{3(g)}]^2}{[N_{2(g)}][H_{2(g)}]^3}.$$

You are correct. You're doing fine.

You remembered that: (1) products belong in the numerator, (2) reactants belong in the denominator, and (3) the coefficients appear as powers *whenever* we write an equilibrium expression.

The equilibrium expression above is for the reversible reaction

$$N_{2(g)} + 3H_{2(g)} \leftrightarrows 2NH_{3(g)},$$

which represents the production of ammonia from nitrogen and hydrogen. Let us interchange the products and reactants. This gives us

$$2NH_{3(g)} \leftrightarrows N_{2(g)} + 3H_{2(g)},$$

which represents the decomposition of ammonia into its elements.

What is the equilibrium expression for the decomposition of ammonia?

$K = \dfrac{[NH_{3(g)}]^2}{[N_{2(g)}][H_{2(g)}]^3}$. section 351

$K = \dfrac{[N_{2(g)}][H_{2(g)}]^3}{[NH_{3(g)}]^2}$. section 369

359

[*from section 369*]

YOUR ANSWER: The value of K is smaller than one.

Let's consider: in general, $K = \dfrac{\text{products}}{\text{reactants}}$.

Now, if the value of this fraction is smaller than one, the concentration of the products must be less than that of the reactants, which is contrary to the assumption of the question: therefore you are wrong. Remember, a fraction is less than one if the denominator is greater than the numerator.

Return to section 369, restudy it, and choose another answer.

360
[from section 347]

YOUR ANSWER: If K is very small, the concentration of the products is much larger than the concentration of the reactants.

Well, let's consider.
It is always true that

$$K = \frac{\text{products}}{\text{reactants}}.$$

(Remember to raise each concentration to the power of its coefficient, and to multiply the resulting terms together.)

You were told that K is a small fraction, much less than one. Since K is less than one, the fraction $\frac{\text{products}}{\text{reactants}}$ is less than one, and if a fraction is less than one, the numerator is less than the denominator. The *concentration of the products* must therefore be less than the *concentration of the reactants*. Hence your answer is wrong!

Return to section 347, reconsider the question, and choose another answer.

361
[from section 356]

YOUR ANSWER: There is an error in (d):

$$\text{If } H_2S \rightleftharpoons H^+ + HS^-, \text{ then}$$
$$V_r \propto [H_2S] \text{ and } V_l \propto [H^+][HS^-].$$

Sorry. This is entirely correct, and you are wrong. Perhaps the symbols for the ions H^+ and HS^- that appeared in the chemical equation bothered you. There is no reason why they should; all you have to do to write a velocity expression is to *use the species just as they appear in the chemical equation.*

Now turn back to section 356 and hunt further for possible errors.

362
[*from section 348*]

YOUR ANSWER: $V_r \propto [A]^a [B]^b [C]^c \ldots$ is correct.

You are correct. The *capital* letters represent chemical species and hence belong inside brackets in the velocity expression, whereas the *small* letters represent coefficients and hence belong as powers in the velocity expression.

Now let's take this same general reversible chemical equation,

$$aA + bB + cC \ldots \rightleftarrows pP + qQ + rR \ldots$$

What is the correct expression for V_l?

$V_l \propto [pP][qQ][rR] \ldots$ **section 338**

$V_l \propto [P]^p[Q]^q[R]^r \ldots$ **section 346**

I don't understand this. What should I do now? **section 357**

363
[*from section 344*]

YOUR ANSWER: The equilibrium expression for the reaction $N_2O_2 \rightleftarrows 2NO$ is

$$K = \frac{[NO]^2}{[N_2O_2]}.$$

You are correct! The answer that you have chosen follows directly from the general equilibrium expression,

$$K = \frac{[P]^p[Q]^q[R]^r \ldots}{[A]^a[B]^b[C]^c \ldots}.$$

What would be the equilibrium expression for the chemical equation $N_{2(g)} + 3H_{2(g)} \rightleftarrows 2NH_{3(g)}$?

$$K = \frac{[NH_{3(g)}]}{[N_{2(g)}][H_{2(g)}]}.$$ **section 345**

$$K = \frac{[NH_{3(g)}]^2}{[N_{2(g)}][H_{2(g)}]^3}.$$ **section 358**

$$K = \frac{[H_{2(g)}]^3[N_{2(g)}]}{[NH_{3(g)}]^2}.$$ **section 368**

364
[from section 369]

YOUR ANSWER: The value of K is equal to one.

Well, let's consider. If K is equal to one, then the concentration of products must equal the concentration of reactants, since $K = \frac{\text{products}}{\text{reactants}}$. The question stated that this was not the case, so you are wrong. Remember, for a fraction to equal one, the numerator must equal the denominator.

Return to section 369, restudy the page, and choose another answer to the question.

365
[from section 337]

YOUR ANSWER: I need more explanation about velocity relationships.

Well, let's consider a nonchemical analogy. Imagine a boy throwing darts toward a board to which we have tied a lot of inflated balloons. Further, let's suppose that the boy is far enough away so that only a few of his throws hit the board at all.

Upon what will the number of balloons that are broken in one minute depend? First, the rate of breaking balloons will depend upon the number of darts that hit the board in one minute. Let's call this the "concentration of hits" on the board, and represent it by the symbol

[hits]. Second, it will depend on how many balloons there are on the board. The closer the balloons are together, the more balloons the boy will break. Let's call the closeness of the balloons the "concentration of balloons" and represent it by the symbol [balloons].

Since the rate of breaking balloons depends on the [hits] and also on the [balloons], the rate of breaking balloons will depend on the product of these two factors. If we use the symbol *R* to represent the rate of breaking balloons, then,

$$R \propto [\text{hits}]\,[\text{balloons}].\dagger$$

Note that it is not correct at this point to say

$$R = [\text{hits}]\,[\text{balloons}],$$

because *R* will depend on other things besides these two quantities. *R* may well depend, for one example, on how effective the hits are at breaking balloons.

It is important to notice the difference between the two symbols " $\propto$ " and "$=$":

"$=$" means "equals";

"$\propto$" means "depends on" or "is proportional to."

Remember that " $\propto$ " does *not* mean "equals."

Now return to section 337 and select another answer after restudying the text carefully.

† Remember: [Hits] means *concentration* of hits, not number of hits. The square-bracket notation means "concentration of."

366

[*from section 346*]

YOUR ANSWER: When a chemical reaction is at equilibrium, the rates for both forward and reverse processes are equal.

You are correct! This is what we mean by equilibrium in a chemical process: the rate to the right equals the rate to the left.

Which of the following statements is correct?

When a reversible chemical reaction is at equilibrium, *no apparent change* is taking place. **section 344**

When a reversible chemical reaction is at equilibrium, *no chemical change* is taking place. **section 352**

367

[*from section 356*]

YOUR ANSWER: There is an error in (e):

$$\text{If } NaCl + H_2SO_4 \rightleftarrows NaHSO_4 + HCl, \text{ then}$$
$$V_r \propto [NaCl][H_2SO_4] \text{ and } V_l \propto [NaHSO_4][HCl].$$

You are wrong; this is entirely correct.

This case is handled exactly as all the others. Return to section 356 and consider this again. *Notice that it is correct,* and continue with the problems.

368

[*from section 363*]

YOUR ANSWER: The equilibrium expression for the reaction $N_{2(g)} + 3H_{2(g)} \rightleftarrows 2NH_{3(g)}$ is

$$K = \frac{[H_{2(g)}]^3[N_{2(g)}]}{[NH_{3(g)}]^2}.$$

You were careless. You reversed the numerator and denominator in the equilibrium expression. Learn this:

Products in numerator.
Reactants in denominator.

Now return to section 363, restudy, and then consider the question again.

369
[*from section 358*]

YOUR ANSWER: The equilibrium expression for the reaction $2NH_{3(g)} \rightleftarrows N_{2(g)} + 3H_{2(g)}$ is

$$K = \frac{[N_{2(g)}][H_{2(g)}]^3}{[NH_{3(g)}]^2}.$$

You are correct. When we reverse the roles of products and reactants in a reversible equation, the equilibrium constant for the new equation is the reciprocal of the previous equilibrium constant.

THE SIGNIFICANCE OF *K*

When a reversible reaction comes to equilibrium, the forward and backward rates of reaction are equal. At equilibrium, the rate at which the reactants form products is exactly equal to the rate at which the reactants *are formed* by the products. At this equilibrium point there is no *observable* change; that is, there is *apparently* no chemical reaction occurring.

When this point is reached, the amounts of products and reactants *are not* necessarily equal to each other.

Let us suppose that when such a reaction is at equilibrium the concentration of the reactants is small and the concentration of the products is large. Would the value of the equilibrium constant, *K*, for this reaction be smaller than one, equal to one, or greater than one?

The value of *K* is greater than one. **section 347**

The value of *K* is smaller than one. **section 359**

The value of *K* is equal to one. **section 364**

[*from section 347*]

YOUR ANSWER: If K is less than one, the concentration of the products is much smaller than the concentration of the reactants.

You are correct. To state that K is less than one, means that the ratio $\frac{[\text{products}]}{[\text{reactants}]}$ is less than one, and this in turn means that the numerator [products] must be less than the denominator [reactants]. Since you were told that K is much less than one, [products] must be *much less* than [reactants].

Continue with section 371.

371
[*from section 370*]

CHAPTER 9—EQUILIBRIUM PHENOMENA—SUMMARY

Many chemical reactions are *reversible,* which means that they can proceed in either direction. To show this, we can write an equation with a double arrow, as,

$$3Fe_{(s)} + 4H_2O \rightleftarrows Fe_3O_{4(s)} + 4H_{2(g)}$$

The subscript letters indicate the physical states: (g) stands for gas, (l) for liquid, (s) for solid, and (aq) for aqueous solution.

By convention we designate the materials written on the left as "reactants," those on the right as "products." Thus, for a reversible reaction, the reactants react to form the products, but the products can react to re-form the reactants.

The *rate* or *velocity* of the forward reaction at a given temperature is proportional to the concentrations of the reactants, while the velocity of the reverse reaction is proportional to the concentrations of the products. Thus for the reaction

$$H_{2(g)} + I_{2(g)} \rightleftarrows 2HI_{(g)},$$

the velocity toward the right

$$V_r \propto [H_{2(g)}]\,[I_{2(g)}],$$

and the velocity toward the left

$$V_l \propto [HI_{(g)}]^2.$$

The brackets mean "concentration of" whatever is inside them. The exponent (2) enters in because there are *two* molecules of HI on the right-hand side of the equation.

When the velocities in both directions are equal, we say that the system is at *equilibrium.* Since at equilibrium $V_r = V_l$, and since

$$V_r = k_r\,[H_{2(g)}]\,[I_{2(g)}] \text{ and } V_l = k_{(l)}\,[HI_{(g)}]^1$$

$$\text{it follows } k_r\,[H_{2(g)}]\,[I_{2(g)}] = k_l\,[HI_{(g)}]^2$$

$$\text{therefore} \qquad \frac{k_r}{k_l} = \frac{[HI_{(g)}]^2}{[H_{2(g)}][I_{2(g)}]} = K.$$

K is called the *equilibrium constant.* It is always equal to the product of the concentrations of the products divided by the product of the concentrations of the reactants.

A large value of K (greater than one) means that the tendency of reactants to form products is greater than the reverse tendency, so that at equilibrium there will be a greater concentration of products than reactants. A small value of K (smaller than one) has just the reverse meaning: at equilibrium there will be a larger concentration of reactants than of products.

Continue with section 372.

CHAPTER 9—REVIEW QUESTIONS AND PROBLEMS

1. Classify the following statements as True or False:

(a) "$[NO_2]$" means "the concentration of NO_2."

(b) In any reversible equation, reactants $\rightleftarrows$ products.

(c) Reactants are always written on the right-hand side of the arrow.

(d) The symbol "$CO_{2(s)}$" refers to carbon dioxide in water solution.

(e) At equilibrium, the amount of the products always equals the amount of the reactants.

(f) At equilibrium, $V_r = V_l$.

(g) At equilibrium, $V_l = V_r$.

(h) At equilibrium all chemical action has come to a standstill.

Given the equation: $H_{2(g)} + Cl_{2(g)} \rightleftarrows 2HCl_{(g)}$,

(i) The velocity to the right, $V_r \propto [H_{2(g)}]\,[Cl_{2(g)}]$.

(j) The velocity to the left, $V_l \propto [HCl_{(g)}]$.

2. Write expressions for the equilibrium constants corresponding to each of the following reactions:

(a) $C + O_2 \rightleftarrows CO_2$

(b) $N_2 + 3H_2 \rightleftarrows 2NH_3$

(c) $H_2O \rightleftarrows H^+ + OH^-$

(d) $2CO + O_2 \rightleftarrows 2CO_2$

(e) $NH_3 + H_2O \rightleftarrows NH_4^+ + OH^-$

(f) $N_2O_4 \leftrightarrows 2NO_2$

(g) $2NO + O_2 \rightleftarrows 2NO_2$

3. Match the items on the left with those on the right:

(a) K is greater than one.
(b) K is less than one.
(c) K is equal to one.
(d) K is zero.

(w) The concentration of the reactants is greater than the concentration of the products.
(x) The concentration of the reactants is less than the concentration of the products.
(y) Reaction in neither direction is favored.
(z) This value is not possible.

Turn to section 552 for the answers, then go on to section 373.

373
[*from section 372*]

Chapter 10

ACID-BASE EQUILIBRIA

ACID-BASE REACTIONS

We can define an acid-base reaction as any reaction in which a single hydrogen atom bearing a positive charge of one unit is transferred from one substance to another.* This charged hydrogen atom is of course a *hydrogen ion* and is also referred to simply as a *proton.*

All acid-base reactions which we will consider are reversible reactions. The details about equilibrium reactions that you studied in Chapter 9 will apply without any exceptions to these acid-base reactions. (A summary of this information was given in section 371.)

ACIDS AND BASES

When an acid-base reaction occurs, the substance providing the proton that is transferred is called the *acid.*

Here is an acid-base reaction:

$$HCl + H_2O \leftrightarrows H_3O^+ + Cl^-.$$

Which of the starting materials in this reaction is the acid?

H_2O is the acid. **section 379**

HCl is the acid. **section 386**

* Other definitions of acid-base reactions are sometimes encountered in more advanced chemistry courses. The acid-base definition above is the one most used in general chemistry, and is called the Brønsted-Lowry concept.

374
[*from section 406*]

YOUR ANSWER: Reaction (3) goes to the right to the largest extent.

$$HSO_3^- + H_2O \leftrightarrows H_3O^+ + SO_3^{--}; K_a = 6.2 \times 10^{-8}.$$

Well, let's consider. The larger the value of K_a, the larger the extent to which the reaction goes. 6.2×10^{-8} is the *smallest* of the three equilibrium constants given, and therefore your answer is wrong.

Turn back to section 406, and be more careful this time.

375
[*from section 386*]

YOUR ANSWER: H_2O is the acid in the reaction

$$NH_3 + H_2O \rightleftarrows NH_4^+ + OH^-.$$

You are correct. H_2O donates a proton, H^+, and hence becomes OH^-.

Many chemical species are able to donate protons in some reactions and to accept protons in other reactions. In the reaction above, H_2O acts as a proton donor and is therefore an acid. In section 373 we gave you the equation $HCl + H_2O \leftrightarrows H_3O^+ + Cl^-$ and pointed out that in this reaction H_2O was a proton acceptor and hence a base.

If a substance accepts a proton in a reaction, we call it a base; if it donates a proton in a reaction, we call it an acid. We can classify it as acid or base only by noting whether it accepts or donates a proton.

Let's see how well you can apply what you have learned so far.

Which of the substances below *cannot* be an acid?

OH^- cannot be an acid. **section 382**

CN^- cannot be an acid. **section 389**

NH_3 cannot be an acid. **section 395**

376
[*from section 385*]

YOUR ANSWER: When H_2SO_4 reacts with HPO_4^{--}, the conjugate acid is H_3PO_4 and the conjugate base is SO_4^{--}.

Well, let's see. Let's write an equation, using the starting materials given in the problem and the products that you selected:

$$\underset{\text{(acid)}}{H_2SO_4} + \underset{\text{(base)}}{HPO_4^{--}} \leftrightarrows SO_4^{--} + H_3PO_4.$$

In this reaction *two* protons were transferred; but in an acid-base reaction *only one proton can be transferred*. Your answer is wrong.

Please return to section 385 and see if you can find the correct answer.

377
[*from section 392*]

YOUR ANSWER: The pH of water is increased by the addition of H_2SO_4.

You are not being careful. Sulfuric acid is a *very* strong proton donor, and adding H_2SO_4 to water will surely make the water more acid–i.e., increase the concentration of H^+.

Turn back to section 392 and restudy it carefully, *especially the table*.

378

[*from section 397*]

YOUR ANSWER: Acetic acid (CH_3COOH) is a better proton donor than sulfuric acid (H_2SO_4).

Sorry, you are wrong!

Perhaps you thought that because CH_3COOH has 4 hydrogen atoms and H_2SO_4 has only 2, acetic acid would be the better able to donate protons (hydrogen ions). This is not so, and *this method does not work.*

Perhaps you misread the table and thought that the weaker acids at the bottom would be the best proton donors. This is not so; the *stronger acids* are the *better proton donors,* and are *at the top* of the table in the column headed *acid.*

Turn back to section 397. Restudy the material, and then choose your answer to the question more thoughtfully.

379

[*from section 373*]

YOUR ANSWER: H_2O is the acid in the reaction

$$HCl + H_2O \leftrightarrows H_3O^+ + Cl^-.$$

Sorry, your answer is incorrect. H_2O does contain hydrogen, and in some reactions it might therefore be able to donate a proton. If it did, it would act as an acid in such a reaction, but in *this* reaction it does not do so.

Turn back now to section 373 and restudy the question; then choose the correct answer.

380

[*from section 387*]

YOUR ANSWER: H_2CO_3 is a stronger acid than $H_2PO_4^-$, which is obvious because it is called an acid.

Your answer is *wrong,* and *your reasoning was not logical. Names* are not good guides to acid strength: e.g., the artificial sweetener saccharin is a fairly strong acid, over 10,000 times as strong as hydrosulfuric acid, whose name certainly sounds "furious."

The comparative strength of two acids is determined solely by noticing which of the two stands higher in the list of acids.

Return to section 387, reconsider the question, and decide more carefully this time.

381

[*from section 398*]

YOUR ANSWER: The reaction

$$H_3PO_4 + CH_3COO^- \leftrightarrows H_2PO_4^- + CH_3COOH$$

is not reasonable.

Well, let's see. To check for reasonableness we must compare the strengths of H_3PO_4 and CH_3COO^- as acids.

In Table A, H_3PO_4 is entry number 6 and CH_3COOH is entry number 8. CH_3COO^- is the conjugate base of CH_3COOH and hence cannot be as strong an acid as CH_3COOH. This is sufficient to assure us that H_3PO_4 is a better proton donor; hence it *is* reasonable for H_3PO_4 to donate a proton to CH_3COO^- and become $H_2PO_4^-$. So your answer was wrong.

Turn back to section 398 and restudy this whole subject carefully. Then choose another answer to the question.

382

[*from section 375*]

YOUR ANSWER: OH^- cannot be an acid.

Sorry, you are wrong. It *can* be an acid. It usually acts as a *base;* that is, it usually accepts a proton. Since OH^- contains a hydrogen atom, however, it *could* donate a proton, and hence your answer was not correct.

Return to section 375, restudy the material given there, and choose your answer more carefully.

383

[*from section 403*]

YOUR ANSWER: The reaction

$$HCl + H_2PO_4^- \rightleftarrows Cl^- + H_3PO_4$$

is not reasonable.

Let's see. In Table A, the stronger of the two acids, HCl, is the proton donor. Thus, we can write

$$HCl \rightleftarrows H^+ + Cl^-.$$

And when HCl donates a proton, Cl^- is a product. The reaction *is reasonable,* and your answer was wrong.

Now go back to section 403 and make a more careful choice.

384

[*from section 392*]

YOUR ANSWER: The pH of water is decreased by adding H_2SO_4.

You are correct. Adding a strong acid such as H_2SO_4 increases the acid content of the water, and the greater the hydrogen ion concentration $[H^+]$, the smaller the value of the pH. Very good.

Human digestive juice from a normal stomach has a pH of about 1.3; human blood has a pH of about 7.4

Which is the more acidic, blood or digestive juice?

Human blood is the more acidic. **section 402**

Human digestive juice is the more acidic. **section 407**

385

[*from section 406*]

YOUR ANSWER: Reaction (1) goes to the right to the largest extent:

$$HCl + H_2O \leftrightharpoons H_3O^+ + Cl^-;\ K_a >> 1.$$

You are correct. Very good.

GENERAL EQUATION FOR ACID-BASE REACTIONS

Let us now look at the two parts of an acid-base reaction: (1) the acidic reaction, in which a proton is donated, and (2) the basic reaction, in which a proton is accepted. These parts, when combined, give us a complete acid-base reaction, in which a proton is transferred.

We can show this in symbolic form as follows:

(1) To symbolize an acid, let us use HA;
to symbolize a base, let us use B.

(2) To symbolize an acidic reaction (donation of a proton), let us write

$$HA \rightleftharpoons H^+ + A^-;$$

to symbolize a basic reaction (acceptance of a proton), let us write

$$B + H^+ \leftrightarrows HB^+.$$

(3) To symbolize an acid-base reaction (transfer of a proton), we add these two equations and get

$$HA + B + H^+ \rightleftarrows H^+ + A^- + HB^+.$$

If we eliminate the H^+ that appears on both sides, we get

$$\underset{\text{(acid)}}{HA} + \underset{\text{(base)}}{B} \leftrightarrows \underset{\text{(acid)}}{HB^+} + \underset{\text{(base)}}{A^-}.$$

In this reaction, A^- is a base, as it can accept a proton; it is called the *conjugate base* of the acid HA. Similarly, HB^+ is an acid, the *conjugate acid* of the base B.

Let us notice the following points about the above equation, which is a general symbolic equation for any acid-base reaction:

(1) There are no coefficients written in this equation. This means that in every acid-base reaction all the coefficients are 1 and need not be expressly written.

(2) When an *acid* and a *base* are the *reactants,* then a *conjugate acid* and a *conjugate base* are the *products.*

Let's apply this.

If the acid H_2SO_4 reacts with the base HPO_4^{--}, what will be the conjugate acid and base formed?

The conjugate acid is H_3PO_4 and the conjugate base is SO_4^{--}.

section 376

The conjugate acid is $H_3SO_4^+$ and the conjugate base is PO_4^{---}.

section 391

The conjugate acid is HSO_4^- and the conjugate base is $H_2PO_4^-$.

section 397

I don't understand. **section 405**

386
[*from section 373*]

YOUR ANSWER: HCl is the acid in the reaction

$$HCl + H_2O \rightleftarrows H_3O^+ + Cl^-.$$

You are correct. HCl donates a proton to the water and hence is the acid in this reaction.

Whenever any chemical species donates a proton, we call the species donating the proton an *acid*. We call the species accepting the proton a *base*. In the reaction we have just considered, H_2O is the base because it accepts the proton.

Any reaction in which a proton is transferred from a *proton donor,* called the acid, to a *proton acceptor,* called the base, is an *acid-base* reaction.

Here is another acid-base reaction:

$$NH_3 + H_2O \rightleftarrows NH_4^+ + OH^-.$$

Which of the reactants is the acid?

H_2O is the acid. **section 375**

NH_3 is the acid. **section 393**

387
[*from section 397*]

YOUR ANSWER: Sulfuric acid (H_2SO_4) is a better proton donor than acetic acid (CH_3COOH).

You are correct. H_2SO_4 stands above CH_3COOH in the acid column; H_2SO_4 is therefore the stronger acid; i.e., it is the better proton donor.

Let's try another comparison.

Which is the stronger acid, dihydrogen phosphate ion ($H_2PO_4^-$) or carbonic acid (H_2CO_3)?

H_2CO_3, because it is called an acid. **section 380**

$H_2PO_4^-$, because it is above H_2CO_3 in the acid list. **section 398**

H_2CO_3, because $H_2PO_4^-$ is a base rather than an acid (line 6 in Table A). **section 404**

388

[*from section 398*]

YOUR ANSWER: The reaction

$$H_3PO_4 + CH_3COO^- \rightleftarrows H_2PO_4^- + CH_3COOH$$

is reasonable and the reactants are favored.

Well, let's see. To check for reasonableness we must compare the strengths of H_3PO_4 and CH_3COO^- as acids.

In Table A, H_3PO_4 is entry number 6 and CH_3COOH is entry number 8. CH_3COO^- is the conjugate base of CH_3COOH and hence cannot be as strong an acid as CH_3COOH. This is sufficient to assure us that H_3PO_4 is a better proton donor; hence it *is* reasonable for H_3PO_4 to donate a proton to CH_3COO^- and become $H_2PO_4^-$. The first half of your answer is correct.

We should decide that reactants are favored only if the new acid on the right is stronger than the strongest acid on the left. Hence we must compare the acid strengths of H_3PO_4 (entry number 6) and CH_3COOH (entry number 8).

Since CH_3COOH is not the stronger acid of these two, the reactants are *not* favored, and the second part of your answer is incorrect.

Turn back to section 398 and restudy this subject carefully. Then choose another answer.

389
[*from section 375*]

YOUR ANSWER: CN^- cannot be an acid.

You are correct. Very good! We have defined an acid as a proton donor. The CN^- ion cannot be an acid, because it contains no hydrogen atoms.

Notice carefully: All acids contain hydrogen, but not all "hydrogen containers" are acids. The donation of a proton, not the mere containing of hydrogen, is the critical distinction. Also,

(1) Some substances can act as either acids or bases—under different conditions, of course.

(2) Some substances neither donate nor accept protons, and hence do not fit into the acid-base category at all.

EQUILIBRIUM IN ACID-BASE REACTIONS

Let us now consider several different acids as they react with water:

(1) $HCl + H_2O \rightleftarrows H_3O^+ + Cl^-$
(2) $HF + H_2O \leftrightarrows H_3O^+ + F^-$
(3) $HSO_3^- + H_2O \leftrightarrows H_3O^+ + SO_3^{--}$.

In each of these reactions, H_2O acts as a base and accepts a proton to become H_3O^+. The protons are furnished by the acids HCl, HF, and HSO_3^-.

If we start with 1 mole of the acid in a liter of water in each of these three reactions, will we produce equal concentrations of H_3O^+ at equilibrium?

Yes. At equilibrium, the concentrations of H_3O^+ in these three reactions will be equal. **section 396**

Not necessarily. At equilibrium, the concentrations of H_3O^+ in these three reactions may not be equal. **section 406**

390
[*from section 403*]

YOUR ANSWER: The reaction

$$HCl + H_2PO_4^- \rightleftarrows Cl^- + H_3PO_4$$

is reasonable, and the reactants are favored.

You are partly right. Since HCl is the stronger acid, the reaction *is* reasonable. The first half of your answer is correct.

To check whether products or reactants are favored, we must consider whether HCl (the strongest acid on the left side of the equation) is stronger or weaker than the new acid on the right (H_3PO_4). Since the HCl (on the left side of the equation) is the stronger acid, the right side (the products) is the favored side. The second part of your answer is therefore incorrect.

Return to section 403, restudy the problem, and choose a better answer.

391
[*from section 385*]

YOUR ANSWER: The conjugate acid is $H_3SO_4^+$ and the conjugate base is PO_4^{---}.

Well, let's consider. The changes you have indicated involve a transfer of one proton, but you reversed the roles of acid and base. You were told H_2SO_4 is the acid, which means it is the proton donor, but you let it accept a proton (which is the role of a base), and thus it became $H_3SO_4^+$, which is incorrect.

Return to section 385 and choose a better answer.

392
[*from section 398*]

YOUR ANSWER: The reaction

$$H_3PO_4 + CH_3COO^- \rightleftarrows H_2PO_4^- + CH_3COOH$$

is reasonable, and the products are favored.

You are correct. H_3PO_4 is a stronger acid than CH_3COO^-, hence the reaction is reasonable. H_3PO_4 is a stronger acid than CH_3COOH, hence the products are favored.

ACID AND BASE STRENGTH IN TERMS OF pH

The acidity of solutions is often expressed in terms of "pH." The lower the pH number the more acid the solution. The general relationship between $[H^+]$ and pH is easily noted from the following table, which you should study carefully:

	Hydrogen-ion Concentration (moles/liter)	pH	Hydroxide-ion Concentration (moles/liter)	
↑	1	0	10^{-14}	↑
	10^{-1}	1	10^{-13}	
	10^{-2}	2	10^{-12}	
acidic	10^{-3}	3	10^{-11}	acidic
	10^{-4}	4	10^{-10}	
	10^{-5}	5	10^{-9}	
	10^{-6}	6	10^{-8}	
neutral—	10^{-7}	7	10^{-7}	—neutral
	10^{-8}	8	10^{-6}	
	10^{-9}	9	10^{-5}	
	10^{-10}	10	10^{-4}	
basic	10^{-11}	11	10^{-3}	basic
	10^{-12}	12	10^{-2}	
	10^{-13}	13	10^{-1}	
↓	10^{-14}	14	1	↓

What happens to the value of the pH of water when sulfuric acid, H_2SO_4, is added to it?

The pH of the solution increases. **section 377**

The pH of the solution decreases. **section 384**

393
[*from section 386*]

YOUR ANSWER: NH_3 is the acid in the reaction

$$NH_3 + H_2O \leftrightarrows NH_4^+ + OH^-.$$

Not so! NH_3 is *not* the acid since it did *not* donate a proton. (If it had donated a proton it would have become NH_2^-.)

Actually, NH_3 *accepted* a proton in this reaction and hence is the *base*.

Perhaps you were mistaken because you remembered that water was the proton acceptor in the previous acid-base reaction,

$$HCl + H_2O \leftrightarrows H_3O^+ + Cl^-,$$

and assumed that it would be the acceptor in every acid-base reaction. Many chemical species are acids in some reactions and bases in other reactions. In any particular acid-base reaction we must decide which substance is the proton donor before we can pick out the acid.

Return to section 386 and choose your answer more carefully.

394
[*from section 405*]

YOUR ANSWER: The products are SO_4^{--} and $CH_3COOH_2^+$.

Well, let's see.

We started with H_2SO_4 and CH_3COO^-, and the products you chose were SO_4^{--} and $CH_3COOH_2^+$. Writing an equation, we obtain

$$\underset{\text{(acid)}}{H_2SO_4} + \underset{\text{(base)}}{CH_3COO^-} \leftrightarrows SO_4^{--} + CH_3COOH_2^+.$$

In this reaction *two* protons are shown as being transferred, but in an acid-base reaction *only one* proton can be transferred.

Return to section 405, check through the problem we worked out for you, and then choose a better answer.

395

[*from section 375*]

YOUR ANSWER: NH_3 cannot be an acid.

Sorry, you are wrong. It *can* be an acid. It usually acts as a *base;* that is, it usually accepts a proton. Since NH_3 contains hydrogen atoms, however, it *could* donate a proton, and your answer was not correct.

Return to section 375, restudy the material given there, and choose your answer more carefully.

396

[*from section 389*]

YOUR ANSWER: Yes. At equilibrium, the concentrations of H_3O^+ in these three reactions will be equal:

$$(1)\ HCl + H_2O \rightleftarrows H_3O^+ + Cl^-$$
$$(2)\ HF + H_2O \leftrightarrows H_3O^+ + F^-$$
$$(3)\ HSO_3^- + H_2O \rightleftarrows H_3O^+ + SO_3^{--}$$

Well, let's consider. These are equilibrium reactions; this fact is indicated by the double arrows.

But you learned in Chapter 9 that at equilibrium a reaction is not complete, either to the right or to the left, and that each equilibrium reaction has its own special equilibrium constant, symbolized by K, which is different for each different reaction.

Remember, acid-base reactions are equilibrium reactions, and the general rules about equilibrium reactions therefore apply to all acid-base reactions.

Return to section 389 and study the question again.

YOUR ANSWER: The conjugate acid is HSO_4^- and the conjugate base is $H_2PO_4^-$.

You are correct:

H_2SO_4 donates a proton and becomes HSO_4^-.
(acid) (conjugate base)

HPO_4^{--} accepts a proton and becomes $H_2PO_4^-$.
(base) (conjugate acid)

This shows that you chose the correct products.

In fact, both H_2SO_4 and HPO_4^{--} are able to donate protons in certain reactions; but we told you which one was the acid (when the two react together) so that you would know which of the two would be the proton donor in this case.

ACID-BASE TABLES

Chemists have prepared extensive lists of acids, their conjugate bases, and their acid constants, so that anybody can tell quickly and easily which of any pair of acids is the better proton donor. The acid that is able to donate protons better is called the stronger of the two acids.

There is a short list (Appendix, Table A) of common acids and their relative strengths, which you will need to use in future work in this book. There is no need to memorize this list, but you must be able to read and interpret it.

Let's practice using this table. Which is the better proton donor—sulfuric acid (H_2SO_4) or acetic acid (CH_3COOH)?

Acetic acid (CH_3COOH) is the better proton donor. **section 378**

Sulfuric acid (H_2SO_4) is the better proton donor. **section 387**

398

[from section 387]

YOUR ANSWER: $H_2PO_4^-$ is a stronger acid than H_2CO_3 because it is located higher in the acid list of Table A.

You are correct. Very good. When we notice which of two acids stands higher in Table A, we know immediately which of the two is the stronger acid (the better proton donor).

PREDICTING ACID-BASE REACTIONS

We can use Table A to predict possible results of reactions. However, since acid-base reactions are reversible, we cannot be sure our "reasonable" prediction is a correct prediction without checking the strength of the new acid found on the right against that of the stronger of the two acids on the left. RULE: *In an acid-base reaction, the products are favored if the new acid formed is weaker than the strongest acid on the reactant side.*

There is, of course, no need to consider whether products or reactants are favored at equilibrium unless the reaction prediction is a reasonable one.

Consider the following equation:

$$H_3PO_4 + CH_3COO^- \rightleftharpoons H_2PO_4^- + CH_3COOH.$$

Which of the following is correct?

This reaction is not reasonable. **section 381**

This reaction is reasonable, and the reactants are favored. **section 388**

This reaction is reasonable, and the products are favored. **section 392**

I am confused. Please work this problem for me as an example. **section 403**

399

[*from section 403*]

YOUR ANSWER: The reaction

$$HCl + H_2PO_4^- \rightleftarrows Cl^- + H_3PO_4$$

is reasonable, and the products are favored.

You are correct. Since you had a bit of confusion on this topic, let's review it by working through this problem step by step together. Since HCl is the stronger acid, the reaction *is* reasonable. So the first part of your answer is correct.

To check whether products or reactants are favored, we must consider whether HCl (the strongest acid on the left side of the equation) is stronger or weaker than the new acid on the right (H_3PO_4). Since the HCl (on the left side of the equation) is the stronger acid, the right side (the products) is the favored side. The second part of your answer is also correct; hence your entire answer is correct.

Now return to section 398, study it carefully, and then proceed with the question on that page.

400

[*from section 405*]

YOUR ANSWER: The products are HSO_4^- and CH_3COOH.

You are correct!

The acid (H_2SO_4) donates H^+ and becomes HSO_4^-.
The base (CH_3COO^-) accepts H^+ and becomes CH_3COOH.
A complete acid-base equation for this reaction is

$$H_2SO_4 + CH_3COO^- \leftrightarrows HSO_4^- + CH_3COOH.$$

You should *now* be able to do the problem that made you ask for special help. Return to section 385, restudy it carefully, and try the question on that page by yourself. Good luck!

401

[*from section 406*]

YOUR ANSWER: I am confused; can you explain this more fully?

Yes. Let's review a bit.

The extent to which an equilibrium reaction goes to completion is indicated by the value of *K*:

If $K_a = 1$, the concentration of products equals the concentration of reactants.

If $K_a < 1$, the concentration of products is less than the concentration of reactants.

If $K_a > 1$, the concentration of products is greater than the concentration of reactants.

If this is not a sufficient refresher as to the significance of the value of K_a, take a few minutes for a special review: study section 369 in Chapter 9, and then return to section 406.

402

[*from section 384*]

YOUR ANSWER: Blood is more acidic than digestive juice.

You are wrong. Human blood has a higher pH value than human digestive juice, but *high* pH does not mean a solution with high acidity.

Return to section 392, restudy the table, and then continue.

403

[*from section 398*]

YOUR ANSWER: I am confused. Please work this problem for me.

Certainly. The reaction given was

$$H_3PO_4 + CH_3COO^- \rightleftarrows H_2PO_4 + CH_3COOH.$$

To check for reasonableness, we must compare the strengths of H_3PO_4 and CH_3COO^- as acids.

In Table A, H_3PO_4 is entry number 6 and CH_3COOH is entry number 8. CH_3COO^- is the conjugate base of CH_3COOH and hence cannot be as strong an acid as CH_3COOH. This is sufficient to assure us that H_3PO_4 is a better proton donor; hence it is reasonable for H_3PO_4 to donate a proton to CH_3COO^- and become $H_2PO_4^-$.

To check whether reactants or products are favored, we must compare the acid strength of H_3PO_4 with that of CH_3COOH, the new acid on the right. H_3PO_4, entry number 6, is a better proton donor than CH_3COOH, entry number 8, so the *products* are favored at equilibrium in this reaction.

To be sure all this is clear, consider the following equation:

$$HCl + H_2PO_4^- \leftrightarrows Cl^- + H_3PO_4.$$

Which of the following best expresses your judgment about this reaction?

This reaction is not reasonable. **section 383**

This reaction is reasonable, and the reactants are favored. **section 390**

This reaction is reasonable, and the products are favored. **section 399**

404

[*from section 387*]

YOUR ANSWER: H_2CO_3 is a stronger acid than $H_2PO_4^-$, because $H_2PO_4^-$ is a base rather than an acid (line 6, Table A).

Not so. You have made the mistake of using the base *and* the acid column in a single comparison. When we use this table to compare the *acid strengths* of two species, we must compare the location of these two species in the *acid column.*

Return to section 387, and be more careful in using Table A.

405

[*from section 385*]

YOUR ANSWER: I don't understand.

We start with this information:

(1) The acid H_2SO_4 donates H^+ to become HSO_4^-, and (2) the base HPO_4^{--} accepts H^+ to become $H_2PO_4^-$.

The acid-base reaction for this is

$$\underset{\text{acid}}{\underset{\uparrow}{H_2SO_4}} + \underset{\text{base}}{\underset{\uparrow}{HPO_4^{--}}} \leftrightarrows \underset{\text{conjugate base}}{\underset{\uparrow}{HSO_4^-}} + \underset{\text{conjugate acid}}{\underset{\uparrow}{H_2PO_4^-}}.$$

Now try this problem:

If the acid H_2SO_4 reacts with the base CH_3COO^-, what are the products?†

The products are SO_4^{--} and $CH_3COOH_2^+$. section 394

The products are HSO_4^- and CH_3COOH. section 400

† In many acids containing carbon, it is customary to write the proton or protons involved in acid-base reactions at the end rather than the beginning of the formula.

406

[*from section 389*]

YOUR ANSWER: No. At equilibrium the concentrations of H_3O^+ in these three reactions may not be equal.

You are correct. These acid-base reactions are all equilibrium reactions, and each goes toward completion to a different extent. Far from having *equal* concentrations of H_3O^+ they will have very different concentrations. Let us proceed.

The extent to which an equilibrium reaction goes to completion is indicated by the value of K, the equilibrium constant for the reaction. Let's look at these three reactions again, this time indicating their respective equilibrium constants by K_a (K_a for the equilibrium constant of an acid):

(1) $HCl + H_2O \leftrightarrows H_3O^+ + Cl^-$; K_a *much* greater than 1.
(2) $HF + H_2O \rightleftarrows H_3O^+ + F^-$; $K_a = 7.2 \times 10^{-4}$.
(3) $HSO_3^- + H_2O \rightleftarrows H_3O^+ + SO_3^{--}$; $K_a = 6.2 \times 10^{-8}$.

Which of these reactions goes to the right to the largest extent?

Reaction (3) goes to the right to the largest extent. **section 374**

Reaction (1) goes to the right to the largest extent. **section 385**

I am confused; can you explain this more fully? **section 401**

407

[*from section 384*]

YOUR ANSWER: Digestive juice is more acidic than blood.

Correct. Lower pH means higher hydrogen-ion concentration, and higher hydrogen-ion concentration means a more acidic solution.

Turn to section 408 for a review of Chapter 10.

[*from section 407*]

CHAPTER 10—ACID-BASE EQUILIBRIA—SUMMARY

In this chapter we have applied the general principles of reversible reactions and equilibrium constants to the very important topic of acids and bases. We are well along in our study of fundamental principles of chemistry.

In an acid-base reaction (commonly called *neutralization*) a proton is *donated* by an *acid* and *accepted* by a *base;* this transfer of a proton results in a new acid and base, referred to as the *conjugate* base and acid.

Acid-base reactions are reversible; the extent to which they go toward completion is indicated by the value of K_a for the reaction. The K_a values of many acids and bases are listed in Table A in the Appendix.

An acid-base reaction is deemed *reasonable* if the proton is donated by the stronger acid. If the newly formed acid is stronger than the original acid, the reactants are favored in the equilibrium; and vice versa, if the newly formed acid is weaker than the original acid, the products are favored.

The degree of acidity of an aqueous solution can be measured by the *pH scale*. The lower the pH, the greater the acidity. Pure water, our arbitrary standard of neutrality, has a pH of 7.

Try the review questions in section 409.

CHAPTER 10—REVIEW QUESTIONS AND PROBLEMS

1. Name the conjugate base of each of the following:
H_2SO_4, H_3PO_4, $H_2PO_4^-$, HCl, H_2O.

2. Name the conjugate acid of the following bases:
Cl^-, NH_3, HSO_4^-, $H_2PO_4^-$, HPO_4^{--}, OH^-.

3. Write equations for the following reactions, indicating the conjugate acids and bases involved:
(a) $HCl + H_2O \rightleftarrows$
(b) $H_3PO_4 + NH_3 \leftrightarrows$
(c) $HNO_3 + CH_3COO^- \rightleftarrows$
(d) $CH_3COOH + SO_3^{--} \rightleftarrows$
(e) $HSO_4^- + H_2PO_4^- \rightleftarrows$

4. Use Table A in the Appendix to decide which member of each of the following pairs is the stronger acid:
(a) H_2CO_3, $H_2PO_4^-$
(b) H_3PO_4, CH_3COOH
(c) HF, HSO_3^-
(d) H_2SO_3, HCl
(e) HSO_3^-, HCO_3^-

5. In each of the following reactions, indicate whether reactants or products are favored:
(a) $H_3PO_4 + CH_3COO^- \rightleftarrows H_2PO_4^- + CH_3COOH$
(b) $HSO_3^- + HPO_4^{--} \rightleftarrows SO_3^{--} + H_2PO_4^-$
(c) $HSO_4^- + HSO_3^- \rightleftarrows H_2SO_3 + SO_4^{--}$
(d) $HF + NH_3 \rightleftarrows F^- + NH_4^+$

6. Calculate the hydrogen-ion concentration in solutions of pH 2, 7, 9. Which of these solutions are more acidic than water?

Turn to section 553 for answers, then go on to section 410.

410
[*from section 409*]

Chapter 11

IONIC SOLUBILITY REACTIONS AND EQUILIBRIA

There are many different kinds of solids, and many different kinds of solvents in which they can be dissolved to form solutions. In this chapter we shall confine our discussion to a single solvent, *water* (the most important solvent in the world). As solutes, we shall consider only *salts,* which are ionic solids that have a crystal structure made up of an intricate lattice network of positive and negative ions.

SOLUTIONS OF SALTS

Sodium chloride is a good example of an ionic salt. The chemical formula of sodium chloride is usually written NaCl; but sometimes, to emphasize its ionic nature, we show the charges and write Na^+Cl^-. If a small pinch of Na^+Cl^- is placed in a beaker of water, the salt will disappear from view. We say the salt has *dissolved.*

We can write a chemical equation for this reaction as follows:

$$Na^+Cl^- + xH_2O \rightarrow Na^+ \cdot yH_2O + Cl^- \cdot zH_2O.$$

This equation emphasizes that water plays an important role in the reaction. The $Na^+ \cdot H_2O$ ions and $Cl^- \cdot H_2O$ ions are called *hydrated* or *aqueous* ions to indicate that they contain water molecules as integral parts of the ions. They may be written $Na^+_{(aq)}$ and $Cl^-_{(aq)}$ if desired.

Do the *x, y,* and *z* in the above equation represent known or unknown numbers of water molecules?

The *x, y,* and *z* represent *definite* and *known* numbers of water molecules. **section 416**

The *x, y,* and *z* represent *indefinite* and *unknown* numbers of water molecules. **section 421**

[*from section 436*]

YOUR ANSWER: $Na^+Cl^-_{(s)} \rightleftarrows Na^+ + Cl^-$ is a less complex equation, but it represents exactly the same theoretical concept of what happens when NaCl dissolves in water as does the equation previously discussed.

You are correct! Very good.

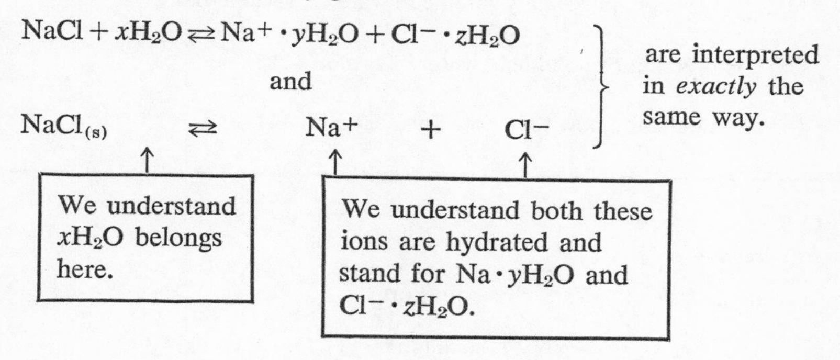

DEGREES OF SOLUBILITY

Water is a good solvent for many substances. Even materials such as glass and chinaware dissolve in water to a *very, very small extent.* To *that* extent they are soluble in water. Water dripping on a marble step will eventually wear a depression in the marble just because the marble is soluble, to a *very, very slight extent,* in water.

If we are to be very precise and exact, we can truthfully state: *Everything will dissolve in water;* i.e., everything is soluble, to some extent, in water. Such a use of the word *soluble* would make it so broad in meaning that it would be of no real value to the chemist. As chemists, let us agree to use the word as follows:

(1) A substance is said to be *soluble* if we can dissolve about one-tenth of a mole or more in a liter of water.
(2) If less than about one-tenth of a mole of a substance (but still a considerable amount) will dissolve in a liter of water, we will refer to the substance as *slightly soluble.*

(3) If the amount of a substance that will dissolve in a liter of water is negligibly small, we will call the substance *insoluble.*

Approximately 0.5 gram of $Ca(OH)_2$ will dissolve in a liter of water. Is $Ca(OH)_2$ soluble, slightly soluble, or insoluble in water?

$Ca(OH)_2$ is soluble in water. **section 418**

$Ca(OH)_2$ is not appreciably soluble in water. **section 424**

$Ca(OH)_2$ is slightly soluble in water. **section 433**

I don't understand how to handle this. **section 441**

412

[*from section 421*]

YOUR ANSWER: Yes, the equation

$$Na^+Cl^- + xH_2O \longrightarrow Na^+ \cdot yH_2O + Cl^- \cdot zH_2O$$

represents an equilibrium reaction, and should be written with a double arrow.

Sorry, you made the wrong choice. Notice that the *reactants* (i.e., substances on the *left*) are Na^+Cl^- and H_2O. Na^+Cl^-, written that way, must represent a *solid,* but we said, ". . . the salt will *completely* dissolve in the water." Can this represent an equilibrium situation?

Think about this. Then return to section 421 and choose another answer.

413

[*from section 431*]

YOUR ANSWER: Sodium chromate is not soluble since it does not appear in the table.

It is true that the table does not contain the chromate ion, but there are many salts, both soluble and insoluble, that do not appear in the table.

In this case, however, you should be able to decide on the basis of information that we have previously given you.

Do this:

(1) Turn back to section 424 and restudy the solubility rules which you were told *should be learned.*

(2) Return to section 431 and answer the question more carefully.

414

[*from section 427*]

YOUR ANSWER: $Na^+Cl^- + xH_2O \longrightarrow Na^+ \cdot yH_2O + Cl^- \cdot zH_2O$ correctly represents what happens when 50 grams of NaCl is added to 100 grams of H_2O at 20°C.

Sorry. You made the wrong choice. You were told that only 36 grams of NaCl can dissolve in 100 grams of H_2O (20°C). When we put 50 grams of NaCl in 100 grams of H_2O (20°C) it *cannot* all dissolve. A total of 36 grams will dissolve, and approximately 14 grams will be left undissolved at the bottom of the beaker. (Exactly the same situation occurs when you add more sugar to iced tea than can be dissolved; the excess sugar remains undissolved at the bottom of your glass.)

Since not all the salt dissolves, the reaction certainly *does not* go to completion and we should *not* use the single arrow in this situation.

Return to section 427 and be more careful in your choice of answer.

415

[*from section 442*]

YOUR ANSWER: The equilibrium constant for the reaction $AgCl_{(s)} \rightleftarrows Ag^+ + Cl^-$ is

$$K = \frac{[AgCl_{(s)}]}{[Ag^+][Cl^-]}.$$

Not exactly. The fraction you have written has the correct expressions in it, but you have the situation upside down. Recall: In any equilibrium expression the products belong in the numerator, and the reactants belong in the denominator.

Return to section 442 and choose your answer to the question more carefully.

416

[*from section 410*]

YOUR ANSWER: In the equation

$$Na^+Cl^- + xH_2O \longrightarrow Na^+ \cdot yH_2O + Cl^- \cdot zH_2O,$$

x, y, and z represent definite and known numbers of water molecules.

Sorry, your answer is incorrect. It is standard practice in mathematics and chemistry to use the letters at the end of the alphabet, such as w, x, y, z, to stand for numbers whose values we do *not* know.

If we knew the value of these numbers we could write them in, just as we put other numbers in equations to represent definite, known amounts of chemical species.

Turn back to section 410, restudy the text, and then choose the correct answer.

417

[*from section 424*]

YOUR ANSWER: If a salt does not contain at least one of these seven ions, it is almost certain to be insoluble.

You are not interpreting the rules correctly. The rules give you a means of classifying certain kinds of salts (those that contain any of these seven ions) as soluble. If a compound does not contain one of these ions, the rules tell us nothing about its solubility.

Return to section 424.

418

[*from section 411*]

YOUR ANSWER: $Ca(OH)_2$ is soluble in water.

No; this would be an unwarranted overstatement.

Did you forget to convert 0.5 gram of $Ca(OH)_2$ to moles of $Ca(OH)_2$ before deciding if it is soluble in water?

Did you forget about our *agreed* meanings for the word "soluble"? The fact that $Ca(OH)_2$ will dissolve in water *does not* mean it is "soluble in water." Remember: *anything* will dissolve in water to some extent, but *not everything* dissolves enough to be classed as "soluble in water."

Return to section 411, restudy the text, learn the gradations of the word "soluble," and then answer the question more carefully.

419

[*from section 432*]

YOUR ANSWER: $[Ag^+] = 4.0 \times 10^{-5}$ molar in a saturated solution of silver bromate.

Sorry. You are wrong. 4.0×10^{-5} is the K_{sp}, the solubility product for $AgBrO_3$. The solubility product is not the same as the concentration of *either* of the ions; it is equal to the product of *both* the concentrations.

Return to section 432 and restudy the problem we gave you.

420

[*from section 436*]

YOUR ANSWER: The equation $Na^+Cl^-_{(s)} \rightleftarrows Na^+ + Cl^-$ represents a less complicated theory of what happens when NaCl dissolves in H_2O.

Sorry. Your interpretation is *wrong!*

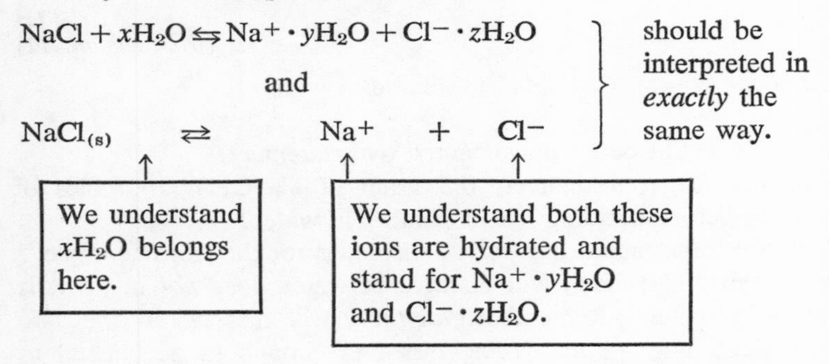

Return to section 436, restudy the explanation given there, and then choose the correct answer to the question.

421

[*from section 410*]

YOUR ANSWER: In the equation

$$Na^+Cl^- + xH_2O \longrightarrow Na^+ \cdot yH_2O + Cl^- \cdot zH_2O,$$

x, y, and *z* represent indefinite and unknown numbers of water molecules.

You are correct. We use these letters x, y, and z precisely because we do *not* know the number of water molecules involved in this reaction.

Whenever any salt dissolves in water the salt forms ions, and *these ions are always hydrated.* Indeed, it is the force or drive of this hydration reaction that provides the energy necessary to disrupt the crystal lattice and allow the salt to dissolve, as hydrated ions, in the water.

If we use a small enough amount of NaCl, e.g., 1 gram, and place it in a beaker containing 100 grams of H_2O, the salt will *completely* dissolve in the water. The equation is the same as before:

$$Na^+Cl^- + xH_2O \longrightarrow Na^+ \cdot yH_2O + Cl^- \cdot zH_2O.$$

Is this an equilibrium reaction, which should therefore be written with a double arrow?

Yes, this is an equilibrium reaction. **section 412**

No, this is not an equilibrium reaction. **section 427**

There is no way we can tell. **section 435**

422

[*from section 434*]

YOUR ANSWER: For the reaction $BaCO_{3(s)} \leftrightarrows Ba^{++} + CO_3^{--}$, the expression for K_{sp} is

$$K_{sp} = \frac{[Ba^{++}][CO_3^{--}]}{[BaCO_{3(s)}]}.$$

You are not paying attention to the material you are studying.

You have written an expression for K, not K_{sp}. Now turn back to section 434 and *reread* it carefully.

423

[from section 440]

YOUR ANSWER: $[Al^{+++}] \cong 4.4 \times 10^{-17}$ molar in a saturated solution of $Al(OH)_3$.

You are wrong. To get this answer you must have assumed:

(1) $[Al^{+++}] = [OH^-]$;
(2) $K_{sp} = [Al^{+++}] [OH^-]$.

Both of these assumptions are wrong.

Return to section 440 and restudy the problem. Be sure you check carefully the entry in Table C for $Al(OH)_3$.

424

[from section 411]

YOUR ANSWER: $Ca(OH)_2$ is not appreciably soluble in water.

You are correct. One mole of $Ca(OH)_2$ weighs 74 grams. 0.5 gram of $Ca(OH)_2$ is thus 2/74, or 0.007 of a mole. This is much less than 1/10 of a mole, and is best considered as a negligibly small amount. Hence our term "not soluble" applies.

Chemists often find it desirable and necessary to know whether large enough amounts of an ionic solid (a salt) can be dissolved to be considered "soluble" in water. Two simple rules of ionic solubility *should be learned,* because they will save much time and effort in the long run.

Ionic Solubility Rules

(1) Any salt (or acid) containing the positive ions K^+, Na^+, NH_4^+, or H^+ is almost certain to be soluble in water.

(2) Any salt containing the negative ions NO_3^-, ClO_3^- (chlorate), or CH_3COO^- is almost certain to be soluble in water.

Let us see whether you can interpret these rules correctly. Which of the statements below is correct?

If an ionic compound does not contain at least one of the above mentioned seven ions, it is almost certain to be insoluble. **section 417**

If an ionic compound does not contain at least one of the above mentioned seven ions, the rules do not tell whether it is soluble or not; further information is needed. **section 439**

425

[*from section 430*]

YOUR ANSWER: About 1.14×10^{-3} grams of $Ca(OH)_2$ can be dissolved in a liter of water.

Apparently you made *these* mistakes to get this answer:

In Table C we found:

$$Ca(OH)_2 \leftrightarrows Ca^{++} + 2OH^-;\ K_{sp} = [Ca^{++}]\,[OH^-]^2 = 1.3 \times 10^{-6}.$$

Your errors were:

(1) You assumed $[Ca^{++}] = [OH^-]$. This is not so!

(2) You forgot to square the $[OH^-]$.

(3) Your answer came out in moles/liter, and you forgot about units and just wrote the value you calculated.

Better take a five-minute break and then return to section 430 and try again.

426

[*from section 442*]

YOUR ANSWER: The equilibrium constant for the reaction $AgCl_{(s)} \rightleftarrows Ag^+ + Cl^-$ is

$$K = \frac{1}{[Ag^+][Cl^-]}.$$

Not so! You are rather mixed up. The products, Ag^+ and Cl^-, belong in the numerator; the numerator is never simply "1."

Apparently you don't remember much about equilibrium expressions. You cannot successfully go ahead until you have this matter mastered.

Turn to section 457 for a brief review.

427

[*from section 421*]

YOUR ANSWER: No, the equation

$$Na^+Cl^- + xH_2O \longrightarrow Na^+ \cdot yH_2O + Cl^- \cdot zH_2O$$

does *not* represent an equilibrium reaction.

You are correct. This is exactly the case.

The clue that tells us that this reaction goes to completion and is *not* an equilibrium reaction is the statement ". . . the salt will *completely* dissolve in the water."

It is important to note, however, that *there is a limit* to the amount of NaCl that will dissolve in a given quantity of water. This limit is about 36 grams of NaCl solid per 100 grams of H_2O (at 20°C).

Which of the two equations below should be used to represent the situation if we place 50 grams of NaCl in a beaker containing 100 grams of H_2O (at 20°C)?

$Na^+Cl^- + xH_2O \rightarrow Na^+ \cdot yH_2O + Cl^- \cdot zH_2O$ **section 414**

$Na^+Cl^- + xH_2O \rightleftarrows Na^+ \cdot yH_2O + Cl^- \cdot zH_2O$ **section 436**

428

[*from section 451*]

YOUR ANSWER: When equal volumes of 0.01 molar solutions of $MgCl_2$ and Na_2CO_3 are mixed, the ion product will be 2.5×10^{-5}.

You are correct.

Each of the original solutions is 0.01 molar. When mixed together in equal volumes, the solutions dilute each other to half their original concentrations, making each concentration 0.005 molar. Hence, the ion product is

$$[Mg^{++}][CO_3^{--}] = (0.005)(0.005)$$
$$= (5 \times 10^{-3})(5 \times 10^{-3})$$
$$= 25 \times 10^{-6}$$
$$= 2.5 \times 10^{-5}.$$

Will a precipitate form if the above-mentioned solutions are mixed together?

Yes, a precipitate will form. **section 443**

No, a precipitate will not form. **section 449**

429

[*from section 449*]

YOUR ANSWER: Yes, a precipitate will form when 10^{-3} molar Cu^{++} and 10^{-4} molar S^{--} solutions are mixed.

You are correct.

To start, we have two solutions having the following concentrations:

$$[Cu^{++}] = 10^{-3} \text{ molar;}$$
$$[S^{--}] = 10^{-4} \text{ molar.}$$

When these solutions are mixed in equal parts by volume, each solution dilutes the concentration of the other to half its original value. Thus, the concentrations after mixing are as follows:

$$[Cu^{++}] = 5 \times 10^{-4} \text{ molar;}$$
$$[S^{--}] = 5 \times 10^{-5} \text{ molar.}$$

We can now calculate the ion product for the mixture:

$$\text{ion product} = [Cu^{++}][S^{--}]$$
$$= (5 \times 10^{-4})(5 \times 10^{-5})$$
$$= 25 \times 10^{-9}$$
$$= 2.5 \times 10^{-8}.$$

Since the K_{sp} for CuS is 8.5×10^{-45}, a precipitate forms.
Go on now to section 459 for a chapter review.

430

[*from section 440*]

YOUR ANSWER: $[Al^{+++}] \cong 2.9 \times 10^{-9}$ molar in a saturated solution of $Al(OH)_3$.

You are correct. Very good. From Table C:

$$Al(OH)_3 \rightleftarrows Al^{+++} + 3OH^-; \quad K_{sp} = [Al^{+++}]\,[OH^-]^3 = 1.9 \times 10^{-33}.$$

From the equation

$$[OH^-] = 3[Al^{+++}],$$

let

$$x = [Al^{+++}] \text{ and } 3x = [OH^-].$$

Insert these values in the K_{sp} equation:

$$(x)(3x)^3 = 1.9 \times 10^{-33}$$

$$27x^4 = 1.9 \times 10^{-33}$$

$$x^4 = \frac{1.9}{27} \times 10^{-33} = .071 \times 10^{-33} = 71 \times 10^{-36}$$

$$x = \sqrt[4]{71 \times 10^{-36}} \cong 2.9 \times 10^{-9} \text{ molar} = [Al^{+++}],$$

which is the answer we are seeking. Going one more step,

$$[OH^-] = 3x \cong 8.1 \times 10^{-9} \text{ molar}.$$

Any other problem calling for us to calculate the concentration of an ion in a saturated solution can be handled in a similar fashion by the use of a table of K_{sp} values, of which Table C is a small sample.

We can use this table to calculate how many grams of marble will dissolve in a liter of water, for example. Marble is calcium carbonate, $CaCO_3$. From Table C:

$$CaCO_3 \rightleftarrows Ca^{++} + CO_3^{--}; K_{sp} = [Ca^{++}][CO_3^{--}] = 1 \times 10^{-8}.$$

$$[Ca^{++}] = [CO_3^{--}] = x = \text{moles of } CaCO_3 \text{ that dissolve per liter.}$$

$$x^2 = 1 \times 10^{-8}$$

$$x = 1 \times 10^{-4} \text{ moles/liter.}$$

$$1 \text{ mole of } CaCO_3 = 100 \text{ grams}$$

$$10^{-4} \text{ moles} = 0.01 \text{ gram.}$$

Hence, at equilibrium in a saturated solution, there is 0.01 gram of $CaCO_3$ dissolved per liter of solution.

You try this problem:
How many grams of $Ca(OH)_2$ can be dissolved in a liter of water?

About 1.14×10^{-3} grams. **section 425**

About 6.7×10^{-3} grams. **section 445**

About 0.5 gram. **section 451**

431

[*from section 439*]

YOUR ANSWER: $FeCl_2$ is soluble in water.

You are correct. The location where the row headed by Fe^{++} meets the column headed by Cl^- contains "S," so we know $FeCl_2$ is soluble, i.e., it will dissolve to a greater extent than 0.1 mole per liter in H_2O.

Is sodium chromate (Na_2CrO_4) soluble in water?

Sodium chromate is not soluble since it does not appear in the table. **section 413**

Sodium chromate is very likely to be soluble in H_2O. **section 442**

I can't tell, because the table does not contain the chromate ion. **section 450**

YOUR ANSWER: For the reaction $Mg(OH)_{2(s)} \rightleftarrows Mg^{++} + 2OH^-$, the K_{sp} expression is

$$K_{sp} = [Mg^{++}]\,[OH^-]^2.$$

You are correct. The K_{sp} always equals the product of the concentrations of the ions present, each concentration being raised to the power of its coefficient in the chemical equation.

Whenever a solution contains all of a dissolved substance that it can hold, we say that the solution is *saturated*. K_{sp} values always apply to saturated solutions of ionic compounds that are insoluble or slightly soluble. A table of K_{sp} values appears in the Appendix, Table C.

Note these three points carefully:

(1) We never use K_{sp} expressions and K_{sp} values for substances that are soluble; i.e., that dissolve more than about 0.1 mole per liter.

(2) K_{sp} applies only to ionic compounds.

(3) K_{sp} applies only to saturated solutions.

CALCULATING ION CONCENTRATIONS

If we have a saturated solution of a salt and know the value of K_{sp}, we can calculate the concentration of each of the ions present. Let us work a typical problem.

What is the concentration of Ag^+ ions in a saturated solution of AgCl?

From Table C (Appendix), we note the following information:

$$AgCl \leftrightarrows Ag^+ + Cl^-;\ K_{sp} = [Ag^+]\,[Cl^-] = 1.6 \times 10^{-10}.$$

The equation on the left tells us that the number of Ag^+ ions is *equal* to the number of Cl^- ions, since the coefficients of Ag^+ and Cl^- are both 1.

$$\begin{aligned} \text{Let } x &= [Ag^+] = [Cl^-]. \\ \text{Then } x^2 &= 1.6 \times 10^{-10}, \\ \text{and } x &= 1.3 \times 10^{-5} \text{ molar.} \end{aligned}$$

Now you try this problem:

What is the concentration of Ag^+ ions in a saturated solution of silver bromate, $AgBrO_3$? That is, what is the value of $[Ag^+]$?

$[Ag^+] = 4.0 \times 10^{-5}$ molar. **section 419**

$[Ag^+] = 6.3 \times 10^{-3}$ molar. **section 440**

$[Ag^+] = 2.0 \times 10^{-5}$ molar. **section 452**

433

[*from section 411*]

YOUR ANSWER: $Ca(OH)_2$ is slightly soluble in water.

You are not correct. You were told that 0.5 gram of $Ca(OH)_2$ will dissolve in a liter of water. Then,

$$\left(\frac{0.5\text{ g }Ca(OH)_2}{\text{liter }H_2O}\right)\left(\frac{\text{mole }Ca(OH)_2}{74\text{ g }Ca(OH)_2}\right) \cong {}^* \frac{0.007\text{ mole}}{\text{liter}}$$

This is much less than 0.1 mole/liter. Is it still a "considerable amount"?

Think this over, then return to section 411 and choose another answer.

* Is approximately equal to.

434

[*from section 442*]

YOUR ANSWER: The equilibrium constant for the reaction $AgCl_{(s)} \rightleftarrows Ag^+ + Cl^-$ is

$$K = \frac{[Ag^+][Cl^-]}{[AgCl_{(s)}]}.$$

You are correct. We can simplify this general expression as described below.

Let us define a new constant, which we will call the *solubility-product constant,* K_{sp}, such that

$$K_{sp} = [Ag^+][Cl^-].$$

We can do this because the denominator of the general equilibrium constant expression is $[AgCl_{(s)}]$, which means "the concentration of solid AgCl." The concentration of a solid is always the same for any given substance, hence is a constant, and can be absorbed into the *K*. Actually, then, $K_{sp} = K[AgCl_{(s)}]$ for the case of AgCl. Notice that the K_{sp} expression is simpler than the corresponding *K* expression.

What is the K_{sp} for the reaction $BaCO_{3(s)} \rightleftarrows Ba^{++} + CO_3^{--}$?

$K_{sp} = \frac{[Ba^{++}][CO_3^{--}]}{[BaCO_{3(s)}]}$. **section 422**

$K_{sp} = [Ba^{++}]^2[CO_3^{--}]^3$. **section 444**

$K_{sp} = [Ba^{++}][CO_3^{--}]$. **section 456**

435

[from section 421]

YOUR ANSWER: There is no way we can tell whether the reaction $Na^+Cl^- + xH_2O \longrightarrow Na^+ \cdot yH_2O + Cl^- \cdot zH_2O$ represents an equilibrium or not.

You should be able to decide this question. Here is a clue: We said, ". . . the salt will *completely* dissolve in the water." Think about the significance of this. Then return to section 421 and select another answer.

[*from section 427*]

YOUR ANSWER: $Na^+Cl^- + xH_2O \leftrightarrows Na^+ \cdot yH_2O + Cl^- \cdot zH_2O$ correctly represents what happens when 50 grams of NaCl is added to 100 grams of H_2O at 20°C.

You are correct; good for you!

Since only about 36 grams of NaCl can dissolve in 100 grams of H_2O, 50 grams of NaCl *cannot* entirely dissolve in 100 grams of H_2O and the reaction *does not* go to completion. The double arrows ($\rightleftarrows$) *are* required to express this situation.

Until now we have written these solubility reactions showing water as a reactant and showing the hydration formula of each ion that is produced. This is a rather time-consuming way of writing these equations. Let's find an easier way.

(1) Throughout this chapter we shall deal with only one solvent, water. *As long as we remember and understand this fact,* there will be no harm in leaving out the xH_2O on the left side of the reaction.

(2) Since we should remember by now that *all ions in water solution are hydrated,* there will be no harm in leaving off the water of hydration of each ion. The water of hydration is always understood to be present.

With these points in mind, we can write the equation at the top of this page in a much simpler fashion, thus:

$$Na^+Cl^-_{(s)} \rightleftarrows Na^+ + Cl^-.$$

What is your interpretation of this last equation?

It is a less complex equation, but it represents exactly the same theoretical concept of what happens when NaCl dissolves in water as does the more complex equation previously discussed. **section 411**

It represents a less complicated theory of what happens when NaCl dissolves in H_2O than does the previous equation. **section 420**

437

[*from section 451*]

YOUR ANSWER: When equal volumes of 0.01 molar solutions of $MgCl_2$ and Na_2CO_3 are mixed, the ion product will be 1×10^{-4}.

You have overlooked something.

To start with, you have two solutions with these concentrations:

$$[Mg^{++}] = 0.01 \text{ molar};$$
$$[CO_3^{--}] = 0.01 \text{ molar}.$$

Apparently you simply multiplied these concentrations together to obtain your answer.

What you have overlooked is this: When equal quantities of two solutions are mixed, there is twice as much solution in the mixture as in either of the original solutions. However, the quantity of each ion remains unchanged. Therefore, the *concentration* of each ion in the mixture is exactly half as much as it was in the original solution.

Turn back to section 451, restudy it, and then choose another answer.

438

[*from section 456*]

YOUR ANSWER: For the reaction $Mg(OH)_{2(s)} \rightleftarrows Mg^{++} + 2OH^-$, the K_{sp} expression is

$$K_{sp} = [Mg^{++}]\,[2OH^-].$$

Sorry; not correct. The coefficients in an equation must appear as *exponents* of their respective concentrations when we write a K_{sp} expression.

Return to section 456 and choose your answer more carefully.

YOUR ANSWER: If a salt does not contain at least one of these seven ions, the rules do not tell whether it is insoluble and further information is necessary.

You are correct. If none of these seven ions appear in a salt, the above rules tell us nothing. $FeCl_2$, for example, does not contain any of the seven ions, and we must find another way of determining whether $FeCl_2$ is soluble.

SOLUBILITY TABLES

The best way to decide such a case is to look up the substance in a chemical reference book or in a table of solubility. Such a table is given as Table B in the Appendix of this TutorText* book.

Turn now to Table B and use it to answer the following question: Is $FeCl_2$ soluble in water?

$FeCl_2$ is soluble in water. **section 431**

$FeCl_2$ is not soluble in water. **section 447**

$FeCl_2$ is slightly soluble in water. **section 454**

---

* Trademark registered in U. S. Patent Office by U. S. Industries, Inc.

440

[from section 432]

YOUR ANSWER: $[Ag^+] = 6.3 \times 10^{-3}$ molar in a saturated solution of silver bromate.

You are correct!
From Table C:

$$AgBrO_3 \leftrightarrows Ag^+ + BrO_3^-; \; K_{sp} = [Ag^+][BrO_3^-] = 4.0 \times 10^{-5}.$$

$$\text{Let } [Ag^+] = x = BrO_3^-$$

$$\text{Hence } x^2 = 4.0 \times 10^{-5} = 40 \times 10^{-6}$$

$$\text{and } x = \sqrt{40 \times 10^{-6}} = 6.3 \times 10^{-3} \text{ molar.}$$

You are doing fine. Let us try a somewhat harder problem.
What is the concentration of Al^{+++} in a saturated solution of $Al(OH)_3$?

$[Al^{+++}] \cong$† 4.4×10^{-17} molar. section 423

$[Al^{+++}] \cong 2.9 \times 10^{-9}$ molar. section 430

$[Al^{+++}] \cong \sqrt[3]{1.9 \times 10^{-33}}$ molar. section 448

$[Al^{+++}] \cong \sqrt[4]{.071 \times 10^{-33}}$ molar. section 453

† Is approximately equal to.

441

[from section 411]

YOUR ANSWER: I don't understand how to handle this.

In section 411 the meaning and gradations of the word "soluble" were discussed; that is probably *not* your trouble.

It is more likely that you have forgotten how to determine the number of moles of $Ca(OH)_2$ there are in 0.5 gram of $Ca(OH)_2$.

The formula weight of $Ca(OH)_2$ is determined as follows:

Element	Number of Atoms	Atomic Weight	Total Weight
Ca	1	40	40
O	2	16	32
H	2	1	2
		Formula weight =	74

Hence 1 mole of $Ca(OH)_2 = 74$ grams.

$$(0.5 \text{ g } Ca(OH)_2)\left(\frac{1 \text{ mole } Ca(OH)_2}{74 \text{ g } Ca(OH)_2}\right) \cong\ddagger\ 0.007 \text{ mole of } Ca(OH)_2.$$

You should now be able to answer the question. Return to the beginning of section 411 and restudy carefully. Then try the question again.

‡ Is approximately equal to.

442

[*from section 431*]

YOUR ANSWER: Sodium chromate is very likely to be soluble in H_2O.

You are correct. The table does not contain the chromate ion; hence it gives us no information about the solubility of sodium chromate. But the general rules of solubility told you that *compounds containing the sodium ion are almost certain to be soluble;* hence Na_2CrO_4 is almost certainly a soluble compound.

The table of solubilities and the two general rules of solubility will enable you to decide in almost every case whether an ionic compound is soluble or insoluble. (Larger and more complete tables and lists are available in standard chemical reference handbooks.)

EQUILIBRIUM IN SOLUTIONS

Keeping in mind that all substances will dissolve in water at least to some slight extent, let us now consider what happens when we place in a liter of water more than 0.1 mole of a substance that is not soluble. As an example of such an insoluble substance, let us use silver chloride, AgCl:

$$AgCl_{(s)} \rightleftarrows Ag^+ + Cl^-.$$

Since we added more AgCl than can dissolve, you should recognize that the reaction cannot go to completion, and hence is an equilibrium reaction. This is indicated by the double arrows.

Since this is a reversible reaction, we can write an equilibrium expression for it. What is the equilibrium expression for the above reaction?

$K = \frac{[AgCl_{(s)}]}{[Ag^+][Cl^-]}$. **section 415**

$K = \frac{1}{[Ag^+][Cl^-]}$. **section 426**

$K = \frac{[Ag^+][Cl^-]}{[AgCl_{(s)}]}$. **section 434**

I don't remember how to write an equilibrium expression. Please give me some help. **section 457**

443

[*from section 428*]

YOUR ANSWER: Yes, a precipitate will form if the ion product for $MgCO_3 = 2.5 \times 10^{-5}$.

You are wrong. K_{sp} for $MgCO_3 = 4 \times 10^{-5}$, and this is *more than* 2.5×10^{-5}.

No precipitate forms unless the value of the ion product for the mixture is greater than K_{sp} for the salt being considered.

Return to section 428 and choose another answer.

444

[*from section 434*]

YOUR ANSWER: For the reaction $BaCO_{3(s)} \leftrightarrows Ba^{++} + CO_3^{--}$, the expression for K_{sp} is

$$K_{sp} = [Ba^{++}]^2 [CO_3^{--}]^3.$$

Sorry. You are wrong. The charges on the ions belong only inside the concentration brackets, and *never* as exponents. Remember: It is only the coefficients in an equilibrium equation that become exponents in equilibrium expressions.

Turn to section 434, restudy, and choose your answer more carefully.

445

[*from section 430*]

YOUR ANSWER: About 6.7×10^{-3} grams of $Ca(OH)_2$ can be dissolved in a liter of water.

You worked this problem perfectly up to a point, but you got careless and forgot about units.

The way you solved the problem,

$$x = [Ca^{++}] = 6.7 \times 10^{-3} \text{ moles/liter.}$$

But your answer *has to be* in grams, because the question called for grams.

Think about how you *convert* moles/liter to grams!

Now return to section 430 and choose a better answer.

446
[from section 456]

YOUR ANSWER: For the reaction $Mg(OH)_{2(s)} \leftrightarrows Mg^{++} + 2OH^-$, the K_{sp} expression is

$$K_{sp} = [Mg^{++}]\,[2OH^-]^2.$$

You are wrong! The coefficient of the OH^- *does* belong as the exponent of the concentration, but it does *not* belong inside the concentration brackets.

Turn to section 456 and be more careful.

447
[from section 439]

YOUR ANSWER: $FeCl_2$ is not soluble in water.

Your answer is incorrect; apparently, you do not understand how to use the table. $FeCl_2$ contains the Fe^{++} and the Cl^- ions. Look down the column of cations at the left until you come to Fe^{++}. Look across the row of anions at the top until you come to Cl^-. Find the location where these headings meet. What symbol appears at this location?

Return to section 439 and reconsider your choice of answers.

448
[from section 440]

YOUR ANSWER: $[Al^{+++}] \cong \sqrt[3]{1.9 \times 10^{-33}}$ molar in a solution of $Al(OH)_3$.

You are wrong.

You failed to notice that the equation is

$$Al(OH)_3 \rightleftharpoons Al^{+++} + 3OH^{-}.$$
If we let $x = [Al^{+++}]$,
then $3x = [OH^{-}]$.

With this hint, return to section 440 and choose a better answer.

449
[*from section 428*]

YOUR ANSWER: No, a precipitate will not form if the ion product for $MgCO_3$ equals 2.5×10^{-5}.

You are right!

$$K_{sp} = 4.0 \times 10^{-5}$$
$$\text{ion product} = 2.5 \times 10^{-5}$$

A precipitate forms if and only if the ion product > K_{sp}.

Will a precipitate of copper sulfide form if a solution containing 10^{-3} moles/liter of Cu^{++} ions is mixed with an equal quantity of a solution containing 10^{-4} moles/liter of S^{--} ions?

Yes, a precipitate will form. **section 429**

No, a precipitate will not form. **section 455**

450
[*from section 431*]

YOUR ANSWER: I can't tell, because the table does not contain the chromate ion.

The table does not contain the chromate ion; therefore the table will not answer this question for you. But you were advised to learn two general rules of solubility. These rules would have helped you answer the question.

Do this:

(1) Turn back to section 424 and restudy the solubility rules which you were told *should be learned*.

(2) Return to section 431 and answer the question more carefully.

451

[*from section 430*]

YOUR ANSWER: About 0.5 gram of $Ca(OH)_2$ can be dissolved in a liter of water.

You are correct. Good!

From Table C we learn:

$$Ca(OH)_2 \leftrightarrows Ca^{++} + 2OH^-; \; K_{sp} = [Ca^{++}][OH^-]^2 = 1.3 \times 10^{-6}.$$

We also know that

$$2[Ca^{++}] = [OH^-].$$

Let

$$x = [Ca^{++}] \text{ and } 2x = [OH^-].$$

Substituting,

$$K_{sp} = (x)(2x)^2 = 1.3 \times 10^{-6}$$
$$4x^3 = 1.3 \times 10^{-6}$$
$$x^3 = 0.3 \times 10^{-6}$$

$x = 0.67 \times 10^{-2} = 6.7 \times 10^{-3} = [Ca^{++}] =$ moles of $Ca(OH)_2$ per liter. $Ca(OH)_2$ weighs 74 grams per mole. Therefore,

$$\left(74 \frac{\text{grams}}{\text{mole}}\right)\left(6.7 \times 10^{-3} \frac{\text{moles}}{\text{liter}}\right) = 0.5 \text{ grams of } Ca(OH)_2 \text{ per liter.}$$

USING K_{sp} TO DETERMINE WHETHER A PRECIPITATE WILL FORM

Another important use of K_{sp} values is to calculate whether or not a precipitate will form if two solutions are mixed together. Suppose we mix together one liter of a 0.001-molar solution of NaCl and one liter of 0.001-molar $AgNO_3$; will a precipitate of AgCl form?

To answer this question, we must consider the concentrations of the Ag^+ and Cl^- ions, multiply them together, and compare the value obtained with the K_{sp} for AgCl.

When we mix equal quantities of the two solutions together, each dilutes the other to half its original concentration. Hence, the concentrations in the mixed solution become

$$[Ag^+] = 0.0005 = 5 \times 10^{-4} \text{ molar;}$$
$$[Cl^-] = 0.0005 = 5 \times 10^{-4} \text{ molar.}$$

Multiplying these two concentrations together gives us the *ion product* for the new solution:

$$\text{ion product} = [Ag^+][Cl^-] = 25 \times 10^{-8} = 2.5 \times 10^{-7}.$$

To determine whether a precipitate will form, we must compare the ion product with the K_{sp} value for AgCl. In an actual solution, the product of the ionic concentrations can never be greater than K_{sp}. If solutions of Ag^+ and Cl^- are mixed and the ion product is greater than the K_{sp} value for AgCl, a precipitate of AgCl will form until enough ions are removed from the solution to make the ion product of the residual concentrations just equal to the K_{sp} value.

The value of K_{sp} for AgCl is given as 1.6×10^{-10} in Table C. Since the ion product calculated above is greater than this, a precipitate will form when the two solutions are mixed.

Now you try this problem:

What will be the ion product of the Mg^{++} and CO_3^{--} ions if we mix equal volumes of 0.01 molar solutions of $MgCl_2$ and Na_2CO_3?

The ion product will be 2.5×10^{-5}. **section 428**

The ion product will be 1×10^{-4}. **section 437**

The ion product will be 4.0×10^{-5}. **section 458**

452

[*from section 432*]

YOUR ANSWER: $[Ag^+] = 2.0 \times 10^{-5}$ molar in a saturated solution of silver bromate.

You are wrong. Apparently you started out correctly, looking up the value of K_{sp} for $AgBrO_3$ and then writing an equation for the concentration of Ag^+ in terms of this value. But you seem to be uncertain about how to take the square root of a number that is expressed in exponential notation.

To take the square root of 4.0×10^{-5} (which is K_{sp} for $AgBrO_3$), follow these steps:

(1) Change 4.0×10^{-5} to its equal, 40×10^{-6}, so that the exponent of 10 will be an even number.

(2) Take the square root of 40:

$$\sqrt{40} = 6.3, \text{ approximately}$$

(3) Take the square root of 10^{-6}. To do so, simply write a power of ten in which the exponent is exactly half the original exponent:

$$\sqrt{10^{-6}} = 10^{-3}.$$

(Note that the exponent in the square root has the same sign as the exponent in the original number.)

(4) Multiply the two roots found in (1) and (2) to obtain the square root of the entire expression:

$$\sqrt{4.0 \times 10^{-5}} = 6.3 \times 10^{-3}.$$

Return to section 432 and try again.

453

[*from section 440*]

YOUR ANSWER: $[Al^{+++}] \cong \sqrt[4]{.071 \times 10^{-33}}$ molar in a saturated solution of $Al(OH)_3$.

What you state is true, but this is not a satisfactory form for your answer. Apparently, you are not sure how to take quartic (fourth) roots. Here's a hint:

Handle the number under the root sign as follows–

$$(10^3)(.071) \times (10^{-33})(10^{-3})$$

–and it becomes

$$71 \times 10^{-36}.$$

Now take the quartic root of each part of this number and multiply the roots together for your final answer.

Return to section 440 and choose another answer.

454

[*from section 439*]

YOUR ANSWER: $FeCl_2$ is slightly soluble in water.

Your answer is incorrect; apparently, you do not understand how to use the table. $FeCl_2$ contains the Fe^{++} and the Cl^- ions. Look down the column of cations at the left until you come to Fe^{++}. Look across the row of anions at the top until you come to Cl^-. Find the location where these headings meet. What symbol appears at this location?

Return to section 439 and reconsider your choice of answers.

455
[*from section 449*]

YOUR ANSWER: No, a precipitate will not form when 10^{-3} molar Cu^{++} and 10^{-4} molar S^{--} solutions are mixed.

You are wrong. Did you just guess, or did you make an error in your calculations?

Return to section 449 and *calculate* the ion product when these solutions are mixed. Then consider another answer.

456
[*from section 434*]

YOUR ANSWER: For the reaction $BaCO_{3(s)} \rightleftarrows Ba^{++} + CO_3^{--}$, the expression for K_{sp} is

$$K_{sp} = [Ba^{++}]\,[CO_3^{--}].$$

You are correct. You are doing fine.

Now consider this equation and determine the K_{sp} expression:

$$Mg(OH)_{2(s)} \rightleftarrows Mg^{++} + 2OH^-.$$

$K_{sp} = [Mg^{++}][OH^-]^2$ **section 432**

$K_{sp} = [Mg^{++}][2OH^-]$ **section 438**

$K_{sp} = [Mg^{++}][2OH^-]^2$ **section 446**

457
[*from section 442*]

YOUR ANSWER: I don't remember how to write an equilibrium expression. Please give me some help.

Of course. We covered this matter in Chapter 9. A reversible chemical equation can be written in general form as

$$aA + bB + cC \ldots \rightleftharpoons pP + qQ + rR \ldots$$

reactants products

K for this reaction is given by

$$K = \frac{[P]^p[Q]^q[R]^r \ldots}{[A]^a[B]^b[C]^c \ldots}$$

and is always written with *products in the numerator* and *reactants in the denominator.*

(If this is not sufficient information to refresh your memory about equilibrium constants, then you should return to Chapter 9 and restudy it carefully before going ahead with the present chapter.)

If you feel prepared to go ahead, return to section 442 and choose the correct answer.

458

[*from section 451*]

YOUR ANSWER: When equal volumes of 0.01 molar solutions of $MgCl_2$ and Na_2CO_3 are mixed, the ion product will be 4.0×10^{-5}.

No. 4.0×10^{-5} is the K_{sp} for $MgCO_3$, but the question asked for the *ion product* when specified solutions are mixed, and this is quite a different thing.

Restudy section 451 and select another answer.

459
[*from section 429*]

CHAPTER 11—IONIC SOLUBILITY REACTIONS AND EQUILIBRIA—SUMMARY

The solvent plays an important part in any solution process. All ions in water solution are hydrated, although we frequently do not show this in writing equations.

Solids dissolve in water only to a limited extent. We say the solid is *soluble* if more than about 0.1 mole will dissolve in a liter of water. The solid is *slightly soluble* if less than 0.1 mole, but still a measurable amount, dissolves. If no measurable amount dissolves, we call the material *insoluble*.

Any compound containing K^+, Na^+, NH_4^+, H^+, NO_3^-, ClO_3^-, or CH_3COO^- ions is almost certain to be soluble in water. A solubility chart is available for reference (Table B in the Appendix).

The *solubility-product constant, K_{sp},* is defined as the product of the concentrations of the ions of a slightly soluble ionic compound, as they exist in a saturated solution, each concentration being raised to a power corresponding to the number of that ion in the formula of the compound. In solutions which are less than saturated, this *ion product* is less than the K_{sp} value. K_{sp} values appear in Table C of the Appendix.

The K_{sp} can be used to calculate (1) the concentration of an ion in a saturated solution, (2) the amount of a salt that will dissolve per liter of water, and (3) whether or not a precipitate will form when two solutions of known concentrations are mixed.

Try the review questions in the next section.

CHAPTER 11—REVIEW QUESTIONS AND PROBLEMS

1. Write simplified equations showing the reaction of each of the following ionic solids dissolving in water:

KCl, $BaCl_2$, $AlCl_3$, $Al_2(SO_4)_3$.

2. Classify each of the following ionic solids as soluble, slightly soluble, or insoluble in water (refer to Table B in the Appendix):

KNO_3, $BaCl_2$, $PbCl_2$, $AgOH$, $Ag(CH_3COO)$, $Fe(NO_3)_3$, $AlCl_3$, $AlBr_3$, $Zn(OH)_2$, $BaSO_4$, $KMnO_4$.

3. Write K_{sp} expressions for: $BaSO_4$, $AgCl$, $PbCl_2$, $CuCO_3$, $AlBr_3$.

4. What is the concentration of:

(a) Ba^{++} ion in a saturated solution of $BaSO_4$?
(b) Ca^{++} ion in a saturated solution of $Ca(OH)_2$?
(c) OH^- ion in a saturated solution of $Ca(OH)_2$?

5. How many grams of $MgCO_3$ can be dissolved in a liter of water?

6. Will a precipitate form if equal volumes of a 0.002 M solution of Mg^{++} ions and a 0.006 M solution of CO_3^{--} ions are mixed?

Turn to section 554 for the answers, then go on to section 461.

Chapter 12

OXIDATION-REDUCTION EQUILIBRIA

REDOX REACTIONS

All chemistry students are familiar with examples of oxidation-reduction reactions long before they ever start to study chemistry. The rusting of iron, the burning of coal or oil, the tarnishing of silver, and the darkening of fruit (once its skin is removed) are everyday examples of oxidation-reduction reactions. We call such reactions *redox* reactions; *redox* is an abbreviation for the longer term oxidation-REDuction.

Redox reactions are always, in principle at least, reversible. Sometimes the equilibrium constant is so extremely large or extremely small that the reaction seems to go to completion or not to go at all. In other cases the redox reaction, which is reversible, is accompanied by side reactions, often caused by heat, so that the over-all process is not reversible. (Who would predict that ashes, carbon dioxide and water could recombine to form a piece of wood!) We will use the double arrows to indicate equilibrium in the redox reactions we shall study, unless we are restricting our thought to the process occurring in one direction only.

Now let us look at a few examples of redox equations:

$$4Fe + 3O_2 \rightleftharpoons 2Fe_2O_3$$
$$2Mg + O_2 \rightleftharpoons 2MgO$$
$$2Fe + 3Cl_2 \rightleftharpoons 2FeCl_3$$
$$2Cu + Br_2 \rightleftharpoons 2CuBr$$
$$Ca + S \rightleftharpoons CaS$$

Note that in each of these reactions, a *metal* combines with a *nonmetal,* and a binary compound results. (Not all redox reactions are between metals and nonmetals, but this makes a convenient way to introduce the subject.)

Which one of the following statements is *false?*

Each metal in the above equations loses electrons when the reaction takes place toward the right. **section 468**

No electron transfer takes place in these reactions. **section 473**

Each nonmetal in these equations gains electrons when the reaction takes place toward the right. **section 479**

462

[*from section 470*]

YOUR ANSWER: Both half-reactions, $Ca \longrightarrow Ca^{++} + 2e^-$, and $S + 2e^- \longrightarrow S^{--}$, are examples of redox.

No, this statement is really meaningless. A half-reaction is never referred to as "redox." This term is used to refer to *complete* (not half-) reactions, in which electron transfer has taken place. Every half-reaction is either an oxidation half-reaction or a reduction half-reaction. Your job in this question is to decide which is which.

Return to section 470 and select another answer.

463

[*from section 486*]

YOUR ANSWER: The reaction $Sn^{++} + 2e^- \longrightarrow Sn$ is a reduction half-reaction.

You are correct. The fact that Sn^{++} *gains electrons* is all we need to know to show that this is a reduction half-reaction.

These half-reactions, as we have seen previously, do not take place singly. The actual case is that *two* half-reactions, an oxidation half-reaction and a reduction half-reaction, take place at the same time. Such a combination of half-reactions is called an oxidation-reduction (redox) reaction. Let's look at an example.

Oxidation half-reaction:	$Ca \longrightarrow Ca^{++} + 2e^-$
Reduction half-reaction:	$S + 2e^- \longrightarrow S^{--}$
Adding them together:	$S + Ca \longrightarrow S^{--} + Ca^{++}$

Note that the two electrons disappear, or "cancel out."

REDOX RULES

Notice the following *redox rules* (*these must be learned*):

(1) The oxidation half-equation has electrons on the *right*.

(2) The reduction half-equation has electrons on the *left*.

(3) The complete redox equation has no electrons.

(4) The total number of electrons provided by the element that is oxidized exactly equals the total number of electrons acquired by the element that is reduced.

(5) The two half-equations that we combine to form a redox equation must be of opposite types; i.e., one must be a reduction and the other an oxidation.

What will be the redox reaction resulting from adding together the two half-reactions given below?

$$Zn \longrightarrow Zn^{++} + 2e^-$$
$$Cu^{++} + 2e^- \longrightarrow Cu$$

$Zn + Cu^{++} + 2e^- \rightarrow Zn^{++} + Cu + 2e^-$. **section 471**

$Zn + Cu^{++} \rightarrow Cu + Zn^{++}$. **section 489**

464

[*from section 473*]

YOUR ANSWER: Oxidation and reduction are independent reactions; a reaction may be of one type or the other, but not both.

No, you are mistaken. Suppose oxidation should take place alone: $Fe \longrightarrow Fe^{++} + 2e^-$. What would happen to the electrons? They have to go somewhere! Similarly, suppose reduction should take place alone: $O_2 + 4e^- \longrightarrow 2O^{--}$. Where would the electrons have come from? They would have had to come from somewhere! These oxidation *half-reactions* and reduction *half-reactions* provide a useful way of *analyzing* actual chemical reactions, but they *never* occur independent of each other.

With this in mind, return to section 473 and select another answer.

465
[*from section 489*]

YOUR ANSWER: $I_2 \longrightarrow 2I^- + 2e^-$ is correct.

No, you are wrong. Your half-reaction does not make sense. No equation or half-equation is ever balanced unless the sum of the charges shown is the same on both sides. According to the equation in your answer, $-4 = 0$!

You were correct in realizing that an oxidation half-equation must have the electrons on the right side, *but* we can't shift just the electrons from one side to the other. To convert a reduction half-reaction to its counterpart oxidation half-reaction, we shift the *entire* right side to the left and the *entire* left side to the right.

Return now to section 489 and choose a better answer.

466
[*from section 484*]

YOUR ANSWER: The net charge will become more positive if we take away some electrons.

You are correct. Let us work out a specific example: A copper atom is a neutral body consisting of 29 protons, 29 electrons, and about 35 neutrons. Thus the atom possesses 29 positive charges and 29 negative charges, resulting in a net charge of zero. If we take away any electrons (negatively charged, of course) the atom will be left with an excess of positive charges.

Which of the two following half-reactions is correct?

$Sn^{++} + 2e^- \rightarrow Sn^{++++}$. **section 472**

$Sn^{++} + 2e^- \rightarrow Sn$. **section 486**

467
[*from section 476*]

YOUR ANSWER: $Mg + Cl_2 + 2e^- \leftrightarrows Mg^{++} + 2Cl^- + 2e^-$ is a complete redox reaction.

Well, almost correct. Your reversal and addition of half-equations is correct, but in a redox equation there should not be any electrons shown. Notice that the same number of electrons appears on each side of the above equation. Subtract two electrons ($2e^-$) from each side of this equation and notice what the result is.

Turn back to section 476 and choose a better answer.

468
[*from section 461*]

YOUR ANSWER: The statement, "Each metal in the equations given loses electrons when the reaction takes place," is *false*.

You are mistaken; the statement is *not* false. The characteristic of a metal is that it has a small number of electrons in its outer shell. In any reactions it undergoes, it can lose these electrons (or some of them). This process, the *loss of electrons,* is called *oxidation,* the metal becomes *oxidized*.

Return to section 461 and select another answer to label "false."

469
[*from section 482*]

YOUR ANSWER: $2Al + 3Cu^{++} \rightleftarrows 2Al^{+++} + 3Cu$ is a complete redox equation.

You are correct. You reversed entry number 3 prior to adding it to number 8, and then you realized that something had to be done about the unequal number of electrons in the two half-reactions. The way to correct this difficulty is to multiply the Al half-reaction by 2 and the Cu half-reaction by 3, so that both show 6 electrons. Then the addition is:

$$\begin{array}{r} 2Al \rightleftarrows 2Al^{+++} + 6e^- \\ 6e^- + 3Cu^{++} \leftrightarrows 3Cu \\ \hline 2Al + 3Cu^{++} \leftrightarrows 2Al^{+++} + 3Cu \end{array}$$

Now let us return to the question of why the entry with the smaller number is the one to be reversed. This cannot be an arbitrary matter, of course, but must be based on chemical reasoning. This is comparable to the question that was raised in Chapter 10 in connection with a similar table of acids and bases.

In Table D,

Entry number 1 is $Na^+ + e^- \rightleftarrows Na$;
Entry number 10 is $Ag^+ + e^- \leftrightarrows Ag$.

From what you already know of the elements sodium and silver, which of them would you expect to be oxidized to the cation more readily?

Silver. **section 477**

Sodium. **section 485**

470

[*from section 488*]

YOUR ANSWER: No, a redox reaction does not always involve the element oxygen.

You are correct.

Let's analyze one of the redox reactions from section 461 more carefully. Consider this equation:

$$Ca + S \leftrightarrows CaS \text{ (or } Ca^{++}S^{--}\text{)}.$$

On the left we find uncharged atoms of the elements, whereas on the right we find *ions* of Ca^{++} and S^{--} combined in a crystal lattice in a ratio of 1 : 1. The neutral atom of Ca becomes doubly *positively* charged by the *loss* of two electrons:

$$Ca \longrightarrow Ca^{++} + 2e^-.$$

Similarly, the neutral S atom becomes doubly *negatively* charged by the *gain* of two electrons:

$$S + 2e^- \longrightarrow S^{--}.$$

Each of these last two expressions is a *half-reaction,* as previously defined (section 473).

Of the two half-reactions $Ca \longrightarrow Ca^{++} + 2e^-$ and $S + 2e^- \longrightarrow S^{--}$, which (if either) represents oxidation and which reduction, as written?

Both half-reactions are examples of redox. **section 462**

The half-reaction $S + 2e^- \rightarrow S^{--}$ is an example of reduction, while $Ca \rightarrow Ca^{++} + 2e^-$ is oxidation. **section 484**

The half-reaction $S + 2e^- \rightarrow S^{--}$ is an example of oxidation, while $Ca \rightarrow Ca^{++} + 2e^-$ is reduction. **section 491**

471

[*from section 463*]

YOUR ANSWER: $Zn + Cu^{++} + 2e^- \longrightarrow Zn^{++} + Cu + 2e^-$ is a correct redox reaction.

You are *almost* right. But remember that in a redox reaction the electrons do not appear.

Turn back to section 463, review the redox rules, and then try again.

472

[*from section 466*]

YOUR ANSWER: $Sn^{++} + 2e^- \longrightarrow Sn^{++++}$ is correct.

Sorry, you are wrong. "$2e^-$" stands for two electrons, with a net charge of −2. "Sn^{++}" means a tin ion with a charge of +2. Now you can't add +2 and −2 and get +4 as an answer! But that is what the symbol "Sn^{++++}" indicates in the answer above.

Turn back to section 466 and try again.

[*from section 461*]

YOUR ANSWER: The statement, "No electron transfer takes place in these reactions," is false.

You are correct, the statement *is* false. In fact, the loss and gain of electrons (the *transfer* of electrons) is the characteristic feature of all redox reactions. The common characteristic of metals is that they have a small number of electrons in their outer shells, whereas nonmetals lack one or more electrons of a complete inert-gas-like electron arrangement. The usual way a metal and a nonmetal react with each other is by transfer of electrons from metal to nonmetal.

HALF-REACTIONS

Chemists find it convenient to resolve reactions of this type into two *half-reactions,* in which the electrons are explicitly shown. For example, the chemical equation $2Fe + O_2 \rightleftarrows 2FeO$ can be resolved into these two half-reactions:

$$Fe \rightleftarrows Fe^{++} + 2e^-;$$
$$O_2 + 4e^- \rightleftarrows 2O^{--}.$$

The first of these half-reactions, which shows a *loss of electrons,* is an *oxidation* half-reaction; the second, showing a *gain of electrons,* is a *reduction* half-reaction.

Which of the following statements is *true?*

Oxidation and reduction are independent chemical reactions; a reaction may be of one type or the other, but not both. **section 464**

All chemical reactions *must* involve oxidation or reduction. **section 483**

Oxidation and reduction always occur together, never alone. **section 488**

474
[*from section 482*]

YOUR ANSWER: $Al + Cu^{++} \rightleftarrows Al^{+++} + Cu$ is a complete redox reaction.

Wait a minute now! You have followed the procedure that worked out all right for the previous equation, but it is not right here. The trouble stems from the fact that the two half-reactions given *do not have the same number of electrons*. You cannot cancel out three electrons in one half-equation against two electrons in the other!

Think about this; you should be able to figure out what to do about it. And remember that any equation or half-equation in which charges are shown must have the same net number of charges on both sides; otherwise it is not balanced properly. The "equation" in your answer above is not balanced in this sense.

Return to section 482 and try again.

475
[*from section 486*]

YOUR ANSWER: The reaction $Sn^{++} + 2e^{-} \longrightarrow Sn$ is an oxidation half-reaction.

Sorry. You appear to be confused or careless about this matter of oxidation and reduction. This *must* be clear in your mind if you are to succeed.

Turn to sections 473 and 488 and review this material carefully. Then return to section 486 and try again.

476
[*from section 489*]

YOUR ANSWER: $2I^{-} \longrightarrow I_2 + 2e^{-}$ is correct.

You are correct. Very good! We convert a reduction half-reaction to an oxidation half-reaction by simply reversing the sides of the half-reaction. In making this conversion we switch left for right and vice versa, but we make *no change within either side*.

Any of the half-reactions in our list will proceed or can be made to proceed in either direction. For this reason they are often written with double arrows!

WRITING REDOX EQUATIONS

It is necessary to make use of this reversal of direction when we want to combine two half-reactions by *adding* them together to form a complete redox reaction. For example, suppose we want to combine entries number 6 and number 8 of Table D. We write one of them (number 8) as it stands, and reverse the other (number 6), then add:

Number 6, reversed:	$Pb \rightleftarrows Pb^{++} + 2e^-$
Number 8:	$Cu^{++} + 2e^- \rightleftarrows Cu$
Add:	$Cu^{++} + Pb \rightleftarrows Pb^{++} + Cu$

Note that the $2e^-$, appearing on both sides, is eliminated.

It *does* make a difference *which* of the two half-reactions we reverse. We will return to this point a little later; for now, reverse the half-reaction with the smaller entry number. This procedure in reversing half-equations results in redox equations that will occur spontaneously.

Combine the following two half-reactions from Table D to form a complete redox reaction:

Entry number 2: $Mg^{++} + 2e^- \rightleftarrows Mg$
Entry number 12: $Cl_2 + 2e^- \leftrightarrows 2Cl^-$

What is the resulting complete redox reaction?

$Mg + Cl_2 + 2e^- \rightleftarrows Mg^{++} + 2Cl^- + 2e^-$ **section 467**

$Mg + Cl_2 \rightleftarrows Mg^{++} + 2Cl^-$ **section 482**

$Mg^{++} + 2Cl^- \rightleftarrows Mg + Cl_2$ **section 492**

477
[*from section 469*]

YOUR ANSWER: I would expect silver to be more readily oxidized to the cation than sodium.

Let's check this. Way back in this TutorText* course, you saw that sodium and silver are both *metals,* but are members of different classes of metals. Sodium is a highly active metal, while silver is one of the group called "noble" metals because they react with so few substances. Think about this a bit, and you will see why your answer is wrong.

Return to section 469 and try again.

* Trademark registered in U. S. Patent Office by U. S. Industries, Inc.

478
[*from section 484*]

YOUR ANSWER: There will be no effect on the net charge if we take away electrons.

No, you are wrong. Each electron carries a negative charge of 1 (i.e., a charge of −1). If we add or remove electrons, that certainly *will* have an effect on the net charge of the atom or ion.

Return to section 484 and select another answer.

479
[*from section 461*]

YOUR ANSWER: The statement, "Each nonmetal in the equations given gains electrons when the reaction takes place," is *false.*

You are mistaken; the statement is *not* false. The characteristic of a nonmetal is that it lacks a few electrons of a complete inert-gas-like arrangement. In any reactions it undergoes, a nonmetal can only gain electrons (or at least a share in some electrons). This process, the *gain of electrons,* is called *reduction;* the nonmetal becomes *reduced.*

Return to section 461 and select another answer to label "false."

480

[*from section 485*]

YOUR ANSWER: $Pb^{++} + Zn \longrightarrow Pb + Zn^{++}$ is a spontaneous reaction.

You are correct. Zn is *above* Pb in the table, which means that Zn is more easily oxidized than Pb and can be oxidized by the Pb^{++} ion itself.

Go on now to the summary in section 494.

481

[*from section 488*]

YOUR ANSWER: Yes, a redox reaction always involves the element oxygen.

Not so. Look back at the sample redox reactions given in section 461, and you will see that although some redox reactions do involve oxygen, many do not. However, there is always some element that plays a role similar to that of oxygen. Chlorine, bromine, and sulfur are familiar elements that can accept electrons in the same way that oxygen can.

Return to section 488 and try again.

482

[*from section 476*]

YOUR ANSWER: $Mg + Cl_2 \rightleftharpoons Mg^{++} + 2Cl^-$ is a complete redox reaction.

You are correct. You have correctly reversed the half-reaction of entry number 2, and added it to number 12:

$$\begin{array}{c} Mg \rightleftharpoons Mg^{++} + 2e^- \\ Cl_2 + 2e^- \rightleftharpoons 2Cl^- \\ \hline Cl_2 + Mg \rightleftharpoons Mg^{++} + 2Cl^- \end{array}$$

(Note that the electrons are eliminated.)

Now let us try another similar problem, but one that involves one more feature.

Consider entries number 3 and number 8 in Table D.

Entry number 3: $Al^{+++} + 3e^- \rightleftharpoons Al$
Entry number 8: $Cu^{++} + 2e^- \rightleftharpoons Cu$

Combine these two entries into a complete redox reaction.

$2Al + 3Cu^{++} \rightleftharpoons 2Al^{+++} + 3Cu$ **section 469**

$Al + Cu^{++} \rightleftharpoons Al^{+++} + Cu$ **section 474**

$3Al + 2Cu^{++} \rightleftharpoons 3Al^{+++} + 2Cu$ **section 487**

483

[*from section 473*]

YOUR ANSWER: All chemical reactions *must* involve oxidation or reduction.

No. Remember those acid-base reactions which we studied in Chapter 10? They involved transfer of a *proton* from one species to another, but not transfer of *electrons*.

Now go back to section 473 and select another answer.

484

[*from section 470*]

YOUR ANSWER: The half-reaction $S + 2e^- \longrightarrow S^{--}$ is an example of reduction, while $Ca \longrightarrow Ca^{++} + 2e^-$ is oxidation.

You are correct. According to our definitions in section 473, oxidation is the *loss of electrons,* reduction is the *gain of electrons.* You have correctly identified the two half-reactions given.

The distinction between oxidation and reduction is just as important to chemistry as the distinction between acids and bases. You must remember it carefully.

Let us see whether we can figure out what happens when an atom or an ion *loses* one or more electrons; i.e., when the atom or ion is *oxidized.* Every atom or ion is composed of a group of protons, neutrons, and electrons: protons are positively charged particles; neutrons are neutral particles; and electrons are negatively charged particles.

What will happen to the net charge on the group if we take away electrons?

The net charge will become more positive if we take away electrons.
section 466

There will be no effect on the *net* charge if we take away electrons.
section 478

The net charge will become more negative if we take away electrons.
section 493

485

[*from section 469*]

YOUR ANSWER: I would expect sodium to be more readily oxidized to the cation than silver.

You are correct. Sodium is one of the most active of metals, and hence is very easily made to lose an electron and become the cation Na^{+}. Silver, on the other hand, is one of the "noble" metals, so-called because they react only with difficulty.

The entries in Table D are carefully arranged so that the species on the *right* (reducing agents) decrease from top to bottom in their ease of reaction; in other words, the strongest reducing agent in the list is *sodium,* Na.

It also follows from this arrangement that the species on the *left* (oxidizing agents) are weakest at the top and strongest at the bottom of the table.

Thus we can state that *any reducing agent will react spontaneously with any oxidizing agent that is lower in the table*. But we must always remember that all these reactions are reversible, and hence in principle never go 100 per cent to completion (unless some product is removed as soon as it is formed).

The principle just stated requires that when two half-reactions are to be added to give a *spontaneous* redox reaction, it must be the higher one in this table that is reversed.

By reference to Table D, decide which of the following two equations is a spontaneous reaction.

$Pb^{++} + Zn \rightarrow Pb + Zn^{++}$ **section 480**

$Zn^{++} + Pb \rightarrow Zn + Pb^{++}$ **section 490**

486

[*from section 466*]

YOUR ANSWER: $Sn^{++} + 2e^- \longrightarrow Sn$ is correct.

You are correct. Sn^{++} has a charge of +2; $2e^-$ have a charge of −2; adding gives a net charge of 0.

Is the reaction $Sn^{++} + 2e^- \longrightarrow Sn$ an oxidation half-reaction or a reduction half-reaction?

It is a reduction half-reaction. **section 463**

It is an oxidation half-reaction. **section 475**

487

[*from section 482*]

YOUR ANSWER: $3Al + 2Cu^{++} \rightleftarrows 3Al^{+++} + 2Cu$ is a complete redox equation.

No. You realized that something must be done about the fact that the two half-reactions show different numbers of electrons, 3 and 2, but you handled the difficulty the wrong way. When you add the two half-equations, they *must* have the same number of electrons, as otherwise you cannot cancel the electrons out against each other. Remember, too, that any equation that shows charges *must* have the same net number of charges on each side; otherwise it is not balanced properly. The "equation" in your answer above is *not balanced,* and if it is not balanced it is incorrect.

Now return to section 482, think this over carefully, and try again.

488

[*from section 473*]

YOUR ANSWER: Oxidation and reduction always occur together, never alone.

You are correct. Electrons cannot be lost in oxidation without being gained in a simultaneous reduction. That is why chemists talk about "oxidation-reduction" reactions (redox reactions). Half-reactions, whether oxidation or reduction, provide a useful means of studying actual reactions, but they can never occur independent of each other.

It is easy to see where the term *oxidation* came from: oxidation is often the combination of something with oxygen. *Reduction* does not have quite so obvious a derivation; we must simply remember that it is the opposite of oxidation.

Does a redox reaction always involve the element oxygen?

No. **section 470**

Yes. **section 481**

489
[*from section 463*]

YOUR ANSWER: $Zn + Cu^{++} \longrightarrow Cu + Zn^{++}$ is a correct redox equation.

You are correct; very good!

HALF-REACTION TABLES

To simplify writing redox equations and to predict whether or not they will take place, chemists have compiled tables of half-reactions. We have prepared such a table (in shortened form) for your use with this TutorText* course.

Table D in the Appendix lists some important half-reactions. All of these are written as reductions; i.e., with the electrons appearing on the left side of each half-reaction. Any of these half-reactions can be converted to the oxidation form of the same half-reaction very easily. Let's try making such a conversion.

Entry number 9 in the table is $I_2 + 2e^- \longrightarrow 2I^-$. If this is converted into the oxidation form, what is the correct expression?

$I_2 \rightarrow 2I^- + 2e^-$. **section 465**

$2I^- \rightarrow I_2 + 2e^-$. **section 476**

* Trademark registered in U. S. Patent Office by U. S. Industries, Inc.

490
[*from section 485*]

YOUR ANSWER: $Zn^{++} + Pb \longrightarrow Zn + Pb^{++}$ is a spontaneous reaction.

Wrong! Zn is *above* Pb in the table. This means that Zn is more easily oxidized than Pb; there is a greater tendency for Zn to become a cation than for Pb, and a greater tendency for Pb to remain as the neutral atom than for Zn.

Think this over, then return to section 485, and try again.

491

[*from section 470*]

YOUR ANSWER: The half-reaction $S + 2e^- \longrightarrow S^{--}$ is an example of oxidation, while $Ca \longrightarrow Ca^{++} + 2e^-$ is reduction.

No. How did we define oxidation? "Oxidation is the loss of electrons." The half-reaction $S + 2e^- \longrightarrow S^{--}$ describes a process of gaining two electrons by a neutral sulfur atom to produce a doubly charged negative ion. Does that meet the definition of oxidation? Think it over.

Return to section 470 and select another answer.

492

[*from section 476*]

YOUR ANSWER: $Mg^{++} + 2Cl^- \rightleftharpoons Mg + Cl_2$ is a complete redox reaction.

Your work is correct except for one point! You reversed the wrong equation. Go back to section 476 and reread the last sentences before the question; then try another answer.

493

[*from section 484*]

YOUR ANSWER: The net charge will become more negative if we take away electrons.

Well, let us review a bit about atomic structure. For example:

A copper atom is a neutral body consisting of 29 protons, 29 electrons, and about 35 neutrons. The 29 protons have a total of 29 positive charges; the 29 electrons have a total of 29 negative charges; the 35 neutrons have no charge. Hence the net charge (+29 −29 +0) is zero. But if we take away one electron from this atom, the net charge will become (+29 −28 +0), which is +1.

The answer you chose was wrong. Turn again to section 484 and restudy. Then choose another answer.

CHAPTER 12—OXIDATION-REDUCTION EQUILIBRIA—SUMMARY

Oxidation is the *loss* of electrons; *reduction* is the *gain* of electrons. Oxidation and reduction must always occur *simultaneously*, since the *net* electron change must always be zero.

A *half-reaction* is one which shows electrons explicitly on one side or the other. For example,

$$Cu \rightleftarrows Cu^{++} + 2e^-$$
$$Fe^{++} \rightleftarrows Fe^{+++} + e^-$$

These two half-reactions are oxidations if read left to right, but reductions if read from right to left. Two reduction half-reactions can be added together to form a complete reaction, if one of them is first reversed, left for right.

If it is desired to obtain a complete reaction which will take place spontaneously, then the half-reaction which is *lower* in Table D in the Appendix should be written as a *reduction;* that which is *higher* should be written as an *oxidation.* Then, many times, one or both must be multiplied through by numerical constants so that both will involve the same number of electrons. Then they can be added with complete cancellation of electrons, to give the required complete equation. Once the electrons gained and lost have been made equal by numerical multipliers, then the rest of the balancing task will fall into place readily by inspection.

Now try the following review questions.

495
[*from section 494*]

CHAPTER 12—REVIEW QUESTIONS AND PROBLEMS

1. Indicate which of the following half-reactions are oxidations, as written, and which are reductions:

(a) $Ba \longrightarrow Ba^{++} + 2e^-$
(b) $Pt^{++} + 2e^- \longrightarrow Pt$
(c) $Sn^{++++} + 2e^- \longrightarrow Sn^{++}$
(d) $2I^- \longrightarrow I_2 + 2e^-$
(e) $2H_3O^+ + 2e^- \longrightarrow 2H_2O + H_2$
(f) $Ag + Cl^- \longrightarrow AgCl + e^-$

2. By reference to the table of half-reactions, determine whether the following reactions will occur *spontaneously* in the direction indicated:

(a) $Pb + Cu^{++} \longrightarrow Cu + Pb^{++}$
(b) $Br_2 + 2Cl^- \longrightarrow Cl_2 + 2Br^-$
(c) $2H^+ + 2I^- \longrightarrow H_2 + I_2$
(d) $I_2 + 2Ag \longrightarrow 2AgI$
(e) $Br_2 + 2Ag \longrightarrow 2AgBr$

3. Balance the following redox equations:

(a) $Fe^{+++} + Sn^{++} \longrightarrow Fe^{++} + Sn^{++++}$
(b) $Fe^{++} + Ce^{++++} \longrightarrow Fe^{+++} + Ce^{+++}$
(c) $Ni^{++} + Br_2 \longrightarrow Ni^{++++} + Br^-$
(d) $Cu + H^+ + NO_3^- \longrightarrow Cu^{++} + NO_2 + H_2O$
(e) $Cu + HNO_3 \longrightarrow Cu(NO_3)_2 + NO_2 + H_2O$

Turn to section 555 for answers, then go on to section 496.

Chapter 13
ELECTROCHEMISTRY

Michael Faraday, early in the nineteenth century, discovered a very important relationship between chemistry and electricity. This relationship depends upon the part played by electrons in a redox process (oxidation-reduction reaction), coupled with the fact that a flow of electrons can be produced, controlled, and measured accurately by methods of physics. The outgrowth of Faraday's discoveries is the science of *electrochemistry.*

ELECTROCHEMICAL REACTIONS

In this chapter, you will learn about two general types of electrochemical reactions. In the first type, an electric current causes a chemical reaction to take place. In the second type, a chemical reaction causes an electric current to flow. Thus, the two types of electrochemical reactions can be thought of as opposites.

To study electrochemistry, you must have an elementary knowledge of current electricity. Test yourself on this subject by answering the following question:

Two of the five statements below are incorrect. Study all five and pick out the incorrect ones.

(a) An electric current in a metallic conductor (such as a wire) consists of electrons in motion.

(b) In general, any electric current consists of electric charges (or charged bodies) in motion.

(c) Current will flow through a wire when it is connected across a source of potential.

(d) An electric current can never flow unless a complete metallic circuit is provided.

(e) Whenever electrons flow in one direction in a wire, protons must flow in the opposite direction.

Statement (a) is incorrect. **section 501**

Statement (b) is incorrect. **section 506**

Statement (c) is incorrect. **section 513**

Statement (d) is incorrect. **section 523**

Statement (e) is incorrect. **section 529**

497

[*from section 516*]

YOUR ANSWER: The electroplating of copper can be characterized by the term *reduction.*

You are correct. We have previously defined reduction as the combination of electrons with some atomic or ionic species, and this clearly is an example. We can write for it the half-reaction

$$Cu^{++} + 2e^{-} \longrightarrow Cu,$$

which emphasizes this relationship.

But this is only half the story. Notice the following parallel: (1) There are *two* electrodes, and we have only considered one of them; (2) we have emphasized previously that the processes of oxidation and reduction can only take place *simultaneously*. Clearly, the process taking place at the other electrode (i.e., the *positive* one) must be *oxidation.*

The complete oxidation-reduction reaction just described is an example of the general class of reactions known as *electrolysis:* the discharge of both the positive and the negative ions of a compound at the same time.

What process would you expect to occur at the positive electrode when current is passed through a solution of $CuBr_2$, as above?

$Cu \rightarrow Cu^{++} + 2e^{-}$. **section 507**

$2Br^{-} \rightarrow Br_2 + 2e^{-}$. **section 517**

$CuBr_2 \rightarrow Cu + Br_2$. **section 524**

498

[*from section 517*]

YOUR ANSWER: Since the nitrate ion cannot be oxidized, no reaction will occur at the positive electrode when electricity is passed through a solution of a nitrate.

No. A chemical process *must* occur at each electrode whenever electricity is passed through a solution. Furthermore, at the positive electrode, only an *oxidation* process can occur. If the nitrate ion cannot be oxidized, then something else must be. What else is present that might be able to release electrons to the electrode?

Think about this. Then return to section 517 and try again.

499

[*from section 526*]

YOUR ANSWER: The reduction potential of zinc is −0.76 volt.

You are correct. The numerical value is obtained by subtracting 1.23 from 1.99; the sign is negative because a more negative voltage is needed to reduce Zn^{++} ions than H^{+} ions.

The voltage figures given here for the various reduction potentials are exact only if the solutions are all of unit concentration: i.e., 1 molar. More advanced chemistry books show how the voltages can be corrected mathematically for different concentrations. The values given here are referred to as $E°$ values. This symbol should be read "E standard."

$E°$ values have been measured for many half-reactions. A tabulation of $E°$ values is given in Table D in the Appendix. This table lists the half-reactions as reductions, and so the corresponding $E°$'s are *reduction potentials.* We saw in Chapter 12 that it is possible to convert an oxidation half-reaction to a reduction half-reaction, and vice versa. Whenever this is done, the algebraic *sign* of the $E°$ value, but *not* its numerical value, is changed.

Just as we can add up two half-reactions to get a redox reaction, so we can add the corresponding $E°$ values to get a voltage corresponding to the entire reaction. For example, we can add together the two following half-reactions:

$$\begin{array}{rll} Cl_2 + 2e^- \longrightarrow 2Cl^-; & E° = +1.36 \text{ volts.} \\ Zn \longrightarrow Zn^{++} + 2e^-; & E° = +0.76 \text{ volt.} \\ \hline Zn + Cl_2 \longrightarrow Zn^{++} + 2Cl^-; & E° = +2.12 \text{ volts.} \end{array}$$

What voltage could you get from the redox reaction

$$2Ag^+ + Fe \longrightarrow 2Ag + Fe^{++}?$$

+0.36 volt. **section 508**

+1.24 volts. **section 520**

+2.04 volts. **section 536**

500

[*from section 520*]

YOUR ANSWER: The $E°$ for a redox reaction is unrelated to the tendency for it to take place spontaneously.

No, you have not thought this through adequately. We saw, in Chapter 12, that when the elements are arranged as in Table D, with the most active reducing agents at the top and the most active oxidizing agents at the bottom, this order can be utilized to predict spontaneity of reactions. Now we should see that the $E°$ values of the elements follow *the same sequence*. There *must* be a significant relation between the $E°$ of a reaction and the tendency of that reaction to occur.

Think this over, then return to section 520 and choose again.

501

[*from section 496*]

YOUR ANSWER: Statement (a), which says, "An electric current in a metallic conductor (such as a wire) consists of electrons in motion," is an incorrect statement.

No; this statement *is* correct. Since you don't understand this, turn to section 518, where you will find a brief summary of the pertinent electrical phenomena.

502

[*from section 509*]

YOUR ANSWER: $2Ag^+ + Cu \longrightarrow Cu^{++} + 2Ag$ is a spontaneous reaction; its $E°$ value is +0.46 volt.

You are correct. +0.34 is "more negative" than +0.80, and you were correct in changing it to −0.34 and reversing the corresponding half-reaction before adding. Thus the two half-reactions, ready to add, are:

$$Cu \longrightarrow Cu^{++} + 2e^-; \quad E° = -0.34 \text{ volt.}$$
$$2Ag^+ + 2e^- \longrightarrow 2Ag; \quad E° = +0.80 \text{ volt.}$$

Adding these together gives the following redox equation:

$$2Ag^+ + Cu \longrightarrow Cu^{++} + 2Ag; \quad E° = +0.46 \text{ volt.}$$

You should realize that *any* oxidation half-reaction can be combined with *any* reduction half-reaction to give a balanced redox reaction. By the sign of the $E°$ value for such a redox reaction, we can tell whether or not it will take place spontaneously. (If not, it may still be a useful reaction, as we shall see presently.)

Add together the following half-reactions *as they are written,* compute $E°$, and state whether or not the reaction is spontaneous:

$$Zn \longrightarrow Zn^{++} + 2e^-; \quad E° = +0.76 \text{ volt.}$$
$$Cu^{++} + 2e^- \longrightarrow Cu; \quad E° = +0.34 \text{ volt.}$$

It is spontaneous. **section 521**

It is not spontaneous. **section 540**

503

[from section 521]

YOUR ANSWER: The reaction

$$2Cr^{+++} + 3Sn \longrightarrow 2Cr + 3Sn^{++}$$

is spontaneous.

No, you are mistaken. Let us add the two half-reactions:

$$\begin{array}{rl} 3Sn \longrightarrow 3Sn^{++} + 6e^{-}; & E° = +0.14 \text{ volt.} \\ 2Cr^{+++} + 6e^{-} \longrightarrow 2Cr; & E° = -0.74 \text{ volt.} \\ \hline 2Cr^{+++} + 3Sn \longrightarrow 2Cr + 3Sn^{++}; & E° = -0.60 \text{ volt.} \end{array}$$

(Notice that the half-equations had to be multiplied by 3 and 2, respectively, so that the electrons would cancel out.)

The resulting $E°$ for the redox reaction is *negative*. What does that tell you about the reaction?

Return to section 521 and choose another answer.

504

[from section 516]

YOUR ANSWER: The electroplating of copper can be characterized by the term *oxidation*.

Your trouble is either not understanding the present situation, or forgetting the definitions of oxidation and reduction.

Note that in the present situation, positive copper ions (Cu^{++}) are combining with electrons to give neutral Cu atoms. Is this oxidation or reduction? If you are not sure, refer to the definitions of oxidation and reduction given in section 473 in the preceding chapter.

Think this over, return to section 516, and try another answer.

505

[*from section 517*]

YOUR ANSWER: Nitrate ions will be reduced at the positive electrode when electricity is passed through a solution of a nitrate.

No. The only process that can occur at the *positive* electrode is *oxidation*. If the nitrate ion cannot be oxidized, then something else must be. What else is present that might be able to release electrons to the electrode?

Think this over, then return to section 517 and try again.

506

[*from section 496*]

YOUR ANSWER: Statement (b), which says, "In general, any electric current consists of electric charges (or charged bodies) in motion," is an incorrect statement.

No; this statement *is* correct. Since you don't understand this, turn to section 518, where you will find a brief summary of the pertinent electrical phenomena.

507

[*from section 497*]

YOUR ANSWER: The process occurring at the positive electrode will be $Cu \longrightarrow Cu^{++} + 2e^-$.

No. This is indeed an example of oxidation, but it can't occur at the positive electrode in this experiment; there are no neutral copper atoms present at that electrode, which you remember is made of platinum, not copper. There must be some other oxidation process occurring.

Return to section 497 and try again.

508
[*from section 499*]

YOUR ANSWER: The redox reaction

$$2Ag^{+} + Fe \longrightarrow 2Ag + Fe^{++}$$

would give +0.36 volt ($E°$).

No, you have not calculated it correctly. Check back on the algebraic signs! Then return to section 499 and select another answer.

509
[*from section 520*]

YOUR ANSWER: A positive $E°$ value for a redox reaction indicates a spontaneous reaction.

You are correct. This is consistent with the method of predicting spontaneity used in Chapter 12, prior to consideration of voltages. We can now state in another way the rule by which we determine which half-reaction to reverse to obtain a spontaneous reaction:

Reverse that half-reaction which has the more negative E° *value.*

Combine the following two half-reactions taken from the table in such a way as to produce a *spontaneous* reaction, and compute the $E°$ value for the reaction:

$$Cu^{++} + 2e^{-} \longrightarrow Cu; \quad E° = +0.34 \text{ volt.}$$
$$Ag^{+} + e^{-} \longrightarrow Ag; \quad E° = +0.80 \text{ volt.}$$

Choose the correct result below:

$2Ag^{+} + Cu \rightarrow Cu^{++} + 2Ag$; $E° = +0.46$ volt. **section 502**

$Cu + 2Ag^{+} \rightarrow Cu^{++} + 2Ag$; $E° = +1.14$ volts. **section 532**

$2Ag + Cu^{++} \rightarrow Cu + 2Ag^{+}$; $E° = +0.46$ volt. **section 537**

510

[*from section 530*]

YOUR ANSWER: Solid $CuBr_2$ will be deposited at the negative electrode.

No, this is not right. This would only happen if *both* copper ions (Cu^{++}) and bromide ions (Br^-) were to move in the *same direction,* namely toward the negative electrode. Since unlike charges attract, it is reasonable to suppose that the positive Cu^{++} ions would move to the negative electrode, but what about the Br^- ions?

Think this over, return to section 530, and try again.

511

[*from section 522*]

YOUR ANSWER: 16.1 moles of sodium can be prepared electrolytically with 6000 coulombs of electric charge.

No, this is not right. You must have made a mistake in arithmetic, such as inverting a factor.

Check your work carefully, then return to section 522 and try again.

512

[*from section 527*]

YOUR ANSWER: The electrode on which chromium is to be deposited should be attached to the *positive* terminal of the external source, the tin electrode to the negative.

No. Would you expect the positive chromium ions (Cr^{+++}) to be attracted to the *positive* electrode?

Think this over, then return to section 527, and select another answer.

513

[*from section 496*]

YOUR ANSWER: Statement (c), which says, "For current to flow through a wire, a source of potential (or voltage) must be connected across it," is an incorrect statement.

No; this statement is correct. Since you don't understand this, turn to section 518, where you will find a brief summary of the pertinent electrical phenomena.

514

[*from section 526*]

YOUR ANSWER: The reduction potential of zinc is -1.99 volts.

No. The algebraic sign is right; zinc must be made at the negative electrode relative to hydrogen. But you have not given the numerical value correctly. It must be relative to hydrogen, too.

Return to section 526 and try again.

515

[*from section 539*]

YOUR ANSWER: Three electrons will be required to deposit 1 mole of metallic chromium.

No, three electrons would only permit the deposition of one *atom* of chromium, not 1 mole!

Return to section 539 and choose another answer.

516

[*from section 530*]

YOUR ANSWER: Elementary copper will be deposited at the negative electrode.

You are correct. Only the positive ions (Cu^{++}) can move toward the negative electrode, and hence be deposited there.

The negative electrode, you will remember, is connected to the negative pole of the battery, which is the pole from which electrons flow out of the battery. These electrons move along through the connecting wires to the negative electrode, where they are available to unite with Cu^{++} ions, neutralizing their two + charges and thus forming neutral copper atoms. Neutral copper atoms, of course, are not soluble in water and therefore precipitate as bulk metal, which often adheres firmly to the metal electrode as *copper plating*.

By what chemical term would you characterize the process just described (electroplating of copper from an ionic solution of Cu^{++})?

Reduction. **section 497**

Oxidation. **section 504**

517

[*from section 497*]

YOUR ANSWER: The process occurring at the positive electrode will be $2Br^- \longrightarrow Br_2 + 2e^-$.

You are correct. This is an example of an oxidation half-reaction, and is the one that would be expected to take place in the experiment described.

Whether the half-reaction above will be the *only* oxidation taking place or not depends on other factors, including especially the *concentrations* of bromide ions and of any other species present that may be oxidizable. For instance, the hydroxide ion can be oxidized according to the half-reaction

$$4OH^- \longrightarrow 2H_2O + O_2 + 4e^-,$$

and since hydroxide ions are always present to some extent in water solutions, it is always possible that some oxygen will be liberated.

It becomes clear, then, that we must have some quantitative way of determining which half-reactions will take place preferentially. We looked into this in Chapter 12, when we were talking about redox reactions in general, not produced specifically by electricity. We can now extend this treatment, using easily made electrical measurements to help us answer the questions that arise.

Suppose we set up a series of experiments similar to that just described, the electrolysis of $CuBr_2$, but using the nitrates of several different metals—namely $NaNO_3$, $Al(NO_3)_3$, $Zn(NO_3)_2$, $Cu(NO_3)_2$, and $AgNO_3$. (The reason for selecting nitrates rather than bromides or chlorides is that all nitrates are soluble in water, whereas AgCl and AgBr are insoluble.) Now it so happens that the nitrate ion cannot be oxidized from water solution as bromide and chloride can.

What chemical process will occur at the *positive* electrode when electricity is passed through a solution of a nitrate?

Since the nitrate ion cannot be oxidized, no reaction will occur. **section 498**

Nitrate ions will be reduced. **section 505**

Oxygen will be liberated. **section 526**

518

[*from sections 501, 506, 513, 523*]

REVIEW OF CURRENT ELECTRICITY

In section 7, we presented a review emphasizing the *electrostatic* aspect of electricity—that is, the attraction of unlike charges and the repulsion of like charges. Now we are concerned with *electric cur-*

rent, which is quite another phase of the subject. The two aspects of electricity complement each other.

Consider a battery lantern. It contains a complete electrical circuit consisting of one or more batteries, a switch, a lamp bulb, and various metallic conductors. (See Figure 26)

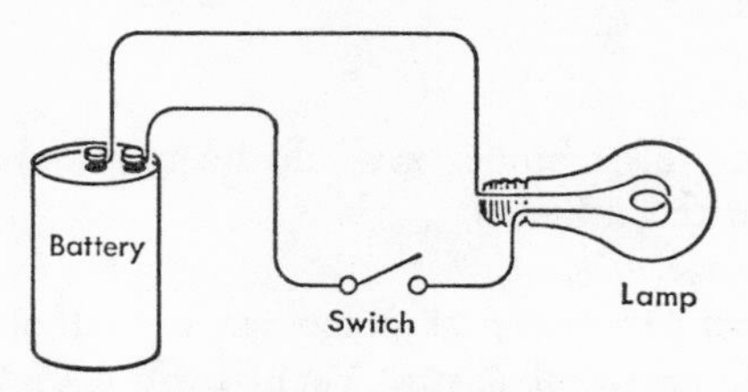

Figure 26. Simple electrical circuit.

The battery is a source of *potential* (also called *voltage,* because potential is measured in *volts*). As soon as the switch is closed, electrons commence to flow from the metal case of the battery, through the switch and the lamp bulb, and back into the battery through its center pole. This flow of electrons is an *electric current.*

In general, we can describe an electric current as a sustained *motion of electric charges.* The charges involved may be positive, negative, or both. Electric current flowing in a metallic conductor (such as a wire) consists of a stream of negative electrons moving through the crystalline lattice of the metal. The positive atomic nuclei of the metal are not free to move, so the electrons alone must carry the current. In conducting liquids and gases, however, both positively and negatively charged particles are free to move, and current is carried by both simultaneously.

You will need to understand three aspects of electricity, each having a corresponding unit of measurement: (1) *potential,* measured in *volts;* (2) *current,* measured in *amperes;* and (3) *charge* (or *quantity of charge*), measured in *coulombs.*

Potential is a measure of "electrical pressure," or the tendency to produce a current. The higher the potential applied across a wire, for example, the greater the current through the wire will be.

Current, in a quantitative sense, is the quantity of charge passing a given point in a circuit per unit of time. Current (in amperes) equals quantity of charge transferred (in coulombs) divided by time (in seconds). Thus,

$$\text{amperes} = \frac{\text{coulombs}}{\text{seconds}} \quad \text{and} \quad \text{coulombs} = \text{amperes} \times \text{seconds}.$$

With this summary to help you, return to section 496 and try again.

519

[from section 535]

YOUR ANSWER: 32.2 amperes would be required to deposit 21.6 grams of silver in ten minutes.

You are correct. In the first place we note that 21.6 grams is $21.6/108 = 0.200$ moles of silver. Then, by use of the dimensional method (Chapter 4),

$$(0.2 \text{ moles})\left(96500 \frac{\text{coulombs}}{\text{mole}}\right)\left(\frac{1 \text{ ampere-second}}{\text{coulomb}}\right)\left(\frac{1}{10 \text{ minutes}}\right)$$
$$\left(\frac{1 \text{ minute}}{60 \text{ seconds}}\right) = \frac{0.2 \times 96500}{10 \times 60} \text{ amperes} = 32.2 \text{ amperes}.$$

Turn to section 542 for a review of the material in this chapter, and then try the review problems in section 543. You will then have completed your elementary study of electrochemistry, and your TutorText* journey through chemistry as well. We hope it has been interesting to you as well as useful.

* Trademark registered in U. S. Patent Office by U. S. Industries, Inc.

520

[from section 499]

YOUR ANSWER: The redox reaction

$$2Ag^{+} + Fe \longrightarrow 2Ag + Fe^{++}$$

would give +1.24 volts ($E°$).

You are correct. You took two entries from the table, namely:

$$Fe^{++} + 2e^{-} \longrightarrow Fe; \quad E° = -0.44 \text{ volt.}$$
$$Ag^{+} + e^{-} \longrightarrow Ag; \quad E° = +0.80 \text{ volt.}$$

To combine these, you must reverse the first half-reaction, changing the sign of its $E°$ at the same time. Then you must double the second half-reaction (but *not* its $E°$), and add the two:

$$\begin{array}{rl} Fe \longrightarrow Fe^{++} + 2e^-; & E° = +0.44 \text{ volt.} \\ 2Ag^+ + 2e^- \longrightarrow 2Ag; & E° = +0.80 \text{ volt.} \\ \hline 2Ag^+ + Fe \longrightarrow 2Ag + Fe^{++}; & E° = +1.24 \text{ volts.} \end{array}$$

Remember well: The $E°$ value for the silver half-reaction is *not* doubled when the half-equation *is* doubled; the voltage does *not* depend on the number of moles taken.

What relation do you think there is between the $E°$ for a redox reaction and the tendency for the reaction to take place spontaneously?

No relation. **section 500**

A positive voltage indicates a spontaneous reaction. **section 509**

A negative voltage indicates a spontaneous reaction. **section 533**

521

[*from section 502*]

YOUR ANSWER: The resulting reaction,

$$Zn + Cu^{++} \longrightarrow Zn^{++} + Cu,$$

is spontaneous.

You are correct. The $E°$ value for the reaction is the sum of +0.76 and +0.34, which is +1.10 volts; the sign is *positive,* which means the reaction *is* spontaneous.

ELECTROCHEMICAL CELLS

It is often possible to arrange electrodes and solutions so that the electrons involved in such a redox reaction are transferred from the reducing agent (here it is Zn) to the oxidizing agent (Cu^{++}) not by direct contact, but through electrical wiring. Such a setup is called an *electrochemical cell,* or sometimes a *galvanic cell* or (colloquially) a *battery*. The voltage that such a cell can produce is calculated as above (assuming that the various chemicals are in 1-molar concentration). The combination of copper and zinc with solutions of copper and zinc sulfates makes an excellent battery, called the *Daniell cell,* which was widely used in the early days of telegraphy.

Now, let's try another reaction. Add together the following half-reactions, compute $E°$, and tell whether the resulting reaction is spontaneous or not:

$$Sn \longrightarrow Sn^{++} + 2e^-; \quad E° = +0.14 \text{ volt.}$$
$$Cr^{+++} + 3e^- \longrightarrow Cr; \quad E° = -0.74 \text{ volt.}$$

The reaction *is* spontaneous. **section 503**

The reaction is *not* spontaneous. **section 527**

522

[*from section 539*]

YOUR ANSWER: Three times Avogadro's number of electrons will be required to deposit 1 mole of metallic chromium.

You are correct. In the half-equation

$$Cr^{+++} + 3e^- \longrightarrow Cr,$$

the electron (e^-) can be considered as a *reactant*. (In the oxidation half-equations, it can similarly be considered as a *product*.) The coefficients of reactants and products represent the relative numbers of *moles* of the various substances. Hence we can logically speak of *moles of electrons,* and we will define the mole of electrons as one Avogadro's number of electrons (6.02×10^{23} electrons). This quantity of electrons is so important that it has been given another name, the *faraday*. The electric charge carried by one faraday of electrons has been shown by experiment to be approximately 96,500 coulombs. You will recall that coulombs are equal to amperes times seconds.

Metallic sodium is prepared commercially by the electrolysis of molten salt. How many moles of sodium can be obtained by this method if 6000 coulombs are utilized?

16.1 moles. **section 511**

1 mole. **section 528**

0.0622 mole. **section 535**

523
[*from section 496*]

YOUR ANSWER: Statement (d) "An electric current can never flow unless a complete metallic circuit is provided," is an incorrect statement.

You are correct; the statement is false. Electric currents can flow under suitable circumstances through gases (think of lightning!), through a vacuum (as in radio tubes), or through liquids. A *metallic* circuit need not be provided.

This is one of the two incorrect statements; have you found the other one? If so, then turn to section 530. If not, then go back to section 496 and continue the hunt. If you are unable to locate another erroneous statement, then you had better go to section 518, where you will find a brief review of the pertinent electrical phenomena.

524
[*from section 497*]

YOUR ANSWER: The process occurring at the positive electrode will be $CuBr_2 \longrightarrow Cu + Br_2$.

No; you should be looking for an *oxidation* process. Which is this, oxidation or reduction? (Answer: It is both!)

Return to section 497, think this over carefully, and try another answer.

525

[*from section 535*]

YOUR ANSWER: 0.0062 ampere would be required to deposit 21.6 grams of silver in ten minutes.

No, this is not right. You have inverted a factor. This is an easy mistake to make if you don't use the dimensional method of Chapter 4.

Check your work carefully and return to section 535 to select another answer.

526

[*from section 517*]

YOUR ANSWER: Oxygen will be liberated at the positive electrode when electricity is passed through a solution of a nitrate.

You are correct. The only process that can take place at the positive electrode is oxidation. The nitrate ion cannot be oxidized; the metal ion (Na^+, Al^{+++}, etc.) is already in its oxidized state. The only other substance present that can possibly be oxidized is the water. Water therefore gives up electrons to the electrode, and oxygen is liberated. The equation for this half-reaction is

$$2H_2O \longrightarrow 4e^- + 4H^+ + O_2.$$

REDUCTION POTENTIALS

Now let us consider what happens at the *negative* electrode. Take first a solution of silver nitrate. If you start with no voltage between the electrodes and gradually raise the applied voltage, you will find that no current at all flows until you reach approximately 0.43 volt; above this voltage, the current increases markedly. In a similar experiment with copper nitrate, the voltage required to cause current to flow is 0.89 volt; for zinc nitrate, the corresponding voltage is 1.99

volts. If you try the experiment with aluminum nitrate, about 2.5 volts is required; but something is different here, because you notice a gas appearing at the negative electrode, which was not true with the other experiments.

Now compare this series of metals with Table D. You will see immediately that the metals fall in the same order in the table and the series of voltages. You have already seen that the relative positions of metals in the table determines the direction in which a reaction will go spontaneously. Now we can make this quantitative by assigning to each metal a voltage that is a measure of the driving force required to reduce ions of that metal to neutral atoms. The voltages we assign are called *reduction potentials.*

Instead of using immediately the voltages we found in the experiments described, we will make one more measurement first. We will imagine another experiment, exactly like those we have done previously, but with *nitric acid* (i.e., hydrogen nitrate) in place of a metal nitrate. In this experiment, hydrogen gas is released at the negative electrode. The voltage needed to cause a current to flow will be found to be about 1.23 volts, which will place hydrogen between copper and zinc in the table. By international agreement, the voltage value for the reduction of H^+ ions to H_2 gas is taken arbitrarily as zero, and all other reduction potentials are given relative to hydrogen. Reduction potentials of substances above hydrogen are regarded as positive and those below as negative. Remember that $2H^+ + 2e^- \longrightarrow H_2$ is our arbitrarily assigned standard with the value of zero volts.

What is the reduction potential of zinc?

−0.76 volt. **section 499**

−1.99 volts. **section 514**

+0.76 volt. **section 534**

527
[from section 521]

YOUR ANSWER: The reaction

$$2Cr^{+++} + 3Sn \longrightarrow 2Cr + 3Sn^{++}$$

is *not* spontaneous.

You are correct. To add the two half-reactions, we must first multiply through by 3 and 2, respectively, so that the electrons will cancel out. Thus we have:

$$\begin{array}{rl} 3Sn \longrightarrow 3Sn^{++} + 6e^{-}; & E^{\circ} = +0.14 \text{ volt.} \\ 2Cr^{+++} + 6e^{-} \longrightarrow 2Cr; & E^{\circ} = -0.74 \text{ volt.} \\ \hline 2Cr^{+++} + 3Sn \longrightarrow 2Cr + 3Sn^{++}; & E^{\circ} = -0.60 \text{ volt.} \end{array}$$

The negative E° value means that the reaction is *not* spontaneous.

Since this reaction is not spontaneous, it cannot serve as a source of electrical energy. However, this does not mean that it lacks significance in electrochemistry. The reaction can still be forced to take place, even though it is not spontaneous, simply by passing an electric current through the cell from some outside source. The voltage of the outside source must be *greater* in absolute magnitude than the negative E° of the reaction.

To make this reaction take place, should the electrode on which chromium is to be deposited be attached to the *negative* or to the *positive* terminal of the external source of electricity?

To the positive terminal. **section 512**

To the negative terminal. **section 539**

528
[*from section 522*]

YOUR ANSWER: 1 mole of sodium can be prepared electrolytically with 6000 coulombs of electric charge.

No. The half-equation $Na^+ + e^- \longrightarrow Na$ shows 1 mole of sodium, but you have to take into account the amount of electric charge used; 6000 coulombs of charge is not equivalent to one faraday.

Think about this, then return to section 522, and try again.

529
[*from section 496*]

YOUR ANSWER: Statement (e), which says, "Whenever electrons flow in one direction in a wire, protons must flow in the opposite direction," is an incorrect statement.

You are correct, the statement *is* false. In a metallic conductor, such as a wire, the only protons present are those in the nuclei of the atoms of the metal, and they are *not* free to move.

This is one of the two incorrect statements; have you found the other one? If so, then turn to section 530. If not, then go back to section 496 and continue the hunt. If you are unable to locate another erroneous statement, then you had better go to section 518, where you will find a brief review of the pertinent electrical phenomena.

530
[*from section 529*]

REACTIONS CAUSED BY CURRENT

Let us consider what happens when an electric current is passed through a water solution of an ionic compound. (See Figure 27) We will choose copper bromide, $CuBr_2$, as an example. The experimental arrangement will look something like the accompanying sketch. Suppose the connections to the solution are made through two *electrodes* made of a metal that is essentially *inert;* i.e., a metal that will not react chemically with anything present. Platinum will come close enough to meeting the requirement of inertness.

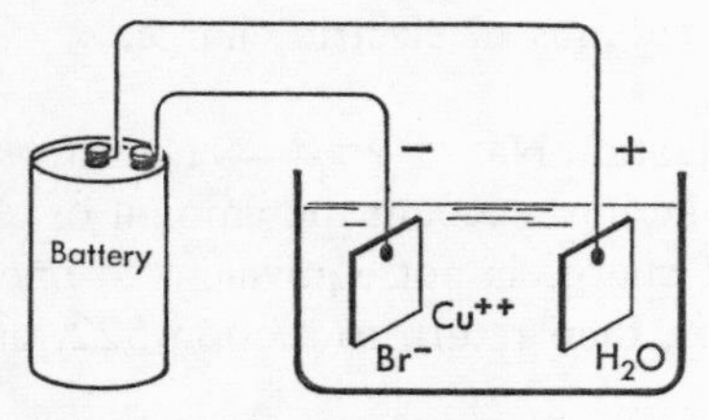

Figure 27. Electrolytic cell.

What would you predict will happen (chemically) at the *negative* electrode?

Solid $CuBr_2$ will be deposited. **section 510**

Elementary Cu will be deposited. **section 516**

Elementary Br_2 will be liberated. **section 538**

531

[*from section 539*]

YOUR ANSWER: Avogadro's number of electrons will be required to deposit 1 mole of metallic chromium.

No. You correctly surmise that Avogadro's number must be involved, but what about that "three"? The half-reaction shows that three electrons are required to deposit a single atom of chromium. Avogadro's number is the number of atoms per mole.

Think this over and return to section 539 to choose another answer.

532

[*from section 509*]

YOUR ANSWER: $Cu + 2Ag^+ \longrightarrow Cu^{++} + 2Ag$ is a spontaneous reaction; its $E°$ is +1.14 volts.

No; your answer is wrong. You failed to make one of the changes you should have made before performing the addition.

Look over your work to see whether you can find your error. Then return to section 509 and choose another answer.

533

[*from section 520*]

YOUR ANSWER: A negative $E°$ value for a redox reaction indicates a spontaneous reaction.

Not so! This answer contradicts your correct answer to the previous question.

Look back at section 520 again, study it carefully, then choose another answer.

534

[*from section 526*]

YOUR ANSWER: The reduction potential of zinc is +0.76 volt.

No, that is not right. The numerical value is all right, but how can you justify that + sign?

Go back to section 526 and try again.

535
[*from section 522*]

YOUR ANSWER: 0.0622 mole of sodium can be prepared electrolytically with 6000 coulombs of electric charge.

You are correct; 6000 coulombs is 6000/96,500 of a faraday, or 6000/96,500 of a mole. Hence, this same fraction of a mole of sodium can be produced, namely 0.0622 mole.

Now let's try another.

How many amperes of electric current would be required to deposit 21.6 grams of silver in a period of ten minutes?

32.2 amperes. **section 519**

0.0062 ampere. **section 525**

1930 amperes. **section 541**

536
[*from section 499*]

YOUR ANSWER: The redox reaction

$$2Ag^{+} + Fe \longrightarrow 2Ag + Fe^{++}$$

would give +2.04 volts ($E°$).

No. You made the mistake of *doubling* one of the half-reaction $E°$ values when you doubled the chemical equation. You *never* should do this. Any given reaction or half-reaction corresponds to a particular $E°$, without regard to the number of moles taken.

Return to section 499 and select another answer.

537

[from section 509]

YOUR ANSWER: $2Ag + Cu^{++} \longrightarrow Cu + 2Ag^{+}$ is a spontaneous reaction; its $E°$ value is +0.46 volt.

No. You have computed the voltage correctly, though it is difficult to understand how you managed to, since you based your work on a wrong equation. Apparently, two wrongs made a right this time.

Look over your work with care; try to discover your mistake. Then return to section 509 and choose another answer.

538

[from section 530]

YOUR ANSWER: Elementary Br_2 will be liberated at the negative electrode.

No, you are mistaken. This answer would imply that bromide ions, which are *negative*, will move toward the *negative* electrode! Would this be likely? Remember: like charges repel, and unlike charges attract.

Think it over, then return to section 530 and try again.

539

[from section 527]

YOUR ANSWER: The electrode on which chromium is to be deposited should be attached to the *negative* terminal of the external source, the tin electrode to the positive.

You are correct. The negative electrode will attract to itself the Cr^{+++} ions, which will be neutralized by electrons coming from the external source. At the positive electrode, tin atoms will give up two electrons each to the external circuit and pass into solution as Sn^{++} ions. (In a practical laboratory setup, the tin electrode would be surrounded by a porous cup to prevent Sn^{++} ions from reaching the negative electrode.)

Consider further the half-reaction

$$Cr^{+++} + 3e^- \longrightarrow Cr.$$

How many electrons will be required to deposit by electrolysis 1 mole (52 grams) of metallic chromium?

Three electrons. **section 515**

Three times Avogadro's number of electrons. **section 522**

Avogadro's number of electrons. **section 531**

540

[*from section 502*]

YOUR ANSWER: The resulting reaction,

$$Zn + Cu^{++} \longrightarrow Zn^{++} + Cu,$$

is *not* spontaneous.

No; it *is* spontaneous, so your answer is incorrect. If you add together the two half-reactions, you obtain this:

$$\begin{array}{rl} Zn \longrightarrow Zn^{++} + 2e^-; & E° = +0.76 \text{ volt.} \\ Cu^{++} + 2e^- \longrightarrow Cu; & E° = +0.34 \text{ volt.} \\ \hline Zn + Cu^{++} \longrightarrow Zn^{++} + Cu; & E° = +1.10 \text{ volts.} \end{array}$$

The resulting $E°$ value is *positive*. What should this tell you about the reaction?

Return to section 502 and select another answer.

[*from section 535*]

YOUR ANSWER: 1930 amperes would be required to deposit 21.6 grams of silver in ten minutes.

No, this is not right. Have you perhaps forgotten to convert minutes to seconds? You ought to use the dimensional method of Chapter 4 to avoid this sort of error.

Check your work again, and return to section 535 to choose another answer.

CHAPTER 13—ELECTROCHEMISTRY—SUMMARY

An *electrode* is a piece of metal wire or foil inserted into a solution containing ionized solutes. Electricity can flow through the solution and an external circuit by way of a pair of electrodes.

Chemical *reduction* will take place at one electrode, as electrons leave the electrode and combine with some reducible species from the solution, for example the Cu^{++} ion:

$$Cu^{++} + 2e^{-} \longrightarrow Cu$$

Metallic copper is *plated* on the electrode in this process.

At the other electrode, *oxidation* occurs, as electrons leave an oxidizable species and pass into the electrode, for example:

$$2Br^{-} \longrightarrow Br_2 + 2e^{-}$$

The combined process (reduction and oxidation) is called *electrolysis*.

The relative tendency to be reduced electrolytically is measured by the *reduction potential* in volts. The process

$$2H^{+} + 2e^{-} \longrightarrow H_2$$

is taken arbitrarily as zero volts. Elements more active than hydrogen are given a *negative* reduction potential; those less active are *positive*. Such potentials are listed in Table D in the Appendix as $E°$ values, which refer to the potential of the metal electrode when dipping into a *1 molar* solution of a salt of the same metal.

An *oxidation potential* can be obtained simply by changing the sign of $E°$.

Just as half-reactions can be added together to give complete reactions, so can the corresponding $E°$ values be added to give a potential corresponding to the complete reaction. This will be the potential available from the two electrodes and their corresponding solutions when assembled as a *cell* (sometimes called a *battery*). For example:

$$
\begin{array}{ll}
Cl_2 + 2e^- \longrightarrow 2Cl^- & E^\circ = +1.36 \text{ volts} \\
Zn \longrightarrow Zn^{++} + 2e^- & E^\circ = +0.76 \text{ volt} \\
\hline
Zn + Cl_2 \longrightarrow Zn^{++} + 2Cl^- & E^\circ = +2.12 \text{ volts}
\end{array}
$$

If one half-reaction has to be doubled (in order to equate electrons with another half-reaction), the voltage should *not* be doubled. Thus the following two voltages are both correct:

$$
\begin{array}{ll}
Ag^+ + e^- \longrightarrow Ag & E^\circ = +0.80 \text{ volt} \\
2Ag^+ + 2e^- \longrightarrow 2Ag & E^\circ = +0.80 \text{ volt}
\end{array}
$$

A positive E° value for a complete reaction indicates a *spontaneous* reaction. To obtain a spontaneous reaction from two half-reactions, reverse the more negative and add them.

A nonspontaneous reaction can be forced to take place by running current through the cell backwards.

In a half-reaction, electrons can be considered to be a reactant (or product). One mole (6.02×10^{23}) of electrons is given the name of one *faraday*. The corresponding quantity of electric charge is very nearly 96,500 coulombs.

543
[from section 542]

CHAPTER 13—REVIEW QUESTIONS AND PROBLEMS

1. By combining half-reactions from Table D (Appendix), write spontaneous reactions and their corresponding $E°$ values for cells constructed of the following electrodes and their appropriate solutions:
(a) Na and Ag
(b) Al and Cu
(c) Fe and Br_2
(d) I_2 and Cl_2
(e) Mg and Ag

2. How many coulombs of electricity would be required to deposit 1 mole of silver from a solution of $AgNO_3$?

3. How many faradays are needed to deposit 2 moles of copper from a solution of $CuSO_4$?

4. How many grams of cadmium would be deposited from a solution of $CdCl_2$ by passage of 10,000 coulombs?

Turn to section 556 for answers.

CHAPTER 1—ANSWERS TO QUESTIONS

1. Chlorine, symbol Cl, atomic number 17, atomic weight 35.45.
Cadmium, symbol Cd, atomic number 48, atomic weight 112.40.
Chromium, symbol Cr, atomic number 24, atomic weight 52.00.
Carbon, symbol C, atomic number 6, atomic weight 12.01.

2. Mn, manganese, atomic number 25, atomic weight 54.94.
Mg, magnesium, atomic number 12, atomic weight 24.31.
Mo, molybdenum, atomic number 42, atomic weight 95.94.
Hg, mercury, atomic number 80, atomic weight 200.59.
H, hydrogen, atomic number 1, atomic weight 1.01.

3. Carbon: the isotope of mass number 12 has 6 electrons, 6 protons, and 6 neutrons.
Oxygen: the isotope of mass number 16 has 8 electrons, 8 protons, and 8 neutrons.
Calcium: the isotope of mass number 40 has 20 electrons, 20 protons, and 20 neutrons.

4. It is an isotope of silver.

5. If an atom contained more electrons than protons it would have a net negative electric charge; if the opposite were true, it would have a net positive charge. But since atoms are electrically neutral, neither of these conditions can be correct. On the other hand, an ion *does* have a charge, and hence must have an excess of either electrons or protons.

6. Phosphorus has 2 electrons in the 1*s* orbital, 2 in the 2*s*, 6 in the 2*p*, 2 in the 3*s*, and one in each of the three 3*p* orbitals.

545
[*from section 69*]

CHAPTER 2—ANSWERS TO QUESTIONS

1. Actinide metals: Fm, U
Lanthanide metals: Ce, Ho
Transition metals: Fe, Mo, Pt, Zr
Other metals: Al, Ba, Ca, K, Na, Rb
Nonmetals: Cl, I, N, O, P, S
Metalloids: As, C, Ge
Noble gases: Kr, He

2. Br lacks one electron of Kr.
Rb has one electron more than Kr.
Sr has two electrons more than Kr.
Br is a halogen.
Rb is an alkali metal.
Sr is an alkaline earth metal.

3. Rb is more metallic than Na, Na than Mg, O than F, Se than Br, Sb than As, Ra than Ca, Al than B, Bi than I, Bi than N, and Ge than As.

4. Co, Ni; Te, I; Ar, K.
In each the normal mixture of isotopes is such that on the average the element with more protons has fewer neutrons.

CHAPTER 3—ANSWERS TO QUESTIONS

1. In ionic bonds electrons are actually *transferred* from one atom to another, while in a covalent bond, electrons are *shared* in pairs between two atoms.

2. Ionic: NaCl, FeI_3, MgO, NaH, SrF_2.
Covalent: C_2H_4, NH_3, CCl_4, H_2O, $C_6H_{12}O_6$.

3. Barium fluoride, BaF_2
Aluminum bromide, $AlBr_3$
Silicon chloride, $SiCl_4$
Actinium chloride, $AcCl_3$
Magnesium oxide, MgO
Aluminum oxide, Al_2O_3
Radium sulfide, RaS
Potassium iodide, KI

4. Ionic crystal: A solid consisting of a regular three-dimensional array in which alternating positions are occupied by positive and negative ions. Examples: NaCl, MgO.

Hydrogen bond: a link formed between two active nonmetals (N, O, or F) by a hydrogen atom which is covalently bound to one of them and attracted electrostatically by the other.

Examples: Water: H–O–H···O–H···O–H···

```
                 |     |
                 H     H
```

Hydrogen fluoride: ···H–F···H–F···H–F···
(The dots represent electric attraction.)

Molecular association: The hanging together in clumps or groups of polar molecules, sometimes through hydrogen bonding. Examples: Water, hydrogen fluoride, as above.

Complex ion: One which contains more than a single atom, the group as a whole bearing the electric charge. Examples: sulfate, SO_4^{--}; hydroxide, OH^-; ammonium, NH_4^+.

547
[*from section 153*]

CHAPTER 4—ANSWERS TO QUESTIONS

1. There are 1000 seconds in one kilosecond.

2. The ratio $\frac{1 \text{ minute}}{60 \text{ seconds}}$ has the value 1, and is therefore a correct conversion factor. The others are incorrect.

3. A "mole" is a "package" of 6.02×10^{23} units.

4. $50 \text{ A.} \left(\frac{10^{-8} \text{ cm}}{1 \text{ A.}}\right) = 50 \times 10^{-8} = 5.0 \times 10^{-7}$ cm.

$$50 \text{ A.} \left(\frac{10^{-8} \text{ cm}}{1 \text{ A.}}\right)\left(\frac{1 \text{ inch}}{2.54 \text{ cm}}\right) = \frac{5.0}{2.54} \times 10^{-7} \text{ inch}$$
$$= 1.97 \times 10^{-7} \text{ inch.}$$

5. The charge on a single electron is the $\frac{1}{6.02 \times 10^{23}}$ part of a faraday;

$$\left(\frac{1}{6.02 \times 10^{23}} \text{ faraday}\right)\left(\frac{96{,}500 \text{ coulombs}}{1 \text{ faraday}}\right) = \frac{9.65 \times 10^{4}}{6.02 \times 10^{23}} \text{ coulomb}$$
$$= 1.59 \times 10^{(4-23)} \text{ coulomb} = 1.59 \times 10^{-19} \text{ coulomb.}$$

6. A formula represents a grouping of atoms, and it represents *one mole of such a grouping.*

CHAPTER 5—ANSWERS TO QUESTIONS

1. 32°F = 0°C = 273°K
140°C = 413°K
−40°C = 233°K
22°C = 295°K
100°C = 373°K

2. (a) $(0.29 \text{ liter})\left(\frac{273°K}{303°K}\right)\left(\frac{800 \text{ mm of Hg}}{760 \text{ mm of Hg}}\right) = 0.275$ liter at STP

(b) $(22.4 \text{ liters})\left(\frac{273°K}{295°K}\right)\left(\frac{760 \text{ mm of Hg}}{760 \text{ mm of Hg}}\right) = 20.72$ liters at STP

(c) $(10 \text{ liters})\left(\frac{273°K}{283°K}\right)\left(\frac{10 \text{ atm}}{1 \text{ atm}}\right) = 96.4$ liters at STP

3. 65 grams at STP occupies 52 liters;
1 mole at STP must occupy 22.4 liters;
hence 65 grams must be 52/22.4, or 2.32 moles;
therefore, 1 mole weighs

$$\left(\frac{65 \text{ grams}}{2.32 \text{ mole}}\right) = 28 \text{ grams/mole;}$$

the molecular weight of the gas is 28.

4. $(39.7 \text{ liters})\left(\frac{273°K}{300°K}\right)\left(\frac{700 \text{ mm of Hg}}{760 \text{ mm of Hg}}\right) = 33.3$ liters at STP;
this weighs 66 grams, and we know that 22.4 liters would weigh 1 molecular weight. Therefore the molecular weight is

$$(66 \text{ grams})\left(\frac{22.4 \text{ liters/mole}}{33.3 \text{ liters}}\right) = 44.4 \text{ grams/mole}$$

5. 22.4 liters (at STP) weighs one molecular weight;
therefore, 1 liter weighs 1/22.4 times the molecular weight.

Hydrogen:	2/22.4 = 0.09 grams/liter
Helium:	4/22.4 = 0.18 grams/liter
Carbon dioxide:	44/22.4 = 1.98 grams/liter
Carbon monoxide:	28/22.4 = 1.25 grams/liter
Uranium hexafluoride:	352/22.4 = 15.8 grams/liter

6. $(50 \text{ ml})\left(\frac{273°K}{297°K}\right)\left(\frac{750 \text{ mm of Hg} - 22 \text{ mm of Hg}}{760 \text{ mm of Hg}}\right) = 44.1$ ml.

This weighs $(44.1 \text{ ml})(0.090 \text{ grams/liter})\left(\frac{1 \text{ liter}}{1000 \text{ ml}}\right)$

$$= \frac{(44.1)(0.090)}{(1000)} = 0.0040 \text{ gram} = 4.0 \text{ mg.}$$

549
[*from section 257*]

CHAPTER 6—ANSWERS TO QUESTIONS

1. (a) There are 1000 ml in 1 liter.
(b) There is approximately 1 quart in 1 liter.
(c) There is 1 mole of solute in 1 liter of a 1 M solution.
(d) There are 6 moles of solute in 3 liters of a 2 M solution.
(e) There is 0.2 mole of solute in 0.5 liter of a 0.4 M solution.
(f) There is 0.24 mole of solute in 400 ml of a 0.6 M solution.

2. (a) The solution is 0.75 M.
(b) The solution is 0.17 M.
(c) The solution is 0.40 M.
(d) The solution is 0.30 M.

3. (a) 208 grams of $BaCl_2$.
(b) 6.06 grams of KNO_3.
(c) 36.0 grams of LiCl.

4. (a) The ratio is 2 : 1, $AgNO_3$ to $BaCl_2$.
(b) There is 0.05 mole of $BaCl_2$ in the solution.
(c) 0.10 mole of $AgNO_3$.
(d) 100 ml of 1 M $AgNO_3$.
(e) 200 ml of 0.2 M $BaCl_2$.
(f) 0.36 M $BaCl_2$ solution.

5. $$\left(\frac{32.7 \text{ grams Zn}}{65.4 \text{ grams Zn/mole Zn}}\right)\left(\frac{2 \text{ moles HCl}}{1 \text{ mole Zn}}\right)\left(\frac{1 \text{ liter}}{6 \text{ moles HCl}}\right)\left(\frac{1000 \text{ ml}}{1 \text{ liter}}\right)$$
= 167 ml, the volume of HCl solution required.

CHAPTER 7—ANSWERS TO QUESTIONS

1. (a) False (f) False
(b) True (g) False
(c) False (h) True
(d) True (i) True
(e) False (j) True

2. (a) The reaction is exoergic.
(b) $Q = +10{,}850$ cals.
(c) $\Delta H = -10{,}850$ cals.
(d) ΔH of combustion $= -10{,}850$ cals/mole.
(e) ΔH of reaction $= -5{,}425$ cals per mole of oxygen.

3. (a) The reaction is exoergic.
(b) $2CO + O_2 \longrightarrow 2CO_2 + 68{,}000$ cals.
(c) ΔH of combustion $= -34$ Kcal/mole.
(d) ΔH of reaction $= -68$ Kcal per mole of oxygen.

4.

	$2C + 2O_2 \longrightarrow 2CO_2$	$\Delta H = -188$ Kcal.
Subtract:	$2CO + O_2 \longrightarrow 2CO_2$	$\Delta H = -136$ Kcal.
	$2C + O_2 - 2CO \longrightarrow$ (nothing)	
Same as:	$2C + O_2 \longrightarrow 2CO$	$\Delta H = -52$ Kcal.

(a) The reaction is exoergic.
(b) $2C + O_2 \longrightarrow 2CO + 52$ Kcal.
(c) $\Delta H = -52$ Kcal.
(d) ΔH of formation of $CO = -26$ Kcal/mole.

551
[from section 334]

CHAPTER 8—ANSWERS TO QUESTIONS

1. $_{-1}e^0$, $_{-1}\beta^0$, symbols for electron
$_1p^1$, $_1H^1$, symbols for proton
$_0n^1$, symbol for neutron
$_1e^0$, symbol for positron
$_0\gamma^0$, symbol for gamma radiation
$_2He^4$, $_2\alpha^4$, symbols for alpha particle
$_1d^2$, symbol for deuteron

2. (a) $_2He^4$ (f) $_{82}Pb^{212}$
(b) $_0n^1$ (g) $_6C^{12}$
(c) $_{92}U^{239}$ (h) $_{18}Ar^{36}$
(d) $_{93}Np^{239}$ (i) $_{50}Sn^{131}$
(e) $_{-1}e^0$ (j) $_7N^{14}$

3. Fission: (i) only
Fusion: (a) and (j).

CHAPTER 9—ANSWERS TO QUESTIONS

1. (a) True (f) True
(b) True (g) True
(c) False (h) False
(d) False (i) True
(e) False (j) False

2. (a) $K = \frac{[CO_2]}{[C][O_2]}$ (e) $K = \frac{[NH_4^+][OH^-]}{[NH_3][H_2O]}$

(b) $K = \frac{[NH_3]^2}{[N_2][H_2]^3}$ (f) $K = \frac{[NO_2]^2}{[N_2O_4]}$

(c) $K = \frac{[H^+][OH^-]}{[H_2O]}$ (g) $K = \frac{[NO_2]^2}{[NO]^2[O_2]}$

(d) $K = \frac{[CO_2]^2}{[CO]^2\,[O_2]}$

3. (a) matches (x)
(b) matches (w)
(c) matches (y)
(d) matches (z)

553
[*from section 409*]

CHAPTER 10—ANSWERS TO QUESTIONS

1. The conjugate base of the acid H_2SO_4 is HSO_4^-.
The conjugate base of the acid H_3PO_4 is $H_2PO_4^-$.
The conjugate base of the acid $H_2PO_4^-$ is HPO_4^{--}.
The conjugate base of the acid HCl is Cl^-.
The conjugate base of the acid H_2O is OH^-.

2. The conjugate acid of the base Cl^- is HCl.
The conjugate acid of the base NH_3 is NH_4^+.
The conjugate acid of the base HSO_4^- is H_2SO_4.
The conjugate acid of the base $H_2PO_4^-$ is H_3PO_4.
The conjugate acid of the base HPO_4^{--} is $H_2PO_4^-$.
The conjugate acid of the base OH^- is H_2O.

3.

	Acid		Base		Conj. Acid		Conj. Base
(a)	HCl	+	H_2O	$\rightleftarrows$	H_3O^+	+	Cl^-
(b)	H_3PO_4	+	NH_3	$\rightleftarrows$	NH_4^+	+	$H_2PO_4^-$
(c)	HNO_3	+	CH_3COO^-	$\rightleftarrows$	CH_3COOH	+	NO_3^-
(d)	CH_3COOH	+	SO_3^{--}	$\rightleftarrows$	HSO_3^-	+	CH_3COO^-
(e)	HSO_4^-	+	$H_2PO_4^-$	$\rightleftarrows$	SO_4^{--}	+	H_3PO_4

4. (a) H_2CO_3 is a stronger acid than $H_2PO_4^-$.
(b) H_3PO_4 is a stronger acid than CH_3COOH.
(c) HF is a stronger acid than HSO_3^-.
(d) HCl is a stronger acid than H_2SO_3.
(e) HSO_3^- is a stronger acid than HCO_3^-.

5. (a) H_3PO_4 is a stronger acid than CH_3COOH, therefore the products are favored.
(b) The reactants are favored.
(c) The reactants are favored.
(d) The products are favored.

6. pH 2: $[H^+] = 10^{-2}$
pH 7: $[H^+] = 10^{-7}$
pH 9: $[H^+] = 10^{-9}$
Only the pH 2 solution is more acidic than water.

CHAPTER 11—ANSWERS TO QUESTIONS

1. $K^+Cl^- + \text{water} \longrightarrow K^+_{(aq)} + Cl^-_{(aq)}$.
$Ba^{++}(Cl^-)_2 + \text{water} \longrightarrow Ba^{++}_{(aq)} + 2Cl^-_{(aq)}$.
$Al^{+++}(Cl^-)_3 + \text{water} \longrightarrow Al^{+++}_{(aq)} + 3Cl^-_{(aq)}$.
$(Al^{+++})_2(SO_4^{--})_3 + \text{water} \longrightarrow 2Al^{+++}_{(aq)} + 3SO_4^{--}_{(aq)}$.

2. Soluble: KNO_3, $BaCl_2$, $Fe(NO_3)_3$, $AlCl_3$, $KMnO_4$.
Slightly soluble: $PbCl_2$, $Ag(CH_3COO)$.
Insoluble: $AgOH$, $AlBr_3$, $Zn(OH)_2$, $BaSO_4$.

3. $BaSO_4$: $K_{sp} = [Ba^{++}][SO_4^{--}]$.
$AgCl$: $K_{sp} = [Ag^+][Cl^-]$.
$PbCl_2$: $K_{sp} = [Pb^{++}][Cl^-]^2$.
$CuCO_3$: $K_{sp} = [Cu^{++}][CO_3^{--}]$.
$AlBr_3$: $K_{sp} = [Al^{+++}][Br^-]^3$.

4. $BaSO_4$:
$[Ba^{++}] = \sqrt{K_{sp}} = \sqrt{1.0 \times 10^{-10}} = 1.0 \times 10^{-5}$ M.
$Ca(OH)_2$:
$[Ca^{++}] = \sqrt[3]{K_{sp}/4} = \sqrt[3]{(1.3 \times 10^{-6})/4} = 6.9 \times 10^{-3}$ M.
$Ca(OH)_2$:
$[OH^-] = 2[Ca^{++}] = 2 \times 6.9 \times 10^{-3} = 1.4 \times 10^{-2}$ M.

5. $MgCO_3$: $K_{sp} = 4.0 \times 10^{-5}$;
$[Mg^{++}] = \sqrt{4 \times 10^{-5}} = \sqrt{40 \times 10^{-6}} = 6.3 \times 10^{-3}$ M.
Molecular weight = 84.3.
Therefore, weight of $MgCO_3$ in 1 liter is $84.3 \times 6.3 \times 10^{-3} = 0.53$ gram.

6. The concentration of each reactant is halved because of the dilution upon mixing. The ion product is:
$[Mg^{++}][CO_3^{--}] = (0.001)(0.003) = 3 \times 10^{-6}$.
This is smaller than K_{sp} (4.0×10^{-5}), so no precipitate can form.

555
[*from section 495*]

CHAPTER 12—ANSWERS TO QUESTIONS

1. Oxidations: (a), (d), (f)
Reductions: (b), (c), (e)

2. Spontaneous reactions: (a), (e)

3. (a) $2Fe^{+++} + Sn^{++} \longrightarrow 2Fe^{++} + Sn^{++++}$.
(b) $Fe^{++} + Ce^{++++} \longrightarrow Fe^{+++} + Ce^{+++}$.
(c) $Ni^{++} + Br_2 \longrightarrow Ni^{++++} + 2Br^{-}$.
(d) $Cu + 4H^{+} + 2NO_3^{-} \longrightarrow Cu^{++} + 2NO_2 + 2H_2O$.
(e) $Cu + 4HNO_3 \longrightarrow Cu(NO_3)_2 + 2NO_2 + 2H_2O$.

CHAPTER 13—ANSWERS TO QUESTIONS

1. (a) $Na + Ag^+ \longrightarrow Na^+ + Ag$ $\quad E° = 3.51$ volts
(b) $2Al + 3Cu^{++} \longrightarrow 2Al^{+++} + 3Cu$ $\quad E° = 2.00$ volts
(c) $Fe + Br_2 \longrightarrow FeBr_2$ $\quad E° = 1.51$ volts
(d) $2I^- + Cl_2 \longrightarrow I_2 + 2Cl^-$ $\quad E° = 0.82$ volt
(e) $Mg + 2Ag^+ \longrightarrow Mg^{++} + 2Ag$ $\quad E° = 3.17$ volts

2. 96,500 coulombs.

3. 4 faradays.

4. 10,000 coulombs is $\frac{10,000}{96,500}$ faraday $=$ 0.104 faraday; $0.104 \times \frac{112.4}{2}$ $=$ 5.85 grams.

Appendix

TABLE A: SELECTED ACIDS AND ACID CONSTANTS

Acid strength	Entry#	Acid HA	⇄	Proton H^+	+	Base strength	Conjugate Base A^-
VERY STRONG ACIDS	1	HCl		H^+		VERY WEAK BASES	Cl^-
	2	HNO_3		H^+			NO_3^-
	3	H_2SO_4		H^+			HSO_4^-
MODERATELY STRONG ACIDS	4	H_2SO_3		H^+			HSO_3^-
	5	HSO_4^-		H^+		WEAK BASES	SO_4^{--}
	6	H_3PO_4		H^+			$H_2PO_4^-$
	7	HF		H^+			F^-
WEAK ACIDS	8	CH_3COOH		H^+			CH_3COO^-
	9	H_2CO_3		H^+		MODERATELY WEAK BASES	HCO_3^-
	10	$H_2PO_4^-$		H^+			HPO_4^{--}
VERY WEAK ACIDS	11	HSO_3^-		H^+			SO_3^{--}
	12	NH_4^+		H^+			NH_3
	13	HCO_3^-		H^+			CO_3^{--}
	14	HPO_4^{--}		H^+		FAIRLY STRONG BASES	PO_4^{---}
	15	HS^-		H^+			S^{--}
	16	H_2O		H^+		VERY STRONG BASES	OH^-
	17	OH^-		H^+			O^{--}
	18	NH_3		H^+			NH_2^-

TABLE B: SOLUBILITY CHART

Solubilities of some common salts and acids in water (at 20°C)

S = soluble (solubility > 0.1 mole per liter)
SS = slightly soluble (solubility > 0.01, but < 0.1 mole per liter)
I = insoluble (< 0.01 mole per liter)
d = decomposes when placed in water
— = compound unknown

Cation	Br^-	CH_3COO^-	Cl^-	CO_3^{--}	I^-	NO_3^-	OH^-	S^{--}	SO_4^{--}
Ag^+	I	SS	I	I	I	S	I	I	SS
Al^{+++}	I	SS	S	—	S	S	I	d	S
Ba^{++}	S	S	S	I	S	S	SS	d	I
Ca^{++}	S	S	S	I	S	S	SS	d	SS
Cu^+	SS	—	I	I	I	—	I	I	d
Cu^{++}	S	S	S	I	S	S	I	I	S
Fe^{++}	S	S	S	I	S	S	I	I	S
Fe^{+++}	S	I	S	—	—	S	I	d	S
H^+	S	S	S	S	S	S	S	SS	S
K^+	S	S	S	S	S	S	S	S	S
Mg^{++}	S	S	S	I	S	S	I	d	S
Na^+	S	S	S	S	S	S	S	S	S
NH_4^+	S	S	S	S	S	S	S	S	S
Pb^{++}	SS	S	SS	I	I	S	I	I	I
Zn^{++}	S	S	S	I	S	S	I	I	S

TABLE C: SELECTED K_{sp} VALUES (at 20°)

EQUATION	K_{sp} EXPRESSION		K_{sp} VALUE
$AgBrO_3 \rightleftarrows Ag^+ + BrO_3^-$	$[Ag^+][BrO_3^-]$	=	4.0×10^{-5}
$AgCl \rightleftarrows Ag^+ + Cl^-$	$[Ag^+][Cl^-]$	=	1.6×10^{-10}
$BaSO_4 \rightleftarrows Ba^{++} + SO_4^{--}$	$[Ba^{++}][SO_4^{--}]$	=	1.0×10^{-10}
$Al(OH)_3 \rightleftarrows Al^{+++} + 3OH^-$	$[Al^{+++}][OH^-]^3$	=	1.9×10^{-33}
$CaCO_3 \rightleftarrows Ca^{++} + CO_3^{--}$	$[Ca^{++}][CO_3^{--}]$	=	1.0×10^{-8}
$Ca(OH)_2 \rightleftarrows Ca^{++} + 2OH^-$	$[Ca^{++}][OH^-]^2$	=	1.3×10^{-6}
$CuS \rightleftarrows Cu^{++} + S^{--}$	$[Cu^{++}][S^{--}]$	=	8.5×10^{-45}
$FeS \rightleftarrows Fe^{++} + S^{--}$	$[Fe^{++}][S^{--}]$	=	3.6×10^{-19}
$MgCO_3 \rightleftarrows Mg^{++} + CO_3^{--}$	$[Mg^{++}][CO_3^{--}]$	=	4.0×10^{-5}
$ZnS \rightleftarrows Zn^{++} + S^{--}$	$[Zn^{++}][S^{--}]$	=	1.4×10^{-23}

TABLE D: SOME HALF-REACTIONS

Entry No.	*Relative Strength of Oxidizing Agents*	*Half-Reaction*	*Relative Strength of Reducing Agents*	*Standard Reduction Potentials, E°, (volts)*
	↑ WEAKEST		STRONGEST ↓	
1.		$Na^{+} + e^{-} \rightleftarrows Na$		−2.71
2.		$Mg^{++} + 2e^{-} \rightleftarrows Mg$		−2.37
3.		$Al^{+++} + 3e^{-} \rightleftarrows Al$		−1.66
4.	Decreases from bottom to top	$Zn^{++} + 2e^{-} \rightleftarrows Zn$	Decreases from top to bottom	−0.76
5.		$Fe^{++} + 2e^{-} \rightleftarrows Fe$		−0.44
6.		$Pb^{++} + 2e^{-} \rightleftarrows Pb$		−0.13
7.		$2H^{+} + 2e^{-} \rightleftarrows H_2$		0.00
8.		$Cu^{++} + 2e^{-} \rightleftarrows Cu$		+0.34
9.		$I_2 + 2e^{-} \rightleftarrows 2I^{-}$		+0.54
10.		$Ag^{+} + e^{-} \rightleftarrows Ag$		+0.80
11.		$Br_2 + 2e^{-} \rightleftarrows 2Br^{-}$		+1.07
12.		$Cl_2 + 2e^{-} \rightleftarrows 2Cl^{-}$		+1.36
	STRONGEST		WEAKEST	

TABLE E: TABLE OF EQUIVALENT VALUES

(1) 1 dozen (dz) = 12 units
(2) 1 mole = 6.02×10^{23} units
(3) 1 liter (l) = 1000 milliliters (ml)
(4) 1 kilogram (kg) = 1000 grams (g)
(5) 1 angstrom (A) = 10^{-8} centimeters (cm)
(6) 1 meter (m) = 100 centimeters
(7) 1 atmosphere (atm) = 760 millimeters of Hg (mm of Hg)
(8) 1 inch (in.) = 2.54 centimeters
(9) 1 centimeter (cm) = 10 millimeters (mm)
(10) 1 atmosphere = 15 pounds per square inch (lb/in^2)
(11) 1 faraday = 96,500 coulombs (cb)
(12) 1 faraday = 6.02×10^{23} electrons
(13) 1 pound (lb) = 454 grams
(14) 1 minute (min) = 60 seconds (sec)
(15) 1 hour (hr) = 60 minutes
(16) 1 molar volume (STP) = 22.4 liters
(17) 1 liter = 1.06 quarts (qt)

To use this table, remember two points:

1. *$a/a = 1$; hence for example,*

$$\frac{\text{1 faraday}}{\text{96,500 coulombs}} = 1 = \frac{\text{96,500 coulombs}}{\text{1 faraday}}$$

or:

$$\frac{\text{454 grams}}{\text{1 pound}} = 1 = \frac{\text{1 pound}}{\text{454 grams}}$$

2. *$a(b/a) = b$; hence for example,*

$$(5\ \cancel{\text{dozen}})\left(\frac{\text{12 units}}{1\ \cancel{\text{doz}}}\right) = \text{60 units}$$

or:

$$(500\ \cancel{\text{atm}})\left(\frac{15\ \text{lb/in}^2}{\cancel{\text{atm}}}\right) = 7{,}500\ \text{lb/in}^2.$$

TABLE F: VAPOR PRESSURE OF WATER

Temperature (°C)	Pressure (mm of Hg)	Temperature (°C)	Pressure (mm of Hg)
0	4.6	35	42.1
5	6.5	40	55.3
10	9.2	45	71.9
15	12.8	50	92.5
20	17.5	60	149.4
23	21.1	70	233.7
25	23.8	80	355.1
27	26.7	90	525.8
30	31.8	100	760.0

Index

(*References apply to sections, not to pages*)

H10

PERIODIC CHART

NOBLE GASES 0	1A	2A	3B	4B	5B	6B	7B	8
	1 1.00797 H HYDROGEN							
2 4.0026 He HELIUM	3 6.939 Li LITHIUM	4 9.0122 Be BERYLLIUM						
10 20.183 Ne NEON	11 22.9898 Na SODIUM	12 24.312 Mg MAGNESIUM						
18 39.948 Ar ARGON	19 39.102 K POTASSIUM	20 40.08 Ca CALCIUM	21 44.956 Sc SCANDIUM	22 47.90 Ti TITANIUM	23 50.942 V VANADIUM	24 51.996 Cr CHROMIUM	25 54.9381 Mn MANGANESE	26 55.847 Fe IRON
36 83.80 Kr KRYPTON	37 85.47 Rb RUBIDIUM	38 87.62 Sr STRONTIUM	39 88.905 Y YTTRIUM	40 91.22 Zr ZIRCONIUM	41 92.906 Nb NIOBIUM	42 95.94 Mo MOLYBDENUM	43 (99) Tc TECHNETIUM	44 101.07 Ru RUTHENIUM
54 131.30 Xe XENON	55 132.905 Cs CESIUM	56 137.34 Ba BARIUM	57 138.91 *La LANTHANUM	72 178.49 Hf HAFNIUM	73 180.948 Ta TANTALUM	74 183.85 W TUNGSTEN	75 186.2 Re RHENIUM	76 190.2 Os OSMIUM
86 (222) Rn RADON	87 (223) Fr FRANCIUM	88 (226) Ra RADIUM	89 (227) †Ac ACTINIUM					

(partial column)
27 58.9 C COBA
45 102. R RHOD.
77 1 Ir IRID

*Lanthanum Series							
	58 140.12 Ce CERIUM	59 140.907 Pr PRASEODYMIUM	60 144.24 Nd NEODYMIUM	61 (147) Pm PROMETHIUM	62 150.35 Sm SAMARIUM	63 151.96 Eu EUROPIUM	64 157 Gd GADOLIN

†Actinium Series							
	90 232.038 Th THORIUM	91 (231) Pa PROTACTINIUM	92 238.03 U URANIUM	93 (237) Np NEPTUNIUM	94 (242) Pu PLUTONIUM	95 (243) Am AMERICIUM	96 (2 Cm CURI